The core syllabus for A level

Book 1

Joyce S. Batty
Formerly Head of the Mathematics Department at King Edward VII School, Sheffield

Schofield & Sims Ltd Huddersfield

0 7217 2356 x
0 7217 2358 6 Net Edition

First printed 1986

Acknowledgements

The author and publishers are grateful for permission to use questions from past G.C.E. examinations in Additional Mathematics and Advanced Mathematics. These are acknowledged as follows:

University of London University Entrance and Schools Examination Council (*L*)

The Associated Examining Board (*AEB*)

Joint Matriculation Board (*JMB*)

University of Cambridge Local Examinations Syndicate (*C*)

Oxford and Cambridge Schools Examination Board:
The School Mathematics Project (*SMP*)
Mathematics in Education and Industry Schools Project (*MEI*)

University of Oxford Delegacy of Local Examinations (*OLE*)

Grateful acknowledgement is also due to the Scottish Examination Board for permission to use questions from past examinations in Higher Mathematics.(*S*)

The Examining Boards whose questions are reproduced bear no responsibility whatever for the answers to examination questions given here, which are the sole responsibility of the author.

References

Questions from past papers in Advanced level Mathematics and Further Mathematics. Collections arranged under the new syllabus headings.

Set 1 Collected and edited by Joyce S. Batty

Set 3 Collected and edited by Joyce S. Batty with Gordon R. Baldock and I. Gwyn Evans

Published by the Joint Matriculation Board and available from the Board, Manchester M15 6EU.

Designed by Graphic Art Concepts, Leeds
Printed in England by Martin's of Berwick

Author's Note

The purpose of this book and its successor 'Pure Mathematics 2' is to provide a reasonably straightforward text to cover the syllabus in Pure Mathematics I of the Joint Matriculation Board. The JMB syllabus contains the proposed national common core for Advanced level Mathematics, and this syllabus is automatically covered by the two books.

With only very minor exceptions, all the work in Book 1 is relevant to the JMB PI syllabus. Book 2 will contain a little work which is not on this syllabus but which is on the corresponding syllabuses of other examining boards, in particular the London Board and the AEB, so that the two books will provide almost complete coverage of at least three syllabuses in Pure Mathematics at single subject level.

The gap between pre-A level mathematics and A level mathematics is considerable. Many students find the first term, at least, of the A level course far more demanding than they had expected. This book attempts to reduce the shock effect in two ways.

First, by starting with some of the less demanding topics—though this is a matter of opinion. The inclusion of a chapter on algebraic manipulation as Chapter 2 is less likely to be controversial, as no progress can be made on other topics until some degree of proficiency has been reached in algebra.

Second, by providing a large number of worked examples, and graded exercises for the student, on each new topic. The author hopes that these exercises are neither so hard as to discourage the less able nor so easy as to bore the more able. There are a few questions more demanding than the rest; these occur late in some of the 'B' exercises and in the Miscellaneous Exercises at the ends of chapters; students or teachers seeking a further supply will find them in the References.

Many of the questions in the Miscellaneous Exercises in Book 1 are taken from past examination papers in Additional Mathematics and in a few cases in Advanced level Mathematics; the author is inclined to regard Advanced level questions as too strong a diet in the earlier months of the course. Book 2 will contain questions from Advanced level papers, though none which are in the References, and some from Special papers to provide a challenge for the more ambitious students. Book 2 will provide revision exercises on the whole of Book 1.

The order of the chapters provides a possible teaching order, though probably no two teachers ever agree about the 'best' teaching order. Many variations are possible, but a knowledge of Chapter 1 is assumed in several later chapters. Some questions in the Miscellaneous Exercises refer back to topics from previous chapters, to provide 'continuous revision'. For suggestions about possible teaching orders see inside back cover.

It is assumed throughout the book that the student has a scientific calculator; the use of trigonometric tables is nowhere mentioned.

The author wishes to express grateful thanks to several colleagues who have helped in the preparation of this book. In particular, to Dr. G. R. Baldock for reading the whole book and making many helpful comments, and to Mr. E. Wilson for reading much of the first draft and suggesting several improvements.

Thanks also to Ian Simmonds and Martin Sykes, students at King Edward VII School, Sheffield, for providing computer graphs.

Finally, special thanks to the staff of Schofield and Sims for their unfailing encouragement and patience, and for their help in many ways.

J. S. Batty

Contents

Chapter 6

Coordinate geometry 1: lines and circles

Chapter 7

Indices; exponential and logarithmic functions

Chapter 8

Vectors 1

Chapter 9

Transformations of graphs: the quadratic and bilinear functions

Chapter 10

Trigonometry 2

Notation

$=$	is equal to
$\approx$	is approximately equal to
$\neq$	is not equal to
$<$	is less than
$\leqslant$	is less than or equal to
$>$	is greater than
$\geqslant$	is greater than or equal to
$\nless$	is not less than
$\ngtr$	is not greater than
$\sqrt{}$	the positive square root
$\Rightarrow$	implies that
$\Leftarrow$	is implied by
$\Leftrightarrow$	implies and is implied by
$x:y$	the ratio of x to y
$\{a, b, c, \ldots\}$	the set with elements $a, b, c, \ldots$
$\in$	is an element of
$\notin$	is not an element of
$\{x: a < x < b\}$	the set of values of x such that a is less than x and also x is less than b
$n(A)$	the number of elements in the set A
$\mathscr{E}$	the universal set
$\varnothing$	the empty set, null set
S'	the complement of the set S
$\cup$	the union of
$\cap$	the intersection of
$\subseteq, \subset$	is a subset of, is a proper subset of, respectively
$\supseteq, \supset$	contains as a subset, contains as a proper subset, respectively
$\leftrightarrow$	corresponds one-to-one with
$\propto$	varies directly as
$\|x\|$	the modulus of x
$\frac{\mathrm{d}y}{\mathrm{d}x}$	the derivative of y with respect to x
$\int y \, \mathrm{d}x$	the indefinite integral of y with respect to x
$\int_a^b y \, \mathrm{d}x$	the definite integral of y with respect to x between the limits $x = a$ and $x = b$
f	a function
$\mathrm{f}(x)$	the function value for x
$\rightarrow$	is mapped into (in the context of a mapping)
$x \overset{\mathrm{f}}{\mapsto} y$	x is mapped into y under the function f
$\mathrm{f}: x \mapsto y$	f is the function under which x is mapped into y
$\rightarrow$	approaches, tends to (in the context of a limit)
Σ	the sum of (precise limits may be given)

$n!$	n factorial
g	the acceleration due to gravity
$\equiv$	is congruent to or is identical to
∞	infinity
$\mathbf{a} \cdot \mathbf{b}$	the scalar product of the vectors **a** and **b**
$\hat{\mathbf{r}}$	the unit vector in the direction defined by the vector **r**
$\lvert\mathbf{r}\rvert$, r	the magnitude of the vector **r**
i, **j**, **k**	unit vectors in the mutually perpendicular directions Ox, Oy, Oz
δx	a small increment of x
$\dot{x}$, $\ddot{x}$	the first and second derivatives, respectively, of x with respect to t
f^{-1}	the inverse function of f
f', f'', $\mathrm{f}^{(3)}$, ... $\mathrm{f}^{(n)}$	the first, second, third, ... n^{th} derivatives, respectively, of f

For functions f and g where domains and ranges are subsets of the set of real numbers:

$\mathrm{f} + \mathrm{g}$	is defined by $(\mathrm{f} + \mathrm{g})(x) = \mathrm{f}(x) + \mathrm{g}(x)$
$\mathrm{f} \cdot \mathrm{g}$	is defined by $(\mathrm{f} \cdot \mathrm{g})(x) = \mathrm{f}(x)\,\mathrm{g}(x)$
fg	is defined by $(\mathrm{fg})(x) = \mathrm{f}[\mathrm{g}(x)]$

$\mathbb{N}$	the set of positive integers and zero $\{0, 1, 2, \ldots\}$
$\mathbb{Z}$	the set of integers $\{0, \pm 1, \pm 2, \ldots\}$
$\mathbb{Q}$	the set of rational numbers
$\mathbb{R}$	the set of real numbers
$\mathbb{C}$	the set of complex numbers

$\ln x$	the natural logarithm of x
$\mathbf{M}^{-1}$	the inverse (when it exists) of the matrix **M**
$\det \mathbf{M}$	the determinant of a square matrix **M**
i	square root of -1
$\lvert z\rvert$	the modulus of the complex number z
$\arg z$	the argument of the complex number z
z^*	the conjugate of the complex number z
d.p.	decimal places
s.f.	significant figures

Chapter 1

Functions

1.1 Functions: domain and range

The concept of related variables and functions is fundamental to the study of mathematics. The student will already have met many examples of related variables: the area of a square is related to the side of the square; the volume of a sphere is related to the radius; time, displacement, velocity and acceleration are all related.

The student has probably met the idea of a function as the means by which each element of a given set is mapped to an element in another set; the given set is called the *domain* of the function and the set to which the domain is mapped is called the *range* of the function. For example, a function could add 3 to each element of the domain $\{2, 3, 4\}$ to give the range $\{5, 6, 7\}$. The mapping may be shown on a mapping diagram or on a graph.

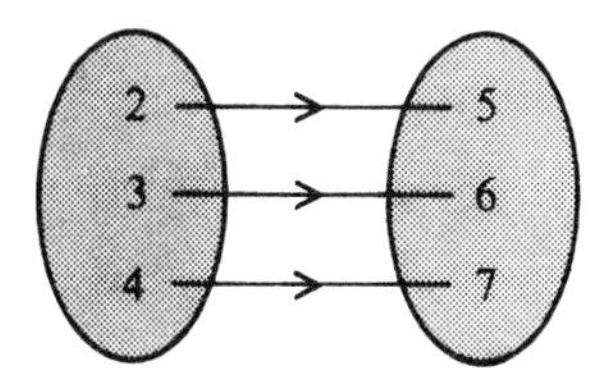

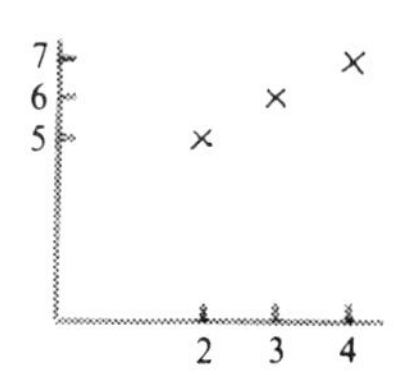

A function may be defined in various ways: for example, it may be given in words, or by a mathematical expression, or by a table or by a graph. A single letter is used to represent a function; often the letter f is used, also g, h, F, etc.

The example above could be described in any of the following ways:

a f adds 3 to each element of $\{2, 3, 4\}$

b f maps x to $x + 3$, where $x \in \{2, 3, 4\}$

c $\mathrm{f}: x \mapsto x + 3$ where $x \in \{2, 3, 4\}$; this is read as in **b**

d $\mathrm{f}(x) = x + 3$ where $x \in \{2, 3, 4\}$; this is read 'f of x is equal to $x + 3$'; $\mathrm{f}(x)$ is called the *image* of x under f

e the mapping diagram could be used

f the graph could be used.

The domain and range of a function are usually sets of numbers, but this is not essential; they could for example be sets of number-pairs or sets of angles. A function could map the number-pair (x, y) to the pair $(x + 2, y + 3)$, or the angle θ to its cosine.

It is an essential property of a function that it maps each element in its domain to *one and only one* element. In a mapping diagram there must therefore be one and only one arrow going *from* each element in the domain *to* some element; how many arrows end at a given element is not relevant. For example in the case of the function defined by $f(x) = 4$ on the domain $\{4, 5, 6\}$ all three arrows end at 4, and the range is $\{4\}$.

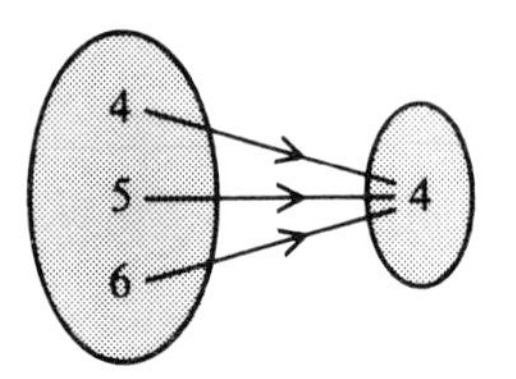

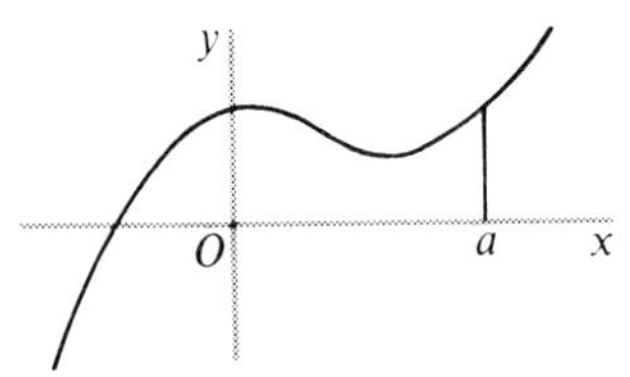

On the graph of a function, a line drawn from a point $(a, 0)$ and parallel to the y-axis must meet the graph in one and only one point if a is an element of the domain, and in no point otherwise.

It follows from this property of a function that a function cannot, for example, map a positive number to its two square roots. A function *can* map any positive number to its *positive* square root; this function is defined by $f(x) = \sqrt{x}$ for $x \geqslant 0$. Equally a function g could be defined by $g(x) = -\sqrt{x}$ for $x \geqslant 0$.

A note on notation

All the numbers in this book are real, i.e. they belong to the set $\mathbb{R}$. Numbers which are not real will be introduced in Book 2. Throughout this book, phrases such as 'all x' and 'all non-zero x' are to be read as abbreviations for 'all real x' and 'all real non-zero x' without further explanation. If some restriction on x is intended, such as that x is an integer, this will be stated. Similarly the notation $\{x : a \leqslant x \leqslant b\}$ is to be read as meaning the set of all x satisfying the inequality, unless some restriction is stated. The fact that x is real here is implied by the inequality; as will be seen later, numbers which are not real do not satisfy inequalities.

Examples 1.1

1 Find the range of each of the following functions.

a the function f defined on the domain $\{1, 3, 5\}$ by
$f(x) = x^2 + 3x - 2$

b the function g defined on the domain $\{0, 1, 2\}$ by
$$g(x) = \frac{1}{x + 2}$$

c the function h defined on the domain $\{1, 2, 3, 4, 5\}$ by
$h(x) = 0$ if x is odd
$h(x) = 1$ if x is even

a $f(1) = 2$, $f(3) = 16$, $f(5) = 38$
So the range is $\{2, 16, 38\}$.

b $g(0) = \frac{1}{2}$, $g(1) = \frac{1}{3}$, $g(2) = \frac{1}{4}$

So the range is $\left\{\frac{1}{2}, \frac{1}{3}, \frac{1}{4}\right\}$.

c $h(1) = 0$, $h(2) = 1$, $h(3) = 0$, $h(4) = 1$, $h(5) = 0$

So the range is $\{0, 1\}$.

2 The function f is defined on $\mathbb{R}$ by $f(x) = 3 - x^2$. Find the range of f.

$f(0) = 3$; for $x \neq 0$, x^2 takes all positive values, so $3 - x^2$ takes all values less than 3.

$\therefore$ the range of f is $\{y : y \leqslant 3\}$.

3 The function g is defined on $\mathbb{R}$ by $g(x) = (x - 3)^2 + 4$.
Find the range of g.

$g(3) = 4$; for $x \neq 3$, $(x - 3)^2$ takes all positive values.

$\therefore$ the range of g is $\{y : y \geqslant 4\}$.

4 The function h is defined by $h(x) = \dfrac{1}{x - 2}$ for $x > 2$.
Find the range of h.

For $x > 2$ the denominator takes all positive values, so its reciprocal takes all positive values.

$\therefore$ the range of h is $\{y : y > 0\}$.

Exercise 1.1A

1 Find the range of each of the following functions.

a the function f defined on the domain $\{1, 2, 3, 4\}$ by

$$f(x) = \frac{1}{x^2 + 1}$$

b the function g defined on the domain $\{-2, -1, 1, 2\}$ by

$g(x) = x$ if x is positive
$g(x) = -x$ if x is negative

c the function h defined on the domain $\{0, 1, 2, 3\}$ by

$h(x) = 2^x$

2 The function f is defined on $\mathbb{R}$ by $f(x) = x^2 + 4$.
Find the range of f.

3 The function f is defined on $\mathbb{R}$ by $f(x) = \dfrac{1}{1 + x^2}$.
Find the range of f.

4 The function f is defined for $x \geqslant 4$ by $f(x) = \sqrt{(x - 4)} + 3$.
Find the range of f.

Exercise 1.1B

1 Find the range of each of the following functions.

a the function f defined on the domain $\{-2, -1, 0, 1, 2\}$ by
$f(x) = x^2 + 4$

b the function g defined on the domain $\{x : 0 \leqslant x \leqslant 2\}$ by
$g(x) = 1$ if $x \in \mathbb{Q}$, $g(x) = 0$ otherwise

c the function h defined on the domain $\{x : 0 \leqslant x \leqslant 3\}$ by
$h(x)$ is the largest integer which does not exceed x

In questions **2**–**5** the domain of f is $\mathbb{R}$. Find the range of f.

2 $f(x) = (x - 1)^2 + 5$

3 $f(x) = \sqrt{(x^2 + 4)} - 2$

4 $f(x) = 4 - (x + 2)^2$

5 $f(x) = \dfrac{1}{\sqrt{(x^2 + 9)}}$

6 The function f is defined by $f(x) = \dfrac{x - 2}{x}$ for $x > 0$.
Find the range of f.

1.2 Composite functions

A composite function is the result of two or more functions acting in succession. For example, if g maps 2 to 5, and f maps 5 to 9, then the composite function formed by 'g followed by f' maps 2 to 9. Numbers in the range of g are 'fed into' f; or, more precisely, all the numbers in the range of g *which also lie in the domain of f* are fed into f. Suppose for example that g and f each have domain $\mathbb{R}$, and that $g(x) = x^2$, $f(x) = x + 5$. Then all the numbers in the range of g lie in the domain of f. In particular, g maps 4 to 16 and f maps 16 to 21. Using function notation,

$$g(4) = 16,\ f(16) = 21;\ \text{or}\ f[g(4)] = 21.$$

The composite function 'g followed by f' is written as fg; note that g is written second but is used first.

The domain of the composite function fg is the set of all x in the domain of g for which $g(x)$ is in the domain of f.

This definition should be remembered.

The composite function gf maps 4 to $g[f(4)] = g(9) = 81$. Thus $fg(4) \neq gf(4)$; composition of functions is not commutative.

Composition of functions may be illustrated by diagrams, as shown below, using 'function boxes'.

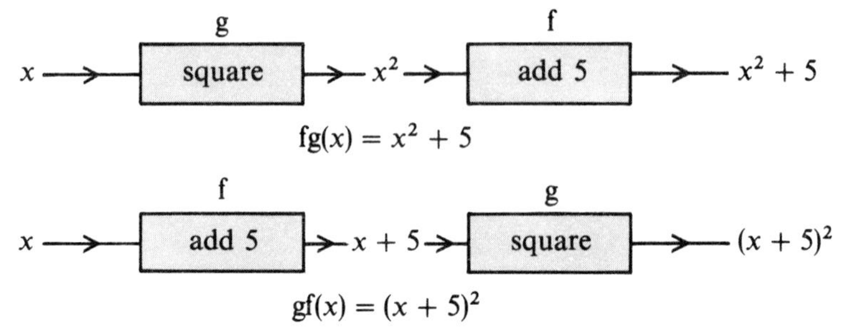

Examples 1.2

In examples **1–4** the domain of each function is $\mathbb{R}$.

1 Given that $f(x) = 2x$, $g(x) = x - 3$, find $fg(x)$, $gf(x)$, $ff(x)$, $gg(x)$.

In words, f doubles and g subtracts 3.

$fg(x) = f(x - 3) = 2(x - 3)$ $\qquad$ $gf(x) = g(2x) = 2x - 3$

$ff(x) = f(2x) = 4x$ $\qquad$ $gg(x) = g(x - 3) = x - 6$

2 Given that $f(x) = x^3$, $g(x) = x + 4$, find $fg(x)$, $gf(x)$, $ff(x)$ and $gg(x)$.

$fg(x) = f(x + 4) = (x + 4)^3$ $\qquad$ $gf(x) = g(x^3) = x^3 + 4$

$ff(x) = f(x^3) = (x^3)^3 = x^9$ $\qquad$ $gg(x) = g(x + 4) = x + 8$

3 Given that $f(x) = 3x + 4$, $g(x) = 2x - 5$, find $fg(x)$ and $gf(x)$.

$fg(x) = f(2x - 5) = 3(2x - 5) + 4 = 6x - 11$

$gf(x) = g(3x + 4) = 2(3x + 4) - 5 = 6x + 3$

4 Given that $f(x) = x^4$, $g(x) = \frac{x}{2}$, $h(x) = x - 2$, find $fg(x)$, $hfg(x)$, $gh(x)$ and $fgh(x)$.

$$fg(x) = f\left(\frac{x}{2}\right) = \left(\frac{x}{2}\right)^4 \qquad hfg(x) = h\left[\left(\frac{x}{2}\right)^4\right] = \left(\frac{x}{2}\right)^4 - 2$$

$$gh(x) = g(x - 2) = \frac{x - 2}{2} \qquad fgh(x) = f\left(\frac{x - 2}{2}\right) = \left(\frac{x - 2}{2}\right)^4$$

5 The functions f and g are defined for all positive x by $f(x) = 2 - x$, $g(x) = \frac{1}{x}$.

a State the range of f and the range of g.

b Find $fg(x)$ and give the domain of fg.

c Find $gf(x)$ and give the domain of gf.

a The range of f is $\{y : y < 2\}$.
The range of g is $\{y : y > 0\}$.

b $fg(x) = f\left(\frac{1}{x}\right) = 2 - \frac{1}{x}$

The domain of fg is the set of x in the domain of g for which $g(x)$ is in the domain of f, i.e. for which $g(x) > 0$. Since $g(x) > 0$ for all x in the domain of g, the domain of fg is the domain of g, the set of all positive x.

c $gf(x) = g(2 - x) = \frac{1}{2 - x}$

The domain of gf is the set of x in the domain of f for which $f(x) > 0$, i.e. the set $\{x : 0 < x < 2\}$.
$\therefore$ the domain of gf is the set $\{x : 0 < x < 2\}$.

Exercise 1.2A

In questions **1–3** the domain of each function is $\mathbb{R}$.

1 Find fg(x), gf(x), ff(x) and gg(x) in each of the cases.

a $f(x) = 3x$, $g(x) = x - 1$ **b** $f(x) = x^2$, $g(x) = x - 6$

c $f(x) = 2^x$, $g(x) = x + 3$

2 Given that $f(x) = x^3$, $g(x) = 2x$, $h(x) = x - 3$, find fg(x), hfg(x), gh(x) and fgh(x).

3 Given that $f(x) = 4x - 3$ and $g(x) = 5x + 2$, find fg(x) and gf(x).

4 The function f is defined by $f(x) = \sqrt{x}$ for $x \geqslant 0$.
The function g is defined by $g(x) = x - 2$ for all x.

a State the range of f and the range of g.

b Find fg(x) and give the domain and range of fg.

c Find gf(x) and give the domain and range of gf.

Exercise 1.2B

1 The domain of f is all non-zero x, and $f(x) = \frac{1}{x}$. The domain of g is $\mathbb{R}$, and $g(x) = x - 4$. Find fg(x), gf(x) and ff(x), giving the domains of fg, gf and ff.

2 The functions f and g are defined for all positive numbers by $f(x) = \sqrt{x}$, $g(x) = \frac{1}{x}$. Show that fg(x) = gf(x), and state the range of fg.

3 Given that, for all x, $f(x) = ax + b$ and $g(x) = cx + d$, and that fg(x) = gf(x) for all x, find a relation between the constants a, b, c and d.

4 The function f is defined by $f(x) = \frac{1}{x}$ for $x \neq 0$.

The function g is defined by $g(x) = \frac{2x + 3}{x - 1}$ for $x \neq 1$.

a Find fg(x) and state the domain of fg.

b Find gf(x) and state the domain of gf.

5 The functions f and g are defined for all positive x by

$$f(x) = 3 - x,\ g(x) = \frac{1}{x + 1}.$$

a State the range of f and the range of g.

b Find fg(x) and give the domain of fg.

c Find gf(x) and give the domain of gf.

6 The functions f and g are defined by

$$f(x) = \frac{1}{x - 1} \text{ for } x > 1,\ g(x) = x + 3 \text{ for } x \geqslant 0.$$

a State the range of f and the range of g.

b Find fg(x) and give the domain and range of fg.

c Find gf(x) and give the domain and range of gf.

1.3 The identity function and the inverse of a function

The identity function is the function which leaves all numbers in its domain unchanged; it maps x to x for every x. The domain may be $\mathbb{R}$ or any subset of $\mathbb{R}$. The graph of the identity function is the line $y = x$, or some part of this line. Given a function f, it may be the case that the effect of f can be 'cancelled out' by some other function g, so that if f maps x to y, then g maps y to x. In this case the composite function gf maps x to x, so that $\mathrm{gf}(x) = x$. The function g is called the *inverse* of the function f, and f is the inverse of g. The inverse function of f is written f^{-1}, so that $\mathrm{f}^{-1}\mathrm{f}(x) = x$.

Simple examples of inverse functions are given by:

a $\mathrm{f}(x) = x + 3, \qquad \mathrm{f}^{-1}(x) = x - 3$

b $\mathrm{f}(x) = 2x, \qquad \mathrm{f}^{-1}(x) = \dfrac{x}{2}$

c $\mathrm{f}(x) = 2x + 3, \qquad \mathrm{f}^{-1}(x) = \dfrac{x - 3}{2}$

d $\mathrm{f}(x) = \dfrac{1}{x}, \qquad \mathrm{f}^{-1}(x) = \dfrac{1}{x}$

e $\mathrm{f}(x) = 3 - x, \qquad \mathrm{f}^{-1}(x) = 3 - x.$

Each of these may be checked by showing that $\mathrm{f}^{-1}\mathrm{f}(x) = x$. Example **c** is a composite function; note that f multiplies by 2 and then adds 3, f^{-1} subtracts 3 and then divides by 2; each inverse must be used and in the opposite order. A useful analogy is undoing a parcel which has been wrapped in paper and then tied with string.

Examples **d** and **e** are examples of self-inverse functions; f is cancelled by using f again. An analogy here is reflecting a point in a line; reflecting the image point in the same line gives the original point.

In each of the examples **a**–**e** an inverse function does exist. This is because each value of $\mathrm{f}(x)$ is the image of only one value of x. The function f maps a number on the x-axis to one and only one number on the y-axis; an inverse function exists if each number on the y-axis is the image of one and only one number on the x-axis. When this condition is satisfied, the function f is said to be one-one.

Fig. 1 shows the graph of a function which has an inverse.

Fig. 2 shows the graph of a function which has no inverse; the value of y shown is the image of four distinct values of x.

Fig. 1

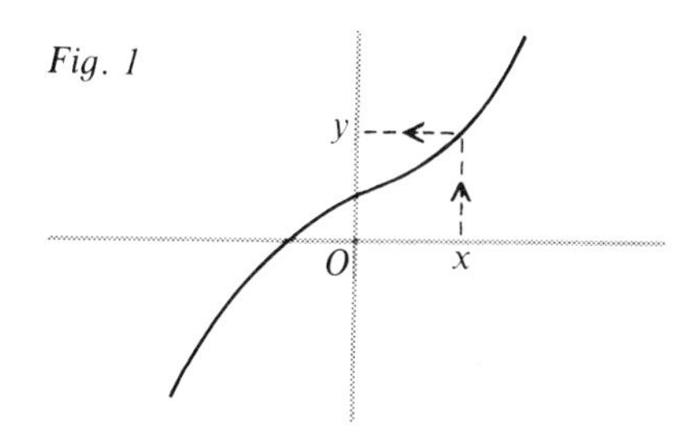

Fig. 2

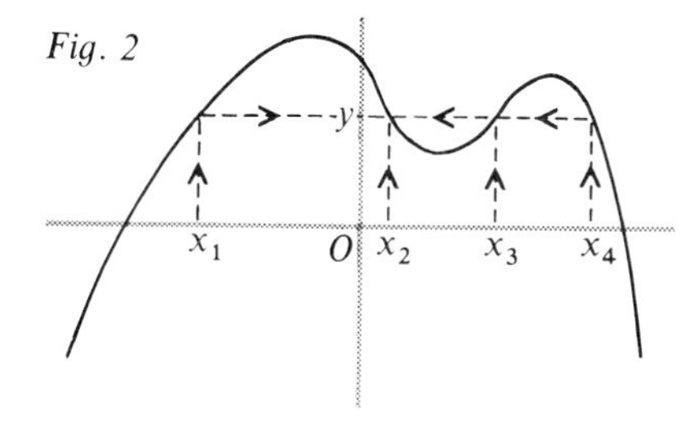

When a function f is one-one, it is in some cases possible to determine the inverse function f^{-1} by 'changing the subject' of the formula $y = f(x)$ from y to x. If $y = f(x)$ then $x = f^{-1}(y)$. Interchanging x and y gives $y = f^{-1}(x)$ as required. Interchanging x and y on the x–y plane corresponds to a reflection in the line $y = x$, so the graph of $f^{-1}(x)$ is the reflection in the line $y = x$ of the graph of $f(x)$. The graph of $y = f(x)$ may also be labelled $x = f^{-1}(y)$; the reflection of this graph in the line $y = x$ may be labelled $x = f(y)$ or $y = f^{-1}(x)$.

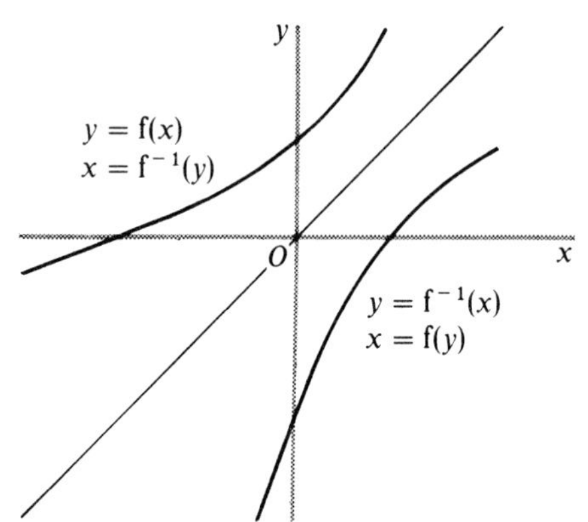

It follows that the domain of f^{-1} is the range of f, and the range of f^{-1} is the domain of f.

Examples 1.3

1 Given that $f(x) = 3x + 4$, find $f^{-1}(x)$. Sketch the graph of $f(x)$ and $f^{-1}(x)$.

Writing y for $f(x)$: $\quad y = 3x + 4$

Changing the subject: $\quad 3x = y - 4$

$$x = \frac{y-4}{3}$$

$$\therefore f^{-1}(y) = \frac{y-4}{3}$$

$$\therefore f^{-1}(x) = \frac{x-4}{3}$$

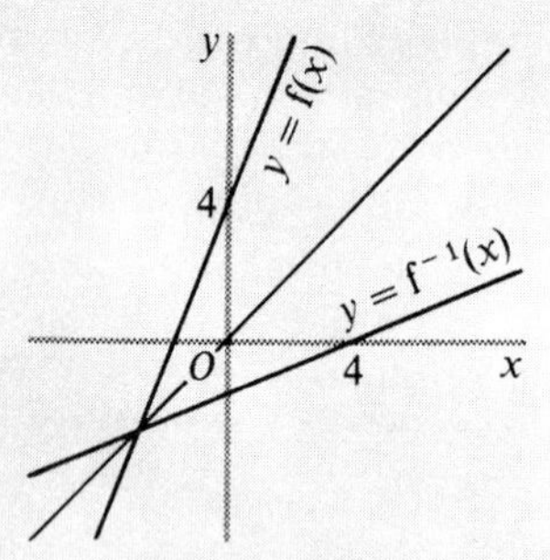

This result agrees with the result obtained by the argument: f multiplies by 3 and then adds 4, $\therefore f^{-1}$ subtracts 4 and then divides by 3. This argument can be used only when x appears in just one position in the formula for $f(x)$.

2 Given that $f(x) = \dfrac{(x-1)^3 + 2}{5}$, find $f^{-1}(x)$.

$$y = \frac{(x-1)^3 + 2}{5}$$

$$\therefore (x-1)^3 = 5y - 2$$

$$x - 1 = \sqrt[3]{(5y - 2)}$$
$$x = \sqrt[3]{(5y - 2)} + 1$$
$$\therefore f^{-1}(y) = \sqrt[3]{(5y - 2)} + 1$$
$$\therefore f^{-1}(x) = \sqrt[3]{(5x - 2)} + 1$$

Note: A check on the working may be made by using numerical values of x, though of course this cannot provide confirmation that the result is correct. For example, in this case:

$f(3) = 2$, $f^{-1}(2) = \sqrt[3]{8} + 1 = 3$
i.e. f maps 3 to 2, f^{-1} maps 2 to 3.

Since x appears in just one position in the formula for $f(x)$, the alternative method may be used here:
f subtracts 1, cubes, adds 2 and divides by 5, therefore
f^{-1} multiplies by 5, subtracts 2, takes the cube root and adds 1.

3 Given that $f(x) = \dfrac{3x + 1}{x - 2}$ for $x \neq 2$, find $f^{-1}(x)$.

$$y = \frac{3x + 1}{x - 2}$$
$$(x - 2)y = 3x + 1$$
$$xy - 3x = 2y + 1$$
$$x(y - 3) = 2y + 1$$
$$x = \frac{2y + 1}{y - 3}$$
$$\therefore f^{-1}(x) = \frac{2x + 1}{x - 3}$$

The alternative method cannot be used here, as x occurs in the numerator and in the denominator.

Exercise 1.3A

1 Find $f^{-1}(x)$ in each of the following. Sketch the graph of $f(x)$ and $f^{-1}(x)$ in each case.

a $f(x) = 5x - 2$ **b** $f(x) = \dfrac{3x + 4}{5}$

2 Given that $f(x) = \dfrac{(x + 4)^3 - 3}{2}$, find $f^{-1}(x)$.

3 Given that $f(x) = \dfrac{2x + 1}{x - 3}$, find $f^{-1}(x)$.

4 Given that $f(x) = \dfrac{x - 3}{2x + 1}$, find $f^{-1}(x)$.

Exercise 1.3B

1 Find $f^{-1}(x)$ in each of the following. Sketch the graph of $f(x)$ and $f^{-1}(x)$ in each case.

a $f(x) = \dfrac{x+3}{2}$ **b** $f(x) = \dfrac{2x-5}{3}$

2 Find $f^{-1}(x)$ in each of the following cases.

a $f(x) = \dfrac{(2x-1)^5+3}{4}$ **b** $f(x) = \dfrac{3x-2}{x+4}$

c $f(x) = \dfrac{x+4}{3x-2}$

1.4 The linear function and the modulus function

The linear function is defined by $f(x) = mx + c$; the domain may be $\mathbb{R}$ or any subset of $\mathbb{R}$. Either or both of the constants m and c may be zero. If the domain is $\mathbb{R}$, the range is also $\mathbb{R}$ unless $m = 0$; in that case the range is $\{c\}$.

The linear function owes its name to the fact that the graph is a line (i.e. a straight line). The gradient of the line is m.

The modulus function is defined by

$$f(x) = x \quad \text{for } x \geqslant 0,$$
$$f(x) = -x \quad \text{for } x < 0.$$

It follows from this definition that the range of the modulus function is all non-negative numbers. The symbol for $f(x)$ as defined above is $|x|$. The graph of $y = |x|$ is shown in the diagram.

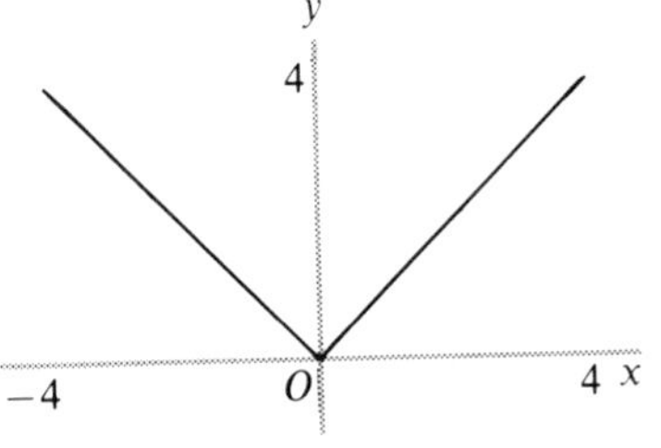

The modulus function gives the *distance* of the point representing x from the origin O, without reference to whether the point x is on the right or the left of O, e.g. $|4| = 4$ and $|-4| = 4$.

Since two values of x give the same value of y, the modulus function has no inverse function.

Examples 1.4

1 Rewrite the statement '$|x| < 5$' without using the modulus notation.

Since the distance of x from the origin is to be less than 5, x must lie between -5 and $+5$, i.e. $-5 < x < 5$.

2 Rewrite the statement '$x^2 < 9$' in a form which uses the modulus notation.

The square of x is the same whether x is positive or negative, so that $x^2 = |x|^2$; and $|x|^2 < 9$ for $|x| < 3$.

3 Sketch the graph of $y = |x - 2|$.

Method 1 Since $|x|$ gives the distance of the point x from the point where $x = 0$, $|x - 2|$ gives the distance of the point x from the point where $x - 2 = 0$, i.e. where $x = 2$. The graph may therefore be drawn by translating the graph of $y = |x|$ through 2 units to the right parallel to the x-axis. The graphs of $|x|$ and $|x - 2|$ are shown in Fig. 3.

Method 2 For $x \geqslant 2$, $x - 2 \geqslant 0$, $y = |x - 2| = x - 2$
For $x < 2$, $x - 2 < 0$, $y = |x - 2| = 2 - x$
$\therefore$ the graph is as shown in Fig. 3.

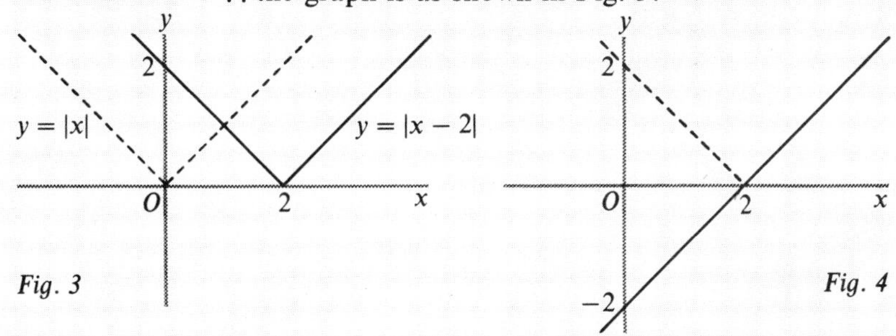

Fig. 3
Fig. 4

Method 3 Draw the line $y = x - 2$ shown in Fig. 4. The part of this line for which $y \geqslant 0$ is part of the graph of $y = |x - 2|$. The part of the line for which $y < 0$ must be reflected in the x-axis to change the sign of each y-coordinate. This gives the broken line shown in Fig. 4. The broken line for $x < 2$ and the solid line for $x \geqslant 2$ are together the required graph, as in Fig. 3.

4 Sketch the graph of $y = |x| - 2$.

Method 1 Draw the graph of $y = |x|$ and subtract 2 from each y-coordinate, i.e. translate the graph through 2 units in the negative direction parallel to the y-axis. See Fig. 5.

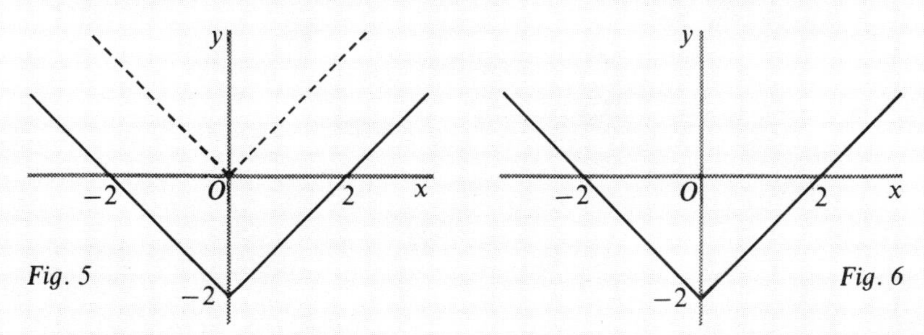

Fig. 5
Fig. 6

Method 2 Draw the graph of $y = x - 2$ for $x \geqslant 0$. This is part of the required graph. Since $|x| - 2$ is unchanged by changing the sign of x, the graph may be completed by reflecting the line already drawn in the y-axis. See Fig. 6.

5 Sketch the graph of $y = |x - 2| + |x + 2|$.

Since $x - 2$ and $x + 2$ change sign at $x = 2$ and $x = -2$ respectively, we have to consider $x < -2$, $-2 \leqslant x \leqslant 2$ and $x > 2$.

$$\begin{aligned} x < -2, &\quad y = (2 - x) + (-x - 2) = -2x \\ -2 \leqslant x \leqslant 2, &\quad y = (2 - x) + (x + 2) \quad = 4 \\ x > 2, &\quad y = (x - 2) + (x + 2) \quad = 2x \end{aligned}$$

The graph is as shown.

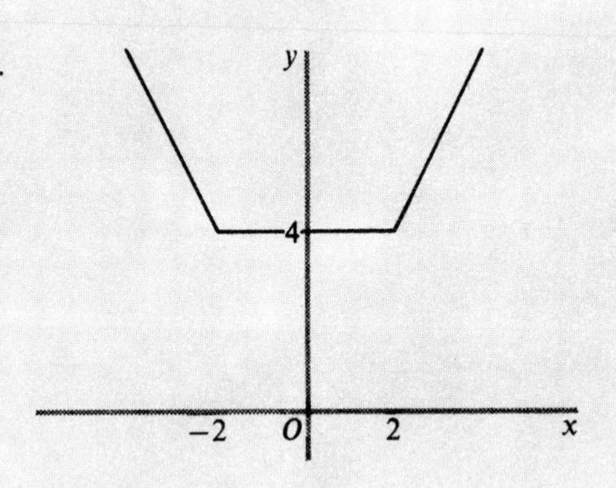

Exercise 1.4A

1 Write each of the following statements in two other forms.

a $x^2 = 16$ **b** $|x| = 2$ **c** $|x| < 5$ **d** $|x| > 6$

2 Sketch the graph of **a** $y = |x - 3|$ **b** $y = |x| - 3$.

3 Sketch the graph of **a** $y = |x + 2|$ **b** $y = |x| + 2$.

4 Sketch the graph of $y = 2x + 3$. Hence sketch on separate axes the graphs of **a** $y = |2x + 3|$ **b** $y = 2|x| + 3$.

5 A particle moves along a line; after t seconds the velocity of the particle is $(5 - 2t)$ cm s^{-1}.

Sketch on separate axes for $0 \leqslant t \leqslant 5$

a the graph of the velocity of the particle

b the graph of the speed of the particle.

Exercise 1.4B

1 Sketch the graph of **a** $y = |x - 4|$ **b** $y = |x| - 4$.

2 Sketch the graph of **a** $y = |2x + 1|$ **b** $y = 2|x| + 1$.

3 Sketch the graph of $y = |x| + |x - 1|$.

4 Sketch the graph of $y = |x + 1| + |x - 2|$.

5 Sketch the graph of $y = |x + 1| + 2|x| + |x - 1|$.

Chapter 2

Polynomials, algebraic fractions, the remainder theorem and the factor theorem

2.1 Polynomials

A polynomial in x, $\mathrm{p}(x)$, is an expression of the form

$$a_n x^n + a_{n-1}x^{n-1} + \ldots + a_1 x + a_0$$

where n is a positive integer and $a_n \neq 0$; the *degree* of this polynomial is n, the highest index which occurs.

Examples of polynomials are

$$4x + 5,\ x^2 + 3x + 7,\ x^3 \text{ and } 2x^4 - 3x^2 - 4x + 2;$$

these examples have degree 1, 2, 3 and 4 respectively.

A polynomial need not be in x; e.g. $4y^2 + 3y - 2$ is a polynomial in y; but x is most frequently used.

The numbers $a_n, a_{n-1}, \ldots, a_1$ and a_0 are the *coefficients* of the polynomial; the term $a_r x^r$ is the term of degree r.

The number x can be a variable in some domain D; in that case the function p defined by $\mathrm{p}(x)$ for $x \in D$ is called a polynomial function. The polynomial functions of degree 0, 1, 2 and 3 are called the constant function, the linear function, the quadratic function and the cubic function respectively.

Equal polynomials have the same degree and the same term of each degree. Thus if the polynomials $ax^2 + bx + c$ and $3x^2 + 4x - 2$ are equal, then $a = 3$, $b = 4$ and $c = -2$, by 'equating coefficients'.

Polynomials may be manipulated as shown in the following examples.

Examples 2.1

1 Given that $\mathrm{p}(x) = 2x + 3$, $\mathrm{q}(x) = 3x^2 + 5x - 4$, calculate

a $\mathrm{p}(x) + \mathrm{q}(x)$ **b** $4\mathrm{p}(x) - \mathrm{q}(x)$ **c** $\mathrm{p}(x)\mathrm{q}(x)$,

giving each answer in descending powers of x.

a $\mathrm{p}(x) + \mathrm{q}(x) = 2x + 3 + 3x^2 + 5x - 4$

$= 3x^2 + 7x - 1$

b $4p(x) - q(x) = 4(2x + 3) - (3x^2 + 5x - 4)$
$= -3x^2 + 3x + 16$

c $p(x)q(x) = (2x + 3)(3x^2 + 5x - 4)$
$= 2x(3x^2 + 5x - 4) + 3(3x^2 + 5x - 4)$
$= 6x^3 + 10x^2 - 8x$
$+ 9x^2 + 15x - 12$
$= 6x^3 + 19x^2 + 7x - 12$

Note that the work is simpler if the same powers are collected in 'columns'.

2 Given that $p(x) = 2x^3 - 6x + 3$ and $q(x) = 4x^3 - 5x^2 + 2x$, calculate $4p(x) - 2q(x)$.

$4p(x) - 2q(x) = 4(2x^3 - 6x + 3) - 2(4x^3 - 5x^2 + 2x)$
$= 10x^2 - 28x + 12$

Note that $p(x)$ and $q(x)$ are each of degree 3, but that $4p(x) - 2q(x)$ is of degree 2. In general, if $p(x)$ has degree n and $q(x)$ has degree m, the degree of $Ap(x) + Bq(x)$, where A and B are constants, cannot exceed the larger of n and m; but no more can be said. The expression $Ap(x) + Bq(x)$ is called a *linear combination* of $p(x)$ and $q(x)$.

3 Find the coefficient of x^3 in the product of $3x^2 + 4x - 2$ and $5x^2 - 2x + 1$.

This may of course be done by expressing the product as a single polynomial, but this is time-wasting and unnecessary. Terms in x^3 arise by multiplying the $3x^2$ on the left by $-2x$ on the right, giving $-6x^3$, and by multiplying $4x$ on the left by $5x^2$ on the right, giving $20x^3$. These products may be indicated as shown:

$$(3x^2 + 4x - 2)(5x^2 - 2x + 1).$$

The coefficient of x^3 is therefore $20 - 6 = 14$.

Exercise 2.1A

1 For each of the following, calculate $p(x) + q(x)$, $p(x) - 2q(x)$ and $p(x)q(x)$, giving each answer in descending powers of x.

a $p(x) = 4x + 3$, $\quad q(x) = 2x^2 - 3x - 6$

b $p(x) = 3x^2 - 2x - 1$, $\quad q(x) = 2x^2 + 5x - 2$

c $p(x) = 2x^4 + 3$, $\quad q(x) = 4x^3 - 2x + 1$

2 Given that $p(x) = 2x^3 + 6x^2 - 3x - 4$ and $q(x) = 4x^3 + 12x^2 - 6x - 3$, find $4p(x) - 2q(x)$ and state the degree of this polynomial.

3 In the product $(4x^2 - 2x + 3)(5x^2 + 4x - 2)$, find the coefficient of
a x^2 **b** x^3.

4 Express $(3x^2 - 5x - 2)^2$ as a polynomial in descending powers of x.

Exercise 2.1B

1 For each of the following, calculate $p(x) + 3q(x)$, $2p(x) - 4q(x)$ and $p(x)q(x)$, giving each answer in descending powers of x.

a $p(x) = 5x - 2$, $q(x) = 4x^2 - 2x - 3$

b $p(x) = 3x^2 - 4x + 2$, $q(x) = 2x^2 + 4x - 1$

c $p(x) = 5x^2 - 3$, $q(x) = 2x^3 + 5x - 4$

2 In the product $(5x^4 + 3x - 2)(2x^3 + 4x^2 - 1)$, find the coefficient of

a x^3 **b** x^4.

3 In the product $(1 + 2x - 4x^2)(3 - 5x + 2x^2)$, find the coefficient of

a x^2 **b** x^3.

4 Find the coefficient of x^2 in $(6 + 4x - 3x^2)^2$.

2.2 Algebraic fractions

If a polynomial $p(x)$ is divided by a polynomial $q(x)$ the result is not in general a polynomial; it is so if the degree of $q(x)$ is zero, i.e. if $q(x)$ is a constant, or if $q(x)$ is a factor of $p(x)$. Otherwise the result is an algebraic fraction. If $p(x)$ and $q(x)$ define functions on some domain, then $\dfrac{p(x)}{q(x)}$ defines a rational function on some domain which excludes the zeros of $q(x)$.

If x is not a variable in some domain, no idea of functionality is involved; x is an unspecified number, the value of which is assumed to exclude zero denominators.

Examples of algebraic fractions are $\dfrac{2x+1}{3x-2}$, $\dfrac{4x^2+3x-2}{x+3}$, $\dfrac{2x+1}{(x-1)(x+2)}$.

Algebraic fractions occur in many branches of mathematics; in particular the student will meet them in calculus as well as in algebra. Accuracy in manipulation of these fractions is of great importance, as is accuracy in all forms of algebraic manipulation; practice is given in this chapter. Ability to factorise quadratics is assumed.

Algebraic fractions may be added, subtracted, multiplied and divided using the same methods as are used in arithmetic fractions.

Examples 2.2

1 Express as a single fraction in its simplest form $\dfrac{3}{x+2} + \dfrac{2}{x-5}$.

The denominators have no factors; the common denominator is their product.

$$\frac{3}{x+2} + \frac{2}{x-5} = \frac{3(x-5) + 2(x+2)}{(x+2)(x-5)}$$

$$= \frac{5x-11}{(x+2)(x-5)}$$

Note that the brackets in the denominator are not removed; those in the numerator are removed, since the result is a simpler form.

2 Given that $y = \dfrac{3x}{x^2 - 4} + \dfrac{2x - 1}{x^2 - 3x + 2}$,
express y as a single fraction in its simplest form.

Each denominator can be factorised:

$$y = \frac{3x}{(x-2)(x+2)} + \frac{2x-1}{(x-1)(x-2)}$$

$$= \frac{3x(x-1) + (2x-1)(x+2)}{(x-2)(x+2)(x-1)}$$

$$= \frac{3x^2 - 3x + 2x^2 + 4x - x - 2}{(x-2)(x+2)(x-1)} = \frac{5x^2 - 2}{(x-2)(x+2)(x-1)}.$$

3 Given that $r(x) = \dfrac{x^2 - 4x + 3}{x^2 - 4x + 4}$, $\quad s(x) = \dfrac{x^2 - 4}{x^2 - x - 6}$,

simplify **a** $r(x)s(x)$ **b** $\dfrac{r(x)}{s(x)}$.

a $r(x)s(x) = \dfrac{(x-1)(x-3)}{(x-2)^2} \times \dfrac{(x-2)(x+2)}{(x+2)(x-3)}$

Three of the factors in the numerator are also in the denominator, and these can be cancelled, giving the answer $\dfrac{x-1}{x-2}$.

It is essential to realise that 'cancelling' in this context means *dividing* the numerator and denominator by the same *factor*.

b $\dfrac{r(x)}{s(x)} = \dfrac{(x-1)(x-3)}{(x-2)^2} \times \dfrac{(x+2)(x-3)}{(x-2)(x+2)}$

Only the factor $x + 2$ can be cancelled, giving the answer $\dfrac{(x-1)(x-3)^2}{(x-2)^3}$.

Note that there is no point in removing these brackets; the factorised form is more useful.

Exercise 2.2A

1 Express each of the following as a single fraction in its simplest form.

a $\dfrac{2}{x-3} + \dfrac{5}{x+4}$

b $\dfrac{4}{x-2} - \dfrac{3}{x-5}$

c $\dfrac{2x+1}{x^2+5x+6} + \dfrac{3x-2}{x^2+x-6}$

d $\dfrac{4x}{x^2-9} - \dfrac{2x+1}{x^2+7x+12}$

e $\dfrac{4x-8}{x^2-7x+12} \times \dfrac{x^2-16}{x^2+2x-8}$

f $\dfrac{x^2-9}{x^2-7x+10} \div \dfrac{x^2-9x+18}{x^2-8x+12}$

g $\dfrac{4x}{x^2+2x+1} + \dfrac{3x-2}{3x^2+x-2}$

h $\dfrac{5x-1}{x^2-10x+24} - \dfrac{4x+2}{2x^2-3x-2}$

i $\dfrac{3x-9}{x^2-5x} \times \dfrac{x^2-25}{x^2-4x+3}$ **j** $\dfrac{x^2+2x}{x^2-6x-7} \div \dfrac{x^2+7x+10}{x^2-49}$

Exercise 2.2B

1 Express as a single fraction in its simplest form.

a $\dfrac{2x}{x+4} + \dfrac{3x+2}{x-6}$ **b** $\dfrac{4x+1}{x-2} - \dfrac{5x-2}{x+4}$

c $\dfrac{3x-1}{2x^2+7x-4} + \dfrac{5-2x}{x^2+10x+24}$ **d** $\dfrac{x^2+8x+16}{3x^2+x-2} \times \dfrac{4x^2+x-3}{x^2+4x}$

e $\dfrac{x^2-2x-15}{8x^2-14x+3} \div \dfrac{x^2-3x-10}{2x^2-5x+3}$ **f** $\dfrac{x+2y}{(x-y)^2} + \dfrac{x+3y}{x^2-y^2}$

g $\dfrac{3a+b}{a+3b} \times \dfrac{a^2+5ab+6b^2}{9a^2-b^2}$ **h** $\dfrac{x}{x^2+xy-2y^2} \div \dfrac{x^2+2xy}{x^2-2xy+y^2}$

2.3 Long division in algebra

By a process similar to long division in arithmetic, a polynomial p(x) may be divided by a polynomial of the same or lower degree than p(x).

Examples 2.3

1 Find the quotient and the remainder when x^3+5x^2+2x+3 is divided by $x+2$.

$$\begin{array}{r} x^2+3x-4 \\ x+2\overline{)x^3+5x^2+2x+3} \\ \underline{x^3+2x^2} \qquad\qquad \\ 3x^2+2x \qquad \\ \underline{3x^2+6x} \qquad \\ -4x+3 \\ \underline{-4x-8} \\ \underline{11} \end{array}$$

Compare:

$$\begin{array}{r} 214 \\ 13\overline{)2792} \\ \underline{26} \\ 19 \\ \underline{13} \\ 62 \\ \underline{52} \\ \underline{10} \end{array}$$

Quotient 214, remainder 10

The quotient is x^2+3x-4 and the remainder is 11.

The result of this division may be written

$$\frac{x^3+5x^2+2x+3}{x+2} = x^2+3x-4+\frac{11}{x+2}$$

or as $x^3+5x^2+2x+3 = (x+2)(x^2+3x-4)+11$.

The second form is an identity true for all values of x, as may be verified by removing the brackets on the right-hand side. The first form is true for all values of x except -2. Note that replacing x by -2 in the identity gives both sides equal to 11: this provides a check on the accuracy of the division, though it is only a partial check; the quotient could still be wrong.

2 Find the quotient and the remainder when $x^3 + 4x + 2$ is divided by $x - 3$, and check the remainder.

Since there is no term in x^2 in the cubic, a space must be left for this term.

$$
\begin{array}{r|l}
 & x^2 + 3x + 13 = \text{quotient} \\
x - 3 & x^3 \qquad + 4x + 2 \\
 & x^3 - 3x^2 \\
 & \quad 3x^2 + 4x \\
 & \quad 3x^2 - 9x \\
 & \qquad 13x + 2 \\
 & \qquad 13x - 39 \\
 & \qquad\quad 41 = \text{remainder}
\end{array}
$$

$\therefore x^3 + 4x + 2 = (x - 3)(x^2 + 3x + 13) + 41$

Check: $x = 3$, left side $= 27 + 12 + 2 = 41 =$ right side.

3 Divide $x + 3$ by $x + 1$ 'by inspection'.

$$\frac{x+3}{x+1} = \frac{(x+1)+2}{x+1} = 1 + \frac{2}{x+1}$$

The quotient is 1 and the remainder is 2.

Exercise 2.3A

1 In each of the following find the quotient and the remainder, and show by a check that both are correct.

a $x^3 + 4x^2 + 3x - 6$ is divided by $x + 2$

b $x^3 + 5x + 4$ is divided by $x - 1$

2 In each of the following find the quotient and the remainder, and show by a check that the remainder is correct.

a $x^3 + 2x^2 - 5$ is divided by $x - 3$

b $6x^3 + 4x - 3$ is divided by $2x - 1$

3 By inspection, divide $x + 4$ by $x + 2$.

4 Find the quotient and the remainder in each of the following.

a $x^4 + 3x^3 - 4x + 2$ is divided by $x^2 + 1$

b $x^3 + 8$ is divided by $x^2 - 2x + 4$

c $x^3 - 27$ is divided by $x^2 + 3x + 9$

Exercise 2.3B

1 In each of the following find the quotient and the remainder, and check that the remainder is correct.

a $x^3 - 3x^2 + 5x - 4$ is divided by $x + 3$

b $3x^3 + 4x^2 - 3$ is divided by $3x + 1$

c $x^3 + 1$ is divided by $x + 1$

d $8x^3 - 1$ is divided by $2x - 1$
e $4x^3 + 5x^2 - 7$ is divided by $2x + 1$
f $x^5 - 32$ is divided by $x - 2$

2 In each of the following find the quotient and the remainder.
a $x^4 + 4x^2 - 5$ is divided by $x^2 - 1$
b $x^4 - 16$ is divided by $x^2 - 4$

3 By inspection or otherwise,
a divide $x + 2$ by $x - 1$
b divide $x + 5$ by $x + 2$
c divide $2x + 3$ by $x - 2$
d divide $3x - 4$ by $2x + 1$.

2.4 The remainder theorem

An important case of division of one polynomial $p(x)$ by another is the case where the second polynomial, the divisor, is linear. This is important because if the remainder is found to be zero, then the divisor is a *factor* of $p(x)$; and it is often necessary to factorise a polynomial. Fortunately the remainder can be found without the trouble of carrying out long division; the remainder theorem provides the method. The theorem states that:

When the polynomial $p(x)$ is divided by the linear polynomial $x - \alpha$, the remainder is $p(\alpha)$.

To prove this, let the quotient be $q(x)$ and let the remainder be r.

Then $\dfrac{p(x)}{x - \alpha} = q(x) + \dfrac{r}{x - \alpha}$

which can be written as the identity

$$p(x) = (x - \alpha)q(x) + r$$

$$\therefore\ p(\alpha) = 0 \,.\, q(\alpha) + r \quad \text{or} \quad r = p(\alpha)\text{, as the theorem states.}$$

A more general form of the theorem states that:

When the polynomial $p(x)$ is divided by the linear polynomial $ax + b$, the remainder is $p\left(-\dfrac{b}{a}\right)$.

The proof follows similar lines to the above proof.

Examples 2.4

1 Given that $p(x) = x^3 + 4x^2 - 5x + 6$, find the remainder when $p(x)$ is divided by $x - 2$.

By the remainder theorem, the remainder is
$p(2) = 8 + 16 - 10 + 6 = 20$.

2 Given that $p(x) = 4x^3 + 3x^2 - 2x + 5$, find the remainder when $p(x)$ is divided by $2x + 1$.

By the remainder theorem, the remainder is

$$p\left(-\frac{1}{2}\right) = -\frac{1}{2} + \frac{3}{4} + 1 + 5 = \frac{25}{4}.$$

Exercise 2.4A

1 Find the remainder in each of the following.

a $x^3 + 5x^2 - 6x + 2$ is divided by $x - 1$

b $x^3 - 27$ is divided by $x - 3$

c $x^5 + 33$ is divided by $x + 2$

d $2x^3 + 4x^2 + 5x - 7$ is divided by $x + 3$

e $4x^3 + x^2 - 8x + 2$ is divided by $2x - 1$

f $6x^3 - 3x^2 + 6x + 4$ is divided by $3x + 1$

Exercise 2.4B

1 Find the remainder in each of the following.

a $x^3 + 8$ is divided by $x + 2$

b $x^4 - 17$ is divided by $x - 2$

c $3x^3 - 6x^2 + x + 4$ is divided by $3x - 1$

d $x^3 - a^3$ is divided by $x - a$

e $x^5 + a^5$ is divided by $x + a$

f $x^6 + a^6$ is divided by $x + a$

2 Given that $p(x) = 2x^3 - 5x^2 + 4x - 6$ and $s(x) = x^2 - 4$, find the remainder when $p(x)$ is divided by $s(x)$.

2.5 The factor theorem

If a polynomial $p(x)$ has a factor $x - \alpha$, then

$$p(x) = (x - \alpha)q(x) \qquad (A)$$

and so $p(\alpha) = 0$. This fact has formed the basis of the method of solving quadratic equations by using factors which the student has probably used for some time. Provided a quadratic can be factorised, the corresponding equation can be immediately solved. The same is true for any polynomial equation, but the factorisation process is harder.

The factor theorem provides the converse of the above statement, (A). It states that:

If $p(x)$ is a polynomial and $p(\alpha) = 0$, then $x - \alpha$ is a factor of the polynomial.

The proof is an immediate consequence of the remainder theorem; the remainder on division of $p(x)$ by $x - \alpha$ is $p(\alpha)$, and so if $p(\alpha) = 0$, then the remainder is 0, so that $x - \alpha$ is a factor.

There is a more general form of the factor theorem, corresponding to the general form of the remainder theorem:

If $p(x)$ is a polynomial and $p\left(-\frac{b}{a}\right) = 0$, then $ax + b$ is a factor of the polynomial.

Examples 2.5

1 Given that $p(x) = x^3 + 3x^2 - 5x + 1$, show that $p(x)$ has a factor $x - 1$ and express $p(x)$ as the product of two factors.

$p(1) = 1 + 3 - 5 + 1 = 0$, $\therefore$ by the factor theorem $p(x)$ has a factor $x - 1$. The other factor must be a quadratic with first term x^2 and last term -1, to give the first and last terms of $p(x)$.

$\therefore x^3 + 3x^2 - 5x + 1 = (x - 1)(x^2 + kx - 1)$

for some constant k. The value of k can be found by inspection, or by equating the coefficients of x^2, which gives $3 = k - 1$, so $k = 4$.

$\therefore p(x) = (x - 1)(x^2 + 4x - 1)$,

which can be mentally checked. Long division can of course be used here. Note that the quadratic factor cannot be further factorised.

2 Given that $p(x) = x^3 - 6x^2 + 3x + 10$, express $p(x)$ as the product of three factors.

Possible factors are $x \pm 1$, $x \pm 2$, $x \pm 5$, $x \pm 10$, since the final number in any factor must be a factor of 10.

$p(1) = 1 - 6 + 3 + 10 \neq 0$

$p(-1) = -1 - 6 - 3 + 10 = 0$, $\therefore x + 1$ is a factor

$\therefore x^3 - 6x^2 + 3x + 10 = (x + 1)(x^2 + kx + 10)$

and equating coefficients of x^2 gives $k = -7$.

$\therefore p(x) = (x + 1)(x^2 - 7x + 10) = (x + 1)(x - 2)(x - 5)$

Exercise 2.5A

1 Use the factor theorem to factorise each of the following.

a $x^3 + 2x^2 - 13x + 10$ **b** $x^3 + 2x^2 - 5x - 6$

c $x^3 - 4x^2 + 5x - 2$ **d** $x^3 - 5x^2 - 2x + 24$

2 Show that $x - 2$ is a factor of $2x^3 - 13x^2 + 22x - 8$ and find the other linear factors.

3 Given that $p(x) = 2x^3 + 3x^2 + 4x - 3$, show that $2x - 1$ is a factor of $p(x)$ and factorise $p(x)$ as far as possible.

4 Given that $p(x) = 3x^3 + 2x^2 + 2x - 1$, show that $3x - 1$ is a factor of $p(x)$ and factorise $p(x)$ as far as possible.

Exercise 2.5B

1 Use the factor theorem to factorise each of the following.

a $x^3 - 13x + 12$ **b** $x^3 - 5x^2 + 4x + 10$

c $x^3 + x^2 - 7x - 15$ **d** $x^3 + 3x^2 + 5x + 6$

2 Show that $x - 2$ is a factor of $3x^3 + x^2 - 20x + 12$ and find the other linear factors.

3 Given that $p(x) = 2x^3 - 3x^2 + 4x + 3$, show that $2x + 1$ is a factor of $p(x)$ and factorise $p(x)$ as far as possible.

4 Factorise $x^4 - 16$ as far as possible.

5 Express $x^5 - 32$ as a product of two factors.

2.6 Some important factors

The following factors should be known.

$$x^2 - a^2 = (x - a)(x + a)$$
$$x^3 - a^3 = (x - a)(x^2 + ax + a^2)$$
$$x^3 + a^3 = (x + a)(x^2 - ax + a^2)$$

The first factor on the right may be found by using the factor theorem, and the other by inspection or by long division. Each identity may of course be verified by removing the brackets on the right-hand side.

These three identities are special cases of the following:

$$x^n - a^n = (x - a)(x^{n-1} + ax^{n-2} + \ldots + a^{n-1})$$

for all values of n,

$$x^n + a^n = (x + a)(x^{n-1} - ax^{n-2} + \ldots + a^{n-1})$$

for all odd values of n. These may be found, and verified, as before. In the case $n = 3$ these factorisations are complete; the quadratic factor cannot be factorised. For $n = 4$, for example, the factorisation is not complete:

$$x^4 - a^4 = (x - a)(x + a)(x^2 + a^2).$$

Exercise 2.6

1 Express each of the following as the product of two or more factors.

a $x^3 - 8$ **b** $x^3 + 27$ **c** $x^5 + 1$ **d** $x^6 - 64$

e $x^3 + 125$ **f** $x^4 - 625$ **g** $8x^3 - 1$ **h** $27 - x^3$

Miscellaneous Exercise 2

1 Simplify $\dfrac{x^3 - 8}{x^3 + 27} \times \dfrac{x^2 + 5x + 6}{x^2 - 3x + 2}$.

2 Express as a single fraction in its simplest form $\dfrac{x + 3}{x^3 + 1} - \dfrac{4}{x^2 + 2x + 1}$.

3 Simplify $\dfrac{x^3 + 1}{x^2 - 4} \div \dfrac{x^2 - x - 2}{x^2 - 4x + 4}$.

4 Given that f is defined by $f(x) = \dfrac{x + 1}{x - 2}$, $x \neq 2$, and that g is defined by $g(x) = \dfrac{x - 3}{x - 1}$, $x \neq 1$, find $fg(x)$ and state the domain of fg.

5 Given that f and g are defined by

$$f(x) = \frac{ax + b}{cx + d}, \; x \neq -\frac{d}{c}, \text{ and } g(x) = \frac{px + q}{rx + s}, \; x \neq -\frac{s}{r},$$

respectively, calculate $fg(x)$. State the relation between c, d, p and r in the case when fg is a linear function. State the domain of fg in this case.

Chapter 3

Arithmetic and geometric series

3.1 Sequences: arithmetic sequences

A sequence is an ordered list of numbers, i.e. it is a list of numbers having a first term, a second term, and so on. The word 'sequence' comes from the Latin verb 'sequor', to follow. It is not a *set* of numbers since two or more terms of the sequence can be equal. Examples of sequences are:

a 1, 3, 5, 7 **b** $1, \frac{1}{2}, \frac{1}{3}, \frac{1}{4}, \frac{1}{5}$ **c** 2, 6, 12, 20, 30, 42

d $1, -1, 1, -1$.

In each of these examples, there is a finite number of terms, but a sequence can be infinite. The natural numbers are an infinite sequence, 1, 2, 3, . . .; there is no 'last term'.

A particularly simple type of sequence is an *arithmetic* sequence. Examples of arithmetic sequences are:

a 2, 6, 10, 14 **b** $3, 3\frac{1}{2}, 4, 4\frac{1}{2}, 5$ **c** $10, 8, 6, 4, 2, 0, -2$.

The definition of an arithmetic sequence is that, from the second term on, each term minus the previous term gives the same number; this number is called the *common difference* of the sequence.

A convenient notation for any sequence is $t_1, t_2, t_3, \ldots$. For the arithmetic sequence the standard notation is a for the first term and d for the common difference, so that $t_1 = a$, $t_2 = a + d$, $t_3 = a + 2d$, and so on. The nth term, t_n, is $a + (n - 1)d$; note that d is not used until the *second* term so that the number of d's to be added to a always lags one behind the suffix of the term.

The *arithmetic mean* of two numbers a and b is defined as the number c such that a, c, b are consecutive terms of an arithmetic sequence. Since the common difference of the sequence $= c - a = b - c$, it follows that $c = \frac{a+b}{2}$,

i.e. the arithmetic mean of a and b is $\frac{a+b}{2}$.

Examples 3.1

1 Given that the sequence 5, 8, 11, ... is arithmetic, find the 8th term and the nth term.

Here $a = 5$ and $d = 3$

$\therefore t_8 = 5 + 7 \times 3 = 26$

$t_n = 5 + 3(n - 1) = 3n + 2$

2 Find the number of terms in the arithmetic sequence 7, 11, 15, ..., 127.

Here $a = 7$ and $d = 4$; let the number of terms be n.

Then $t_n = 7 + 4(n - 1) = 4n + 3$

$\therefore 4n + 3 = 127$

$n = 31$

$\therefore$ the number of terms is 31.

3 The 4th term of an arithmetic sequence is 15; the 8th term is 23. Find the common difference and the first term.

Let the first term be a and the common difference d.

Then $t_4 = a + 3d = 15$

$t_8 = a + 7d = 23$

$\therefore 4d = 8$

$d = 2, a = 9$

$\therefore$ the common difference is 2 and the first term is 9.

Exercise 3.1A

1 Find the 8th term and the nth term in each of the following arithmetic sequences.

a 2, 6, 10, ... **b** 6, 4, 2, ... **c** 3, $3\frac{1}{2}$, 4, ... **d** 10, 9.9, 9.8, ...

2 Find the number of terms in each of the following arithmetic sequences.

a 3, 8, ..., 83 **b** 10, 12, ..., 362

c 4, $5\frac{1}{2}$, ..., 79 **d** 36, 32, ..., -84

3 The 3rd term of an arithmetic sequence is 12; the 9th term is 42. Find the 21st term.

4 Find the arithmetic mean of 3.5 and 4.7.

Exercise 3.1B

1 Find the nth term in each of the following arithmetic sequences.

a 5, 7, 9, ... **b** 4, 4.2, 4.4, ... **c** 20, 15, 10, ... **d** 2, $3\frac{1}{3}$, $4\frac{2}{3}$, ...

2 Find the number of terms in each of the following arithmetic sequences.

a 4, 11, ..., 445 **b** $-5, -3, \ldots, 75$

c 2, 2.3, ..., 32.3 **d** $50, 47, \ldots, -241$

3 The 7th term of an arithmetic sequence is $8\frac{1}{2}$, the 13th term is 13. Find the 25th term.

3.2 Series: arithmetic series

When successive terms of a sequence are added, the result is called a *series*. The sequence $t_1, t_2, t_3, \ldots, t_n$ gives the series $t_1 + t_2 + t_3 + \ldots + t_n$.

This sum of terms may be written in a concise form by using the summation sign $\sum$, which is a Greek S, pronounced 'sigma'. Using this sign, the above sum of terms is written $\sum_{r=1}^{n} t_r$, and is read 'the sum of t_r from $r = 1$ to $r = n$', or 'sigma t_r from $r = 1$ to $r = n$'.

For the present, this definition of a series is confined to *finite* series obtained from finite sequences.

When the sequence $t_1, t_2, \ldots$ is arithmetic, the series $t_1 + t_2 + \ldots$ is called an arithmetic series. The name 'arithmetic progression' is often used for such a series, and this is abbreviated to 'A.P.' The word 'progression' is also used for the sequence.

The standard notation is to use l for the last of n terms of an A.P. and S_n for the sum of n terms. The numbers $S_1, S_2, \ldots, S_n$ themselves form a new sequence. The sum S_n may be written in several ways:

$$\begin{aligned} S_n &= a + (a + d) + \ldots + l \\ &= a + (a + d) + \ldots [a + (n - 1)d] \\ &= \sum_{r=1}^{n} [a + (r - 1)d]. \end{aligned}$$

It is easy to prove that $S_n = \dfrac{n(a + l)}{2}$.

Proof $\quad S_n = a + (a + d) + \ldots + (l - d) + l$

Reversing: $\quad S_n = l + (l - d) + \ldots + (a + d) + a$

Adding: $\quad 2S_n = (a + l) + (a + l) + \ldots + (a + l) + (a + l)$

$$\therefore S_n = \frac{n(a + l)}{2}$$

$$= (\text{number of terms}) \times (\text{mean of first and last terms}).$$

This is a useful form in which to remember the formula.

Replacing l by $a + (n - 1)d$ gives the alternative form

$$S_n = \frac{n}{2}[2a + (n - 1)d].$$

Examples 3.2

1 Write using the summation sign $1^3 + 2^3 + 3^3 + \ldots + (2n)^3$.

This is equal to $\sum_{r=1}^{2n} r^3$.

2 Write without using the summation sign $\sum_{r=2}^{6} (2r + 1)$.

This is equal to $5 + 7 + 9 + 11 + 13$.

3 Given that the series $2 + 8 + 14 + \ldots$ is arithmetic, find the 100th term and the sum of the first 100 terms.

Here $a = 2$ and $d = 6$

$\therefore l = 2 + 99 \times 6 = 596$

$\therefore S_{100} = 100\dfrac{(2 + 596)}{2} = 29900.$

4 The 10th term of an A.P. is 47, and the sum of the first 10 terms is 245. Find the first term and the common difference.

$t_{10} = a + 9d = 47$

$S_{10} = 10\dfrac{(a + 47)}{2} = 245$

$\therefore a = 2$ and $d = 5$

$\therefore$ the first term is 2 and the common difference is 5.

Exercise 3.2A

1 Write the following using the summation sign $\sum$.

a $1^2 + 2^2 + 3^2 + \ldots + n^2$

b $1 + \frac{1}{2} + \frac{1}{3} + \ldots + \frac{1}{10}$

c $1 + 2 + 2^2 + \ldots + 2^{n-1}$

d $1.2 + 2.3 + 3.4 + \ldots + n(n + 1)$

2 Write without using the summation sign.

a $\sum_{r=1}^{n} r^3$

b $\sum_{r=1}^{2n} 3^r$

c $\sum_{r=1}^{6} [4 + 3(r - 1)]$

d $\sum_{r=0}^{5} (-1)^r 4^r$

3 Find the 50th term and the sum of the first 50 terms for each of the following A.P.s.

a $3 + 5 + 7 + \ldots$

b $4 + 3 + 2 + \ldots$

c $1 + 1.1 + 1.2 + \ldots$

d $2 + 2\frac{1}{7} + 2\frac{2}{7} + \ldots$

4 The first term of an A.P. is 5 and the sum of the first 21 terms is 630. Find the 21st term and the common difference.

5 The 29th term of an A.P. is 10 and the sum of the first 33 terms is 231. Find the sum of the first 29 terms.

6 The sum of the first n terms of an A.P. is $2n^2 + n$ for all values of n. Find the first three terms.

Exercise 3.2B

1 Write the following using the summation sign $\sum$.

a $4 + 6 + \ldots + 2n$ **b** $\frac{1}{3^2} + \frac{1}{4^2} + \ldots + \frac{1}{n^2}$

c $3 + 3(2) + 3(2^2) + 3(2^3)$ **d** $\frac{1}{1.3} + \frac{1}{3.5} + \ldots + \frac{1}{(2n-1)(2n+1)}$

2 Write without using the summation sign.

a $\sum_{r=1}^{n} \frac{1}{2^{r-1}}$ **b** $\sum_{r=0}^{2n} (-1)^r x^r$ **c** $\sum_{r=1}^{7} r(r+1)(r+2)$ **d** $\sum_{r=1}^{n} 2$

3 Find the 60th term and the sum of the first 60 terms for each of the following A.P.s.

a $5 + 8 + 11 + \ldots$ **b** $10 + 8 + 6 + \ldots$ **c** $2 + 3.2 + 4.4 + \ldots$

4 The common difference of an A.P. is 5 and the sum of the first 30 terms is 2235. Find the first term.

5 Prove that

a the sum of the first n positive integers is $\frac{n(n+1)}{2}$

b the sum of the first n odd positive integers is n^2.

6 The first term of an A.P. is 4, the common difference is $\frac{2}{3}$, and the sum is 434. Find the number of terms.

7 The sum of the first n terms of a series is $\frac{n}{2}(3n + 13)$ for all values of n.

Find the first two terms and the nth term. Show that the series is arithmetic.

3.3 Geometric sequences and series

The following are examples of geometric sequences.

a 2, 6, 18, 54, ... **b** $1, \frac{1}{2}, \frac{1}{4}, \frac{1}{8}, \frac{1}{16}, \ldots$ **c** 5, −10, 20, ...

The defining property of a geometric sequence is that, from the second term on, each term divided by the previous term gives the same number; this number is called the *common ratio* of the sequence. The standard notation for a geometric sequence is a for the first term and r for the common ratio, so that $t_1 = a$, $t_2 = ar$, $t_3 = ar^2$, ..., $t_n = ar^{n-1}$. For each term the index for r lags one behind the suffix of the term, since r is first used on the *second* term.

The nth terms in the sequences **a**, **b**, **c** above are $2(3^{n-1})$, $\frac{1}{2^{n-1}}$ and $5(-2)^{n-1}$ respectively.

The *geometric mean* of two positive numbers a and b is defined as the positive number c such that a, c, b are consecutive terms of a geometric sequence.

Since the common ratio of the sequence $= \frac{c}{a} = \frac{b}{c}$, it follows that $c^2 = ab$ and $c = \sqrt{(ab)}$, i.e. the geometric mean of a and b is $\sqrt{(ab)}$.

A *geometric series* is formed by adding successive terms of a geometric sequence. The first n terms of the sequences **a**, **b**, **c** above give the series

a $2 + 6 + 18 + 54 + \ldots + 2.3^{n-1}$ **b** $1 + \frac{1}{2} + \frac{1}{4} + \frac{1}{8} + \frac{1}{16} + \ldots + \frac{1}{2^{n-1}}$

c $5 - 10 + 20 - \ldots + 5(-2)^{n-1}$.

There is a simple formula for the sum of the first n terms of the geometric series with first term a and common ratio r.

Let the sum be S_n.

Then $S_n = a + ar + ar^2 + \ldots + ar^{n-1}$

$\therefore rS_n = \quad ar + ar^2 + \ldots + ar^{n-1} + ar^n$.

Subtract: $S_n - rS_n = a - ar^n$

$S_n(1 - r) = a(1 - r^n)$

$\therefore S_n = \dfrac{a(1 - r^n)}{1 - r}$ provided $r \neq 1$.

In the case $r = 1$, all the terms of the series are equal to a, and so $S_n = na$.

In the case $r > 1$, the formula may be more conveniently written

$$S_n = \frac{a(r^n - 1)}{r - 1}.$$

A geometric series is often called a 'geometric progression' and this may be abbreviated to 'G.P.' The word 'progression' is also used for the sequence.

Examples 3.3

1 The 7th term of a geometric sequence is 384; the 10th term is 3072. Find the common ratio and the first term.

Let the common ratio be r and the first term a.

Then $t_7 = ar^6 = 384$

$t_{10} = ar^9 = 3072$.

Dividing: $r^3 = \dfrac{3072}{384} = 8$

$\therefore r = 2$

$\therefore a = \dfrac{384}{2^6} = 6$.

$\therefore$ the common ratio is 2 and the first term is 6.

2 Find the sum of the first 20 terms of the G.P. with first term 3 and common ratio $\frac{1}{2}$, giving the answer (i) in index form and (ii) to six d.p.

$$S_{20} = 3\left(1 + \frac{1}{2} + \frac{1}{4} + \ldots + \frac{1}{2^{19}}\right)$$

$$= \frac{3\left(1 - \frac{1}{2^{20}}\right)}{1 - \frac{1}{2}}$$

(i) $S_{20} = 6\left(1 - \frac{1}{2^{20}}\right)$

(ii) $S_{20} = 5.999994$ to six d.p.

3 Given that £P is invested at 7% per annum compound interest, show that the values of the investment at the end of each successive year form a geometric sequence. Find the value of the investment at the end of six years.

The interest for the first year is 7% of £P = £$(0.07)P$ and this is added to the original investment of £P.

∴ the amount invested at the end of one year

$= £P + £(0.07)P$

$= £P(1 + 0.07)$

$= £P(1.07)$.

∴ the effect of one year's interest is to multiply the amount invested at the beginning of that year by the factor 1.07.

∴ the values of the investment at the end of each successive year form a geometric sequence, with first term £$P(1.07)$ and common ratio 1.07.

At the end of six years the value of the investment is £$P(1.07)^6 \approx$ £$1.5P$.

Exercise 3.3A

1 Write down in index form the 6th term and the nth term in each of the following geometric sequences.

a 4, 12, 36, ... **b** 2, 20, 200, ... **c** $\frac{1}{2}, -2, 8, \ldots$ **d** $6, 2, \frac{2}{3}, \ldots$

2 The 10th term of a geometric sequence is eighty-one times the 6th term. Find the possible values of the common ratio.

3 Find the geometric mean of 3.6 and 5.4, correct to one d.p.

4 Find the sum of the first 15 terms in each of the following G.P.s, giving the answers correct to three s.f.

a $2 + 8 + 32 + \dots$ **b** $4 + 2 + 1 + \dots$ **c** $10 - 2 + \frac{2}{5} + \dots$

5 Write down the sum of the series $1 + x + x^2 + \dots + x^{n-1}$. Hence express $1 - x^n$ as the product of two factors.

6 In a G.P. the first term is a, the second term is p more than the first term and the fourth term is q more than the first term. Show that the sum of the first 3 terms is $\frac{aq}{p}$.

Exercise 3.3B

1 Write down the term indicated, and the nth term, in each of the following geometric sequences.

a $2, 8, 32, \dots$; 6th term **b** $12, -3, \frac{3}{4}, \dots$; 5th term

c $0.2, 0.02, 0.002, \dots$; 7th term

2 In a geometric sequence the sum of the 5th and 6th terms is nine times the sum of the 3rd and 4th terms. Given that the common ratio is not -1, find its possible values.

3 Find the sum of the first 20 terms in each of the following G.P.s, giving the answers in index form.

a $12 + 4 + \frac{4}{3} + \dots$ **b** $3 - 6 + 12 - \dots$ **c** $27 - 9 + \frac{1}{3} - \dots$

4 Write down and simplify the sum of the G.P.

$$x^{n-1} + ax^{n-2} + a^2x^{n-3} + \dots + a^{n-1}.$$

Hence express $x^n - a^n$ as the product of two factors.

5 The sum of £100 is invested on the first of January in each of five successive years, and the whole investment earns compound interest at the rate of 8% per annum. Find the total amount by the end of the fifth year, to the nearest penny.

3.4 Infinite geometric series

For the geometric series $1 + \frac{1}{2} + \frac{1}{4} + \dots$, the sum, S_n, of the first n terms is

$$\frac{1 - \left(\frac{1}{2}\right)^n}{1 - \frac{1}{2}} = 2\left(1 - \frac{1}{2^n}\right) = 2 - \frac{1}{2^{n-1}}.$$

Since $\frac{1}{2^{n-1}} > 0$ for all n, this result shows that S_n remains less than 2, no matter how many terms of the series are added, i.e. no matter how large n becomes. Not only does S_n remain less than 2 for all values of n, but the larger n is, the closer S_n is to 2; and S_n can be made as close as we like to 2, by choosing a large enough n. For example, S_{100} falls short of 2 by $\frac{1}{2^{99}}$, which is less than 2×10^{-30}; S_{1000} is much closer still to 2. The number 2 has this unique relation to S_n, that S_n can be made as near as we like to 2; 2 is called the *limit* of S_n as $n \to \infty$ and the 'sum to infinity' of the series. We write

$$S_n \to 2 \text{ as } n \to \infty;$$

the series is said to *converge* to 2.

For the general geometric series $a(1 + r + r^2 + \ldots)$,

$$S_n = \frac{a(1 - r^n)}{1 - r} = \frac{a}{1 - r} - \frac{a}{1 - r} \cdot r^n.$$

Provided $|r| < 1$, r^n can be made as small as we like by making n large enough, and so

$$S_n \to \frac{a}{1 - r} \text{ as } n \to \infty$$

i.e. the sum to infinity of the general geometric series is $\frac{a}{1 - r}$ *provided* $|r| < 1$. For other values of r the series is not convergent. It is said to be 'divergent'.

Examples 3.4

1 Show that the geometric series $2 + 1.8 + 1.62 + \ldots$ converges, and find its sum to infinity.

The common ratio $= r = 0.9 < 1$, $\therefore$ the series converges; the sum $= \frac{2}{1 - 0.9} = 20$.

2 Find the values of x for which the geometric series $1 + 2x + 4x^2 + \ldots$ converges, and find its sum to infinity.

The common ratio is $2x$, $\therefore$ the series converges for $|2x| < 1$, $|x| < \frac{1}{2}$.

The sum $= \frac{1}{1 - 2x}$.

3 Express the recurring decimal $0.\dot{2}\dot{4}$ as an infinite geometric series and hence express the decimal as a fraction in its simplest form.

$$0.\dot{2}\dot{4} = 0.242424\ldots$$
$$= \frac{24}{100} + \frac{24}{(100)^2} + \cdots$$
$$= \frac{24}{100}\left(1 + \frac{1}{100} + \cdots\right)$$

This is an infinite geometric series with first term $\frac{24}{100}$ and common ratio $\frac{1}{100}$; $\therefore$ the series converges to the sum

$$\frac{\frac{24}{100}}{1 - \frac{1}{100}} = \frac{24}{99} = \frac{8}{33}.$$

Exercise 3.4A

1 Write down the common ratio, and the sum to infinity where it exists, for each of the following geometric series.

a $2 + \frac{4}{3} + \frac{8}{9} + \ldots$ **b** $\frac{1}{3} - \frac{1}{6} + \frac{1}{12} - \ldots$

c $1 + 0.9 + 0.81 + \ldots$ **d** $2 + 2.2 + 2.42 + \ldots$

2 Find the values of x for which each of the following geometric series converges, and state the sum to infinity.

a $1 + 3x + 9x^2 + \ldots$ **b** $1 + \frac{2}{x} + \frac{4}{x^2} + \ldots$ **c** $1 + (2 - x) + (2 - x)^2 + \ldots$

3 Express each of the following recurring decimals as an infinite geometric series, and hence express the decimal as a fraction in its simplest form.

a $0.\dot{2}$ **b** $0.\dot{5}\dot{4}$ **c** $0.\dot{1}2\dot{3}$ **d** $0.0\dot{2}\dot{1}$

Exercise 3.4B

1 Write down the common ratio, and the sum to infinity where it exists, for each of the following geometric series.

a $3 + \frac{1}{3} + \frac{1}{27} + \ldots$ **b** $4 - 3 + \frac{9}{4} - \ldots$

c $12 + \frac{144}{11} + \frac{1728}{121} + \ldots$ **d** $64 + \frac{128}{3} + \frac{256}{9} + \ldots$

2 Find the values of x for which each of the following geometric series converges, and state the sum to infinity.

a $1 + 5x + 25x^2 + \ldots$ **b** $1 - \frac{x}{4} + \frac{x^2}{16} - \ldots$

c $1 + x^2 + x^4 + \ldots$ **d** $1 + 8x^3 + 64x^6 + \ldots$

3 Express each of the following recurring decimals as an infinite geometric series, and hence express the decimal as a fraction in its simplest form.

a $0.\dot{5}$ **b** $0.\dot{2}\dot{7}$ **c** $0.\dot{5}2\dot{8}$ **d** $0.00\dot{1}\dot{5}$

Miscellaneous Exercise 3

1 Evaluate $\sum_{r=1}^{100} (3r - 2)$.

2 In an arithmetic progression the third term is four times the first term and the fifth term is 14. Find the tenth term. *(L)*

3 The first term of a progression is 24 and the fourth term is 81. Calculate the second and third terms
(i) if the progression is arithmetic (ii) if the progression is geometric.

4 The first and last terms of an arithmetic progression are -2 and 73 respectively, and the sum of all the terms is 923. Calculate the number of terms and the common difference of the progression.

5 The three positive numbers $x - 2$, x, $2x - 3$ are successive terms of a geometric progression. Calculate the value of x.
Given that x is the second term of the progression, calculate the value of the seventh term.

6 A triangle has a perimeter of 14.25 cm and its shortest side is 3 cm in length. Calculate the lengths of the other sides of the triangle
(i) when the lengths of the sides are in arithmetic progression
(ii) when the lengths of the sides are in geometric progression.

7 A piece of wire 216 cm long is cut into 27 pieces whose lengths are in arithmetic progression. The sum of the lengths of the three shortest pieces is 15 cm. Calculate
(i) the length of the shortest piece
(ii) the sum of the lengths of the three longest pieces.

8 The three real, distinct and non-zero numbers a, b, c are such that
a, b, c are in arithmetic progression and
a, c, b are in geometric progression.
Find the numerical value of the common ratio of the geometric progression.
Hence find an expression, in terms of a, for the sum to infinity of the geometric series whose first terms are a, c, b. *(JMB)*

9 **a** If the nth term of an arithmetic progression is $4n - 7$, find the sum of the first 40 terms.

b A geometric progression has first term a and common ratio r. Given that the sum of n terms is 422, show that $ar^{n-1} = \dfrac{422(r-1) + a}{r}$.
If, in addition, the first and nth terms are 32 and 162 respectively, find r and n. *(C)*

Chapter 4

Trigonometry 1

4.1 Introduction

Trigonometry is an important subject; it is widely used in many branches of mathematics, science and engineering. The word trigonometry means measurement of triangles, and the subject first developed through relations between the sides and angles of triangles. The definitions were then generalised to apply to angles of any size and with positive and negative signs; it is at this stage that the present chapter begins. The definitions are then generalised again so that they apply to real numbers, and later to complex numbers. The last stage is beyond the scope of the A level course.

Before starting on the main work of this chapter, a simple but important result will be proved; it will be used in this chapter and in some later chapters.

The distance formula

This formula gives the distance between two points with given coordinates. Let P_1 be (x_1, y_1) and P_2 be (x_2, y_2).

Draw the triangle P_1NP_2 as shown in the diagram, with sides parallel to the axes.

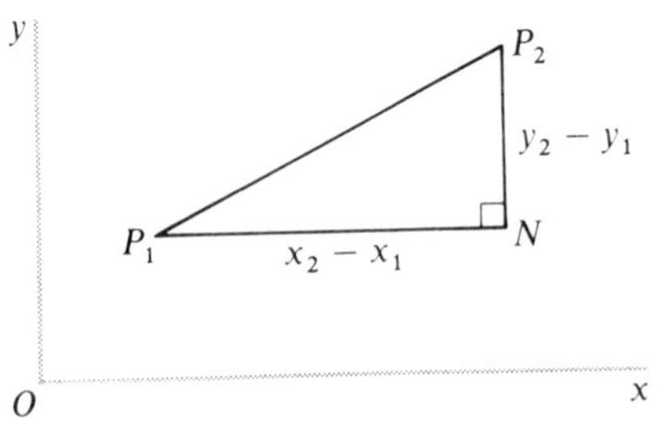

Then
$P_1N = x_2 - x_1, \quad NP_2 = y_2 - y_1$

Pythagoras' Theorem gives
$P_1P_2 = \sqrt{[(x_2 - x_1)^2 + (y_2 - y_1)^2]}$.

This is the distance formula.

In general, $P_1N = |x_2 - x_1|, \quad NP_2 = |y_2 - y_1|$ and the formula is unchanged.

Cosines, sines and tangents

These are the basic tools of trigonometry. They will shortly be defined for an angle θ which is of any size and may be positive or negative. The symbol θ is used for the present to denote an angle, not a number. Angles may be measured in various units; at the present stage they are measured in degrees.

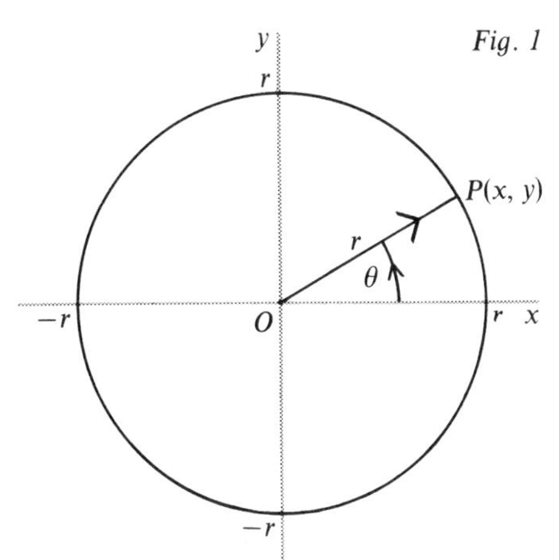

Fig. 1

Fig. 1 shows a circle with centre O and radius r, drawn in the x-y plane.

The point P on the circle has Cartesian coordinates (x, y). The rotation from the direction of the positive x-axis to the direction of the vector $\overrightarrow{OP}$ is the angle θ. If the rotation to $\overrightarrow{OP}$ is anticlockwise, θ is positive; if it is clockwise, θ is negative. If neither, θ is zero.

The number r and the angle θ together describe the position of the point P in the plane, relative to the point O and the x-axis. They are called the polar coordinates of P; the point O is called the pole and the positive x-axis is called the initial line. The angle θ corresponding to a given point P will be called its polar angle. Polar coordinates will be written (r, θ); ambiguity is avoided by a statement when necessary.

For a given point P, r is unique; it measures the length of OP, so that $r \geqslant 0$. (If $r = 0$, θ is undefined.) The angle θ is unique in the interval $-180° < \theta \leqslant 180°$, or alternatively in the interval $0° \leqslant \theta < 360°$; but any multiple of 360° can be added or subtracted. For example, the polar coordinates (2, 60°), (2, 420°), (2, −300°) all give the same point.

For all angles θ, the cosine, sine and tangent of θ are defined by

$$\cos\theta = \frac{x}{r}, \qquad \sin\theta = \frac{y}{r}, \qquad \tan\theta = \frac{y}{x} \quad (x \neq 0),$$

where the usual abbreviations are used.

These relations may also be written

$$x = r\cos\theta, \qquad y = r\sin\theta, \qquad y = x\tan\theta.$$

Also, $\tan\theta = \dfrac{y}{x} = \dfrac{r\sin\theta}{r\cos\theta} = \dfrac{\sin\theta}{\cos\theta}$.

The importance of these definitions lies in the fact that $\cos\theta$, $\sin\theta$ and $\tan\theta$ depend only on the angle θ, not on the radius of the circle on which $P(x, y)$ lies. If the circle were enlarged, for example, by a scale factor 2, then each of x, y and r would be doubled, and $\cos\theta$, $\sin\theta$ and $\tan\theta$ would be unchanged. It is the *ratios* $x : r$, $y : r$ and $y : x$ which determine $\cos\theta$, $\sin\theta$ and $\tan\theta$. For this reason, $\cos\theta$, $\sin\theta$ and $\tan\theta$ are often called the trigonometric ratios.

Since the definitions determine a unique cosine, sine and tangent for a given θ, they define functions; these are called the trigonometric functions. They are also called the circular functions, for obvious reasons.

The domain of the cosine function and of the sine function is the set of all angles. For the tangent function, x must be non-zero, so $\tan\theta$ is not defined when θ is ±90°, 270°, or any other odd multiple of 90°. These angles are therefore excluded from the domain of the tangent function.

Since at every point on the circle of radius r in Fig. 1, $|x| \leqslant r$ and $|y| \leqslant r$, the range of the cosine function and of the sine function is the set of numbers between -1 and 1 inclusive. The range of the tangent function is $\mathbb{R}$.

Since for every integer n the polar coordinates (r, θ) and $(r, \theta + n\,.\,360°)$ represent the same point, it follows that

$$\left.\begin{aligned} \cos\theta &= \cos(\theta + n\,.\,360°) \\ \sin\theta &= \sin(\theta + n\,.\,360°) \\ \tan\theta &= \tan(\theta + n\,.\,360°) \end{aligned}\right\} n \in \mathbb{Z} \qquad (1)$$

There is therefore an unlimited number of angles with a given cosine, sine or tangent, so that the trigonometric functions with the domains given above are not one-one and do not have inverse functions. By restricting the domains, inverse functions may be defined. The inverse trigonometric functions will be discussed in detail in Chapter 10; for the present the student needs to know the range of the functions $\cos^{-1}$, $\sin^{-1}$ and $\tan^{-1}$, since these functions are given on calculators and their use is essential. The following table gives the domain and range of each inverse function.

Function defined by	domain	range
$\theta = \cos^{-1}x$	$-1 \leqslant x \leqslant 1$	$0° \leqslant \theta \leqslant 180°$
$\theta = \sin^{-1}y$	$-1 \leqslant y \leqslant 1$	$-90° \leqslant \theta \leqslant 90°$
$\theta = \tan^{-1}t$	$\mathbb{R}$	$-90° < \theta < 90°$

An alternative notation to $\cos^{-1}x$ is arccos x, and similarly arcsin y and arctan t for $\sin^{-1}y$ and $\tan^{-1}t$, respectively.

It is essential to appreciate that, for example,

'$\cos\theta = x$' and '$\theta = \cos^{-1}x$' are *not* equivalent statements.

The statement

'$\cos\theta = x$ and $0° \leqslant \theta \leqslant 180°$' is equivalent to $\theta = \cos^{-1}x$.

A note on notation

The squares of $\cos\theta$, $\sin\theta$ and $\tan\theta$ occur frequently; strictly they should be written as $(\cos\theta)^2$ etc. but the abbreviations $\cos^2\theta$ etc. are commonly used. Similar abbreviations are used for other *positive* powers.

Examples 4.1

Give all angles in the interval $-180° < \theta \leqslant 180°$ and to the nearest degree when not exact.

1 Find three angles for which the cosine has the same magnitude as $\cos 30°$.

Let P be the point with polar angle 30° on the circle in Fig. 2. We require the polar angles of the three points on the circle for which the x-coordinate has the same magnitude as x_P. These points are Q, the reflection of P in the x-axis; R, the reflection of

P in the y-axis; and S, obtained by a half-turn about O from P. The polar angles of Q, R and S are $-30°$, $150°$ and $-150°$ respectively.

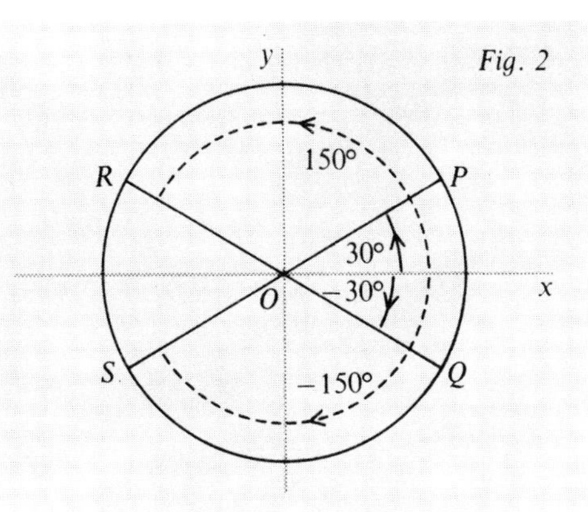

2 In each of the following use a calculator to find one angle θ and use a diagram to find a second angle.
a $\cos\theta = 0.26$ **b** $\sin\theta = 0.76$ **c** $\tan\theta = -2.75$

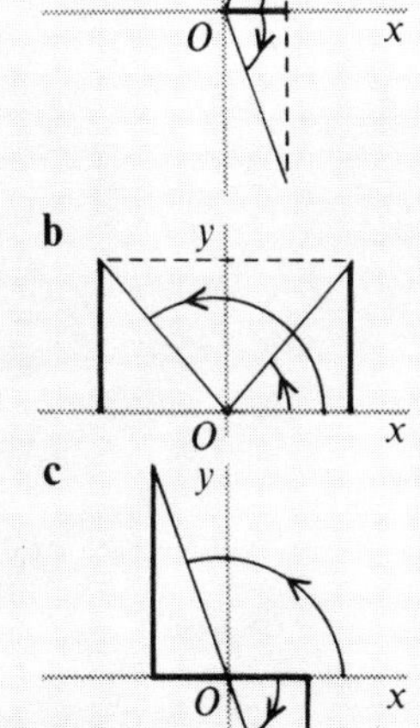

a $\cos\theta = 0.26$
One value of θ is $\cos^{-1}0.26 = 75°$.

A reflection in the x-axis is needed to give the same x-coordinate.

$\therefore$ the second angle is $-75°$.

b $\sin\theta = 0.76$
One value of θ is $\sin^{-1}0.76 = 49°$.

A reflection in the y-axis is needed to give the same y-coordinate.

$\therefore$ the second angle is $180° - 49° = 131°$.

c $\tan\theta = -2.75$
One value of θ is $\tan^{-1} -2.75 = -70°$.

A half-turn about O is needed to give the same value for $\frac{y}{x}$.

$\therefore$ the second angle is $-70° + 180° = 110°$.

Note that in each case the second angle may be checked by calculator.

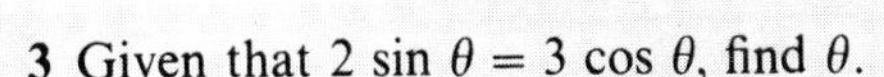

3 Given that $2\sin\theta = 3\cos\theta$, find θ.

$2\sin\theta = 3\cos\theta$

$\therefore \frac{\sin\theta}{\cos\theta} = \frac{3}{2}$

$\therefore \tan\theta = 1.5$

One value of θ is $\tan^{-1}1.5 = 56°$.

Another value of θ is $56° - 180°$, using a half-turn.

$\therefore \theta = 56°$ or $-124°$.

4 Calculate the polar coordinates (r, θ) for the points $P(-3, 4)$ and $Q(3, -4)$.

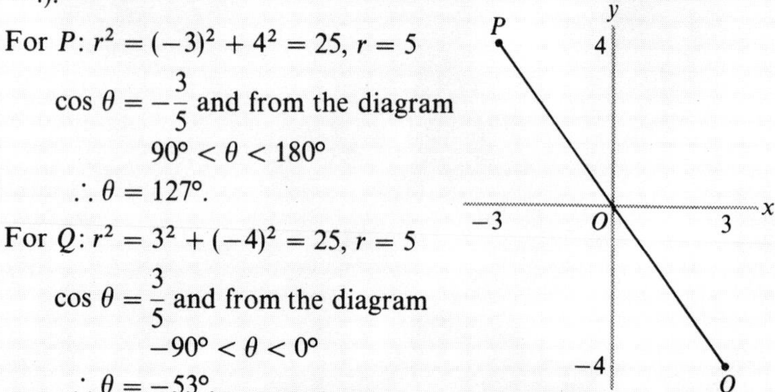

For P: $r^2 = (-3)^2 + 4^2 = 25$, $r = 5$

$\cos\theta = -\dfrac{3}{5}$ and from the diagram

$$90° < \theta < 180°$$

$\therefore \theta = 127°$.

For Q: $r^2 = 3^2 + (-4)^2 = 25$, $r = 5$

$\cos\theta = \dfrac{3}{5}$ and from the diagram

$$-90° < \theta < 0°$$

$\therefore \theta = -53°$.

Note that θ may be found using $\cos\theta$ or $\sin\theta$ or $\tan\theta$, provided that either a diagram or the sign of a second function is also used.

5 Solve the equation $3\sin^2\theta - 8\sin\theta + 4 = 0$.

Writing s for $\sin\theta$ the equation may be written

$$3s^2 - 8s + 4 = 0$$

and this is a quadratic equation for s, i.e. for $\sin\theta$.

Factorising the left-hand side gives

$$(3s - 2)(s - 2) = 0,$$

giving $\sin\theta = \dfrac{2}{3}$ or 2.

Since 2 is outside the range of $\sin\theta$, the only solutions are given by $\sin\theta = \dfrac{2}{3}$.

$$\therefore \theta = 42° \text{ or } 180° - 42°$$
$$= 42° \text{ or } 138°.$$

6 The function f is defined on the set of all angles by $f(\theta) = \sin\theta$; the function g is defined for all real x by $g(x) = x^2 + 1$. Find $gf(\theta)$ and state the domain and range of gf.

$$gf(\theta) = g(\sin\theta) = (\sin\theta)^2 + 1$$
$$= \sin^2\theta + 1$$

The domain of gf is the set of all angles.

Since $\sin\theta$ takes all values from -1 to 1 inclusive, $\sin^2\theta$ takes all values from 0 to 1 inclusive; so the range of gf is the set of all numbers from 1 to 2 inclusive, i.e. $\{y : 1 \leqslant y \leqslant 2\}$.

Exercise 4.1A

Give all angles in the interval $-180° < \theta \leqslant 180°$, and to the nearest degree when not exact.

1 Write down three angles for which the cosine has the same magnitude as the cosine of

a $40°$ **b** $110°$ **c** $170°$ **d** $-20°$ **e** $-100°$.

2 Write down an angle which has the same cosine as

a $35°$ **b** $128°$ **c** $-25°$ **d** $-160°$.

3 Find two angles θ for which

a $\sin\theta = 0.57$ **b** $\sin\theta = -0.31$ **c** $\cos\theta = 0.08$.

4 Find two angles θ for which

a $\tan\theta = 0.26$ **b** $\tan\theta = 2.14$ **c** $\tan\theta = -5.67$.

5 Find correct to one decimal place the Cartesian coordinates (x, y) of the points P, Q, R with polar coordinates $(4, 60°)$, $(6, 140°)$, $(10, -30°)$ respectively. Use the distance formula to calculate the sides of the triangle PQR, correct to the nearest integer.

6 Solve the equation $4\tan^2\theta - 9\tan\theta + 2 = 0$

a for $\tan\theta$ **b** for θ.

7 Draw accurate graphs of $\cos\theta$ and $\sin\theta$ for $-180° \leqslant \theta \leqslant 180°$. Keep these graphs for later use.

8 The function f is defined on the set of all angles by $f(\theta) = \cos\theta$. In each of the following cases find $gf(\theta)$ and state the domain and range of gf.

a $g(x) = 2x + 3$ for all x **b** $g(x) = x^2 + 3$ for all x

c $g(x) = \dfrac{1}{x}$ for $x \neq 0$

Exercise 4.1B

Give all angles in the interval $-180° < \theta \leqslant 180°$, and to the nearest degree when not exact.

1 Find an angle with the same cosine as

a $90°$ **b** $105°$ **c** $79°$ **d** $130°$.

2 Find an angle with the same sine as

a $170°$ **b** $50°$ **c** $-85°$ **d** $-108°$.

3 Find an angle with the same tangent as

a $40°$ **b** $175°$ **c** $-89°$ **d** $-110°$.

4 Solve

a $\cos\theta = 0.53$ **b** $\sin\theta = -0.46$ **c** $\tan\theta = -1.26$.

5 Find an angle θ for which

a $\cos\theta = -\frac{3}{5}$ and $\sin\theta = -\frac{4}{5}$

b $\cos\theta = -\frac{5}{13}$ and $\sin\theta = \frac{12}{13}$.

6 Solve the equation $6\cos^2\theta + \cos\theta - 1 = 0$

a for $\cos\theta$ **b** for θ.

7 Find the polar coordinates of the points with Cartesian coordinates

a (5, 12) **b** (−5, −12) **c** (2, −2) **d** (−2, 2).

8 Draw an accurate graph of $\tan\theta$ for $-180° \leqslant \theta \leqslant -100°$, $-80° \leqslant \theta \leqslant 80°$, $100° \leqslant \theta \leqslant 180°$.
Keep this graph for later use.

9 The function f is defined on the set of all angles by $\mathrm{f}(\theta) = \sin\theta$. In each of the following cases find $\mathrm{gf}(\theta)$ and state the domain and range of gf.

a $\mathrm{g}(x) = 3x + 1$ for all x **b** $\mathrm{g}(x) = x^3 + 2$ for all x

c $\mathrm{g}(x) = \frac{1}{x^2}$ for $x \neq 0$

4.2 The sign of the trigonometric functions

In the definitions of $\cos\theta$ and $\sin\theta$ the number r is positive; it follows that

$\cos\theta > 0$ where $x > 0$, i.e. where OP is in quadrant 1 or 4

$\sin\theta > 0$ where $y > 0$, i.e. where OP is in quadrant 1 or 2.

Since $\tan\theta = \frac{y}{x}$, $\tan\theta > 0$ where both $x > 0$ and $y > 0$, and also where both $x < 0$ and $y < 0$, i.e. where OP is in quadrant 1 or 3.

Summarising the above facts:

$\cos\theta$, $\sin\theta$ and $\tan\theta$ are positive for OP in quadrant 1
$\sin\theta$ is positive " " " " 2
$\tan\theta$ is positive " " " " 3
$\cos\theta$ is positive " " " " 4.

As a diagram:

$\sin\theta$ positive	all positive
$\tan\theta$ positive	$\cos\theta$ positive

Some reflections

As in Fig. 1 (page 35), the point P has Cartesian coordinates (x, y) and polar coordinates (r, θ).

1 Reflect P in the x-axis to give the point Q. Then Q is $(x, -y)$ with polar coordinates $(r, -\theta)$.

$$\therefore \cos(-\theta) = \frac{x}{r}, \qquad \sin(-\theta) = -\frac{y}{r}, \qquad \tan(-\theta) = -\frac{y}{x}$$

$$\therefore \cos(-\theta) = \cos\theta, \qquad \sin(-\theta) = -\sin\theta, \qquad \tan(-\theta) = -\tan\theta$$

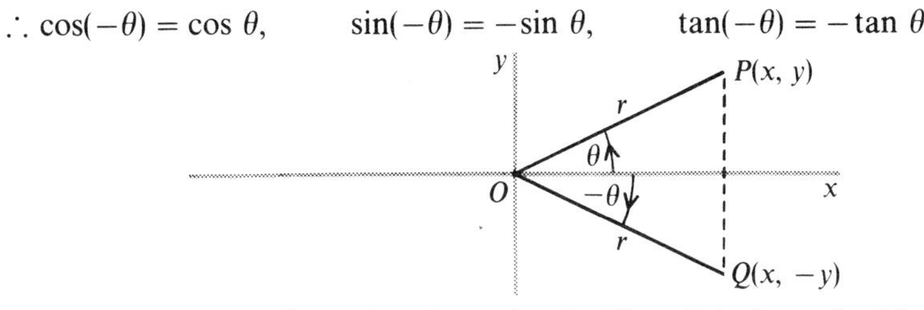

2 Reflect P in the y-axis to give the point R. Then R is $(-x, y)$ with polar coordinates $(r, 180° - \theta)$.

$$\therefore \cos(180° - \theta) = -\frac{x}{r}, \qquad \sin(180° - \theta) = \frac{y}{r}, \qquad \tan(180° - \theta) = -\frac{y}{x}$$

$$\therefore \cos(180° - \theta) = -\cos\theta, \quad \sin(180° - \theta) = \sin\theta, \quad \tan(180° - \theta) = -\tan\theta$$

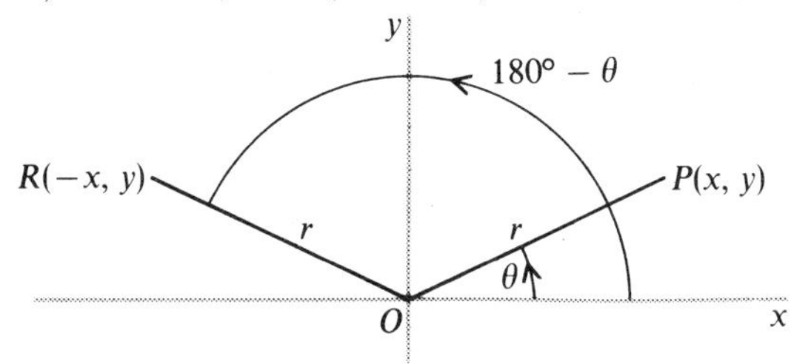

3 Reflect P in the line $y = x$ to give the point S. Then S is (y, x) with polar coordinates $(r, 90° - \theta)$.

$$\therefore \cos(90° - \theta) = \frac{y}{r}, \qquad \sin(90° - \theta) = \frac{x}{r}, \qquad \tan(90° - \theta) = \frac{x}{y}, \ (y \neq 0)$$

$$\therefore \cos(90° - \theta) = \sin\theta, \quad \sin(90° - \theta) = \cos\theta, \quad \tan(90° - \theta) = \frac{1}{\tan\theta}, \ (\theta \neq 0)$$

The angle $90° - \theta$ is called the complementary angle to θ; the sine of θ is the *co*sine of the *co*mplementary angle.

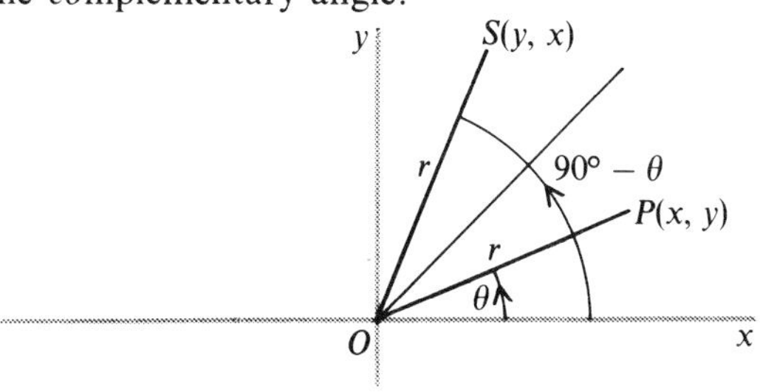

Some rotations

1 Rotate P through 180° about O to give the point U. Then U is $(-x, -y)$ with polar coordinates $(r, \theta \pm 180°)$.

$$\therefore \cos(\theta \pm 180°) = -\frac{x}{r}, \qquad \sin(\theta \pm 180°) = -\frac{y}{r}, \qquad \tan(\theta \pm 180°) = \frac{-y}{-x} = \frac{y}{x}$$

$$\therefore \cos(\theta \pm 180°) = -\cos\theta, \quad \sin(\theta \pm 180°) = -\sin\theta, \quad \tan(\theta \pm 180°) = \tan\theta.$$

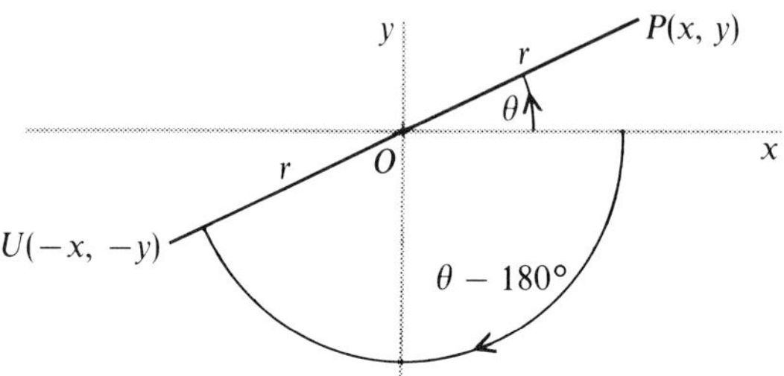

2 Rotate P through 90° about O to give the point V. Then V is $(-y, x)$ with polar coordinates $(r, \theta + 90°)$.

$$\therefore \cos(\theta + 90°) = -\frac{y}{r}, \qquad \sin(\theta + 90°) = \frac{x}{r}, \qquad \tan(\theta + 90°) = -\frac{x}{y}, \ (y \neq 0)$$

$$\therefore \cos(\theta + 90°) = -\sin\theta, \ \sin(\theta + 90°) = \cos\theta, \ \tan(\theta + 90°) = -\frac{1}{\tan\theta}, \ (\theta \neq 0).$$

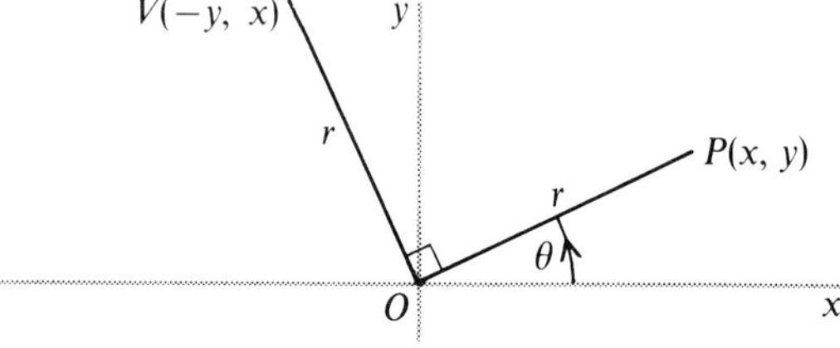

The solution of equations

All the relations obtained by using reflections and rotations are true for any angle θ.

Three of the relations found are of particular importance:

by reflection in the x-axis: $\cos(-\theta) = \cos\theta$
by reflection in the y-axis: $\sin(180° - \theta) = \sin\theta$
by a half-turn about O: $\tan(\theta \pm 180°) = \tan\theta$.

Using these relations and the functions $\cos^{-1}$, $\sin^{-1}$ and $\tan^{-1}$ on a calculator, the solutions may be found in the interval $-180° < \theta \leqslant 180°$ of each of the equations

$$\cos\theta = x, \qquad \sin\theta = y, \qquad \tan\theta = t.$$

These solutions are:

for $\cos\theta = x$,	$\theta = \pm\cos^{-1}x$			
for $\sin\theta = y$,	$\theta = \sin^{-1}y$	and either	$180° - \sin^{-1}y$,	$y > 0$
		or	$-180° - \sin^{-1}y$,	$y < 0$
for $\tan\theta = t$,	$\theta = \tan^{-1}t$	and either	$\tan^{-1}t - 180°$,	$t > 0$
		or	$\tan^{-1}t + 180°$,	$t < 0$

To find solutions in the interval $0° \leqslant \theta < 360°$, add 360° to any negative solutions in the interval $-180° < \theta \leqslant 180°$; the former interval is rarely used in this book.

To find the *general solutions* of the equations, add $n \,.\, 360°$ to each solution in either of the intervals considered above, where n is a positive or negative integer, i.e. $n \in \mathbb{Z}$.

In future references to general solutions, it will be assumed that m and n are integers without specific mention.

Note that since $\tan(\theta + 180°) = \tan\theta$, the general solution of the equation $\tan\theta = t$ may be written $\theta = \tan^{-1}t + n \,.\, 180°$.

Examples 4.2

1 Find to the nearest degree the solutions of the equation $\sin\theta = -0.482$ which lie between **a** $-180°$ and $180°$ **b** $0°$ and $360°$.

a $\sin\theta = -0.482 \;\therefore\; \theta = \sin^{-1}(-0.482) = -29°$ (to nearest degree)
or $\theta = -180° + 29° = -151°$
$\therefore$ the solutions are $-29°$ and $-151°$.

b Both solutions in **a** are negative.
$\therefore$ add $360°$ to each to give the solutions $331°$ and $209°$.

Note that a calculator will *find* only one solution of an equation of this type, but it takes negligible time to check that another solution, which has been obtained and is still displayed, does satisfy the equation. Such an equation should never lead to a wrong solution.

2 Find the solutions of the equation $\sin 2\theta = 0.5$ which lie between $-180°$ and $180°$.

Method 1 $\sin 2\theta = 0.5$
Two values of 2θ which lie in the required interval are $30°$ and $150°$, so two solutions are $15°$ and $75°$. But since θ is to lie between $-180°$ and $180°$, we must double this interval for 2θ; we need all the values of 2θ which lie between $-360°$ and $360°$. Two more values are $30° - 360°$ and $150° - 360°$.

$\therefore 2\theta = -330°, -210°, 30°, 150°$

$\therefore \theta = -165°, -105°, 15°, 75°$

Method 2 $\sin 2\theta = 0.5$
First find the *general solution*.

$2\theta = 30° + n \,.\, 360°,\; 2\theta = 150° + n \,.\, 360°$

$\therefore\; \theta = 15° + n \,.\, 180°,\; \theta = 75° + n \,.\, 180°$

Using $n = 0$ and $n = -1$ in each case gives the solutions as above.

Note that the general solution using $n = 0$ and $n = 1$ in each case gives four solutions between $0°$ and $360°$, namely

$15°, 75°, 195°, 255°$.

Method 2 is recommended, particularly when larger multiples of θ are involved.

3 Sketch the graph of $\cos\theta$ for $-360° \leqslant \theta \leqslant 360°$. Interpret the relation $\cos(-\theta) = \cos\theta$ in terms of the symmetry of the graph.

The accurate graph of $\cos\theta$ drawn for Exercise 4.1A, Q7, gives the sketch for $-180° \leqslant \theta \leqslant 180°$ as shown in Fig. 3.

Fig. 3

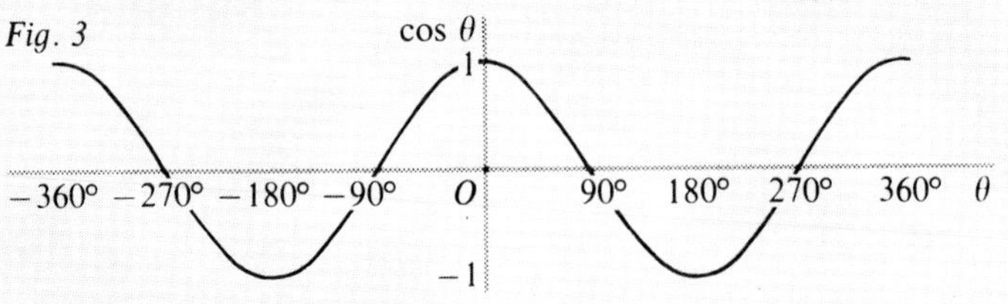

By 4.1 (1), $\cos\theta = \cos(\theta + n\,.\,360°)$

$\therefore$ the curve is repeated in each interval of length 360°, and the sketch is as shown. The graph is said to have period 360°.

The relation $\cos(-\theta) = \cos\theta$ corresponds to the symmetry of the graph about the line $\theta = 0$.

4 Sketch the graph of $\sin 2\theta$ for $-270° \leqslant \theta \leqslant 270°$.

The accurate graph of $\sin\theta$ drawn for Exercise 4.1A, Q7, gives the sketch shown in Fig. 4.

Fig. 4

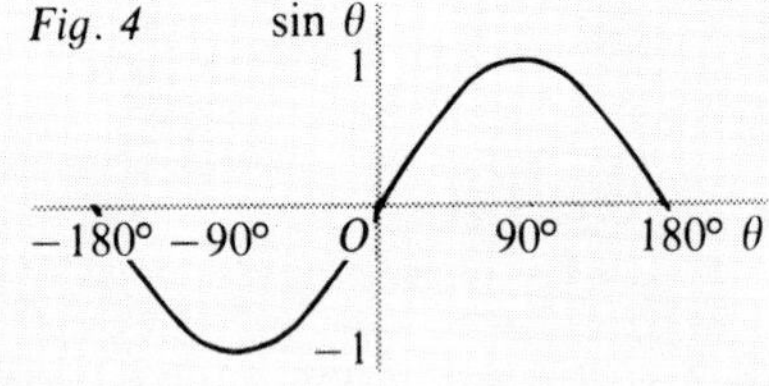
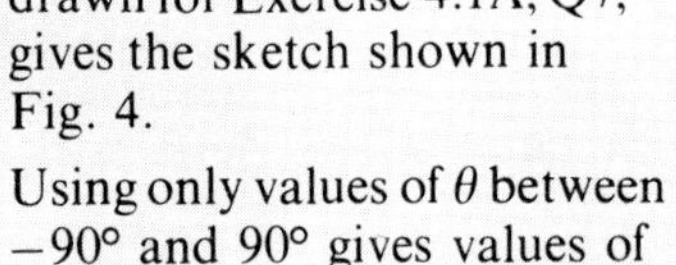

Using only values of θ between $-90°$ and $90°$ gives values of 2θ between $-180°$ and $180°$, and gives the graph for these values as shown in Fig. 5.

Since $\sin 2(\theta + n\,.\,180°) = \sin(2\theta + n\,.\,360°) = \sin 2\theta$, the curve is repeated in each interval of length 180°, i.e. the graph has period 180°. The complete sketch is shown in Fig. 5.

Fig. 5

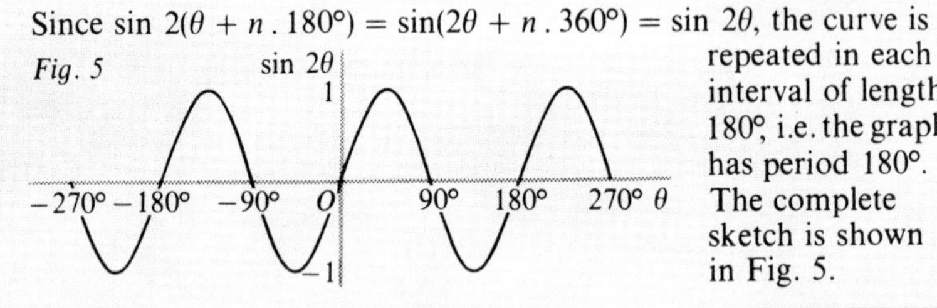

Exercise 4.2

1 Find to the nearest degree the solutions between $-180°$ and $180°$ of the equations

a $\cos\theta = 0.36$ **b** $\sin\theta = -0.56$ **c** $\tan\theta = -0.78$.

2 Find to the nearest degree the solutions between $0°$ and $360°$ of the equations

a $\cos\theta = -0.72$ **b** $\sin\theta = -0.23$ **c** $\tan\theta = 2.45$.

3 Find to the nearest degree the solutions between $-180°$ and $180°$ of the equations

a $\cos 2\theta = 0.67$ **b** $\sin 2\theta = 0.56$ **c** $\tan 2\theta = -2.76$.

4 Sketch the graph of $\sin\theta$ for $-540^\circ \leqslant \theta \leqslant 540^\circ$. Interpret the relation $\sin(-\theta) = -\sin\theta$ in terms of a rotational symmetry of the graph.

5 Describe the property of the graph of $\tan\theta$ which corresponds to the relation $\tan(\theta + 180^\circ) = \tan\theta$.

6 Sketch the graph for $-180^\circ \leqslant \theta \leqslant 180^\circ$ of

a $\cos 2\theta$ **b** $\sin\dfrac{\theta}{2}$.

4.3 Three important angles

1 Construct the equilateral triangle OAP with side 2 units, as shown in the diagram. Draw PN at right angles to OA.

Then $PN^2 = 2^2 - 1^2 = 3$, $PN = \sqrt{3}$

$\therefore P$ is $(1, \sqrt{3})$

$\therefore \cos 60^\circ = \dfrac{1}{2}$, $\sin 60^\circ = \dfrac{\sqrt{3}}{2}$,

$\tan 60^\circ = \sqrt{3}$.

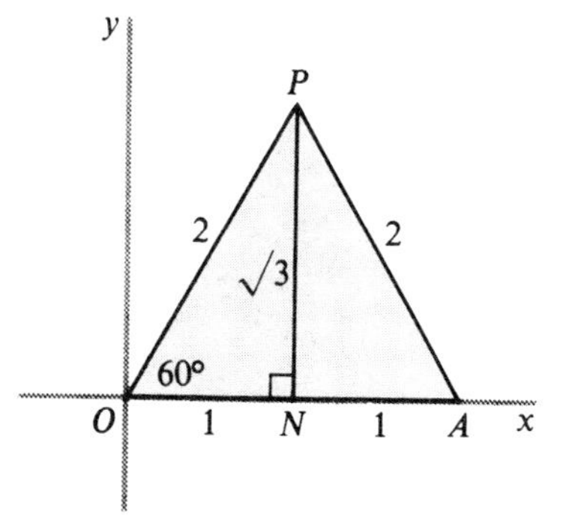

Using the relations for complementary angles, or the diagram,

$\cos 30^\circ = \dfrac{\sqrt{3}}{2}$, $\sin 30^\circ = \dfrac{1}{2}$,

$\tan 30^\circ = \dfrac{1}{\sqrt{3}}$.

2 Construct the right-angled triangle ONP as shown in the diagram, with $ON = NP = 1$, so that P is $(1, 1)$.

Then $r = OP = \sqrt{2}$.

$\therefore \cos 45^\circ = \dfrac{1}{\sqrt{2}}$, $\sin 45^\circ = \dfrac{1}{\sqrt{2}}$,

$\tan 45^\circ = 1$.

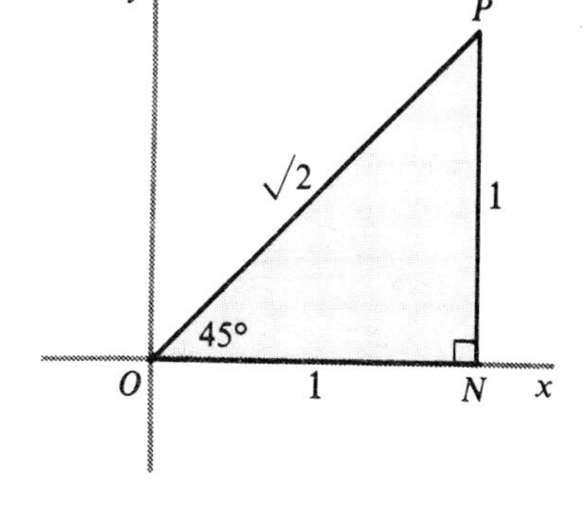

The results of **1** and **2** can conveniently be shown in a table:

angle θ	$\cos\theta$	$\sin\theta$	$\tan\theta$
60°	$\frac{1}{2}$	$\frac{\sqrt{3}}{2}$	$\sqrt{3}$
30°	$\frac{\sqrt{3}}{2}$	$\frac{1}{2}$	$\frac{1}{\sqrt{3}}$
45°	$\frac{1}{\sqrt{2}}$	$\frac{1}{\sqrt{2}}$	1

These results should be remembered.

Three more trigonometric functions

The reciprocals of $\cos\theta$, $\sin\theta$ and $\tan\theta$ occur quite frequently and it is convenient to give them separate names. The functions sec, cosec and cot are defined by:

$$\sec\theta = \frac{1}{\cos\theta}, \quad \operatorname{cosec}\theta = \frac{1}{\sin\theta}, \quad \cot\theta = \frac{1}{\tan\theta};$$

in each case the domain of the function is the set of all values of θ for which the corresponding denominator is non-zero. For example, the domain of cosec is the set of all angles which are not multiples of 180°, so that $\sin\theta \neq 0$.

The names sec, cosec and cot are abbreviations for secant, cosecant and cotangent; the prefix 'co' again arises from the complementary angle. Note that in each of the above definitions one of each related pair has the prefix 'co'.

Note also that since $\tan(90° - \theta) = \dfrac{1}{\tan\theta}$, it follows that $\tan(90° - \theta) = \cot\theta$.

Three identities

An identity is an equation which relates one or more variables and is true for all relevant values of the variables. An important identity relating $\cos\theta$ and $\sin\theta$ for all angles θ is the trigonometric form of Pythagoras' Theorem:

$$\cos^2\theta + \sin^2\theta = 1.$$

The proof of this identity follows directly from the definitions of $\cos\theta$ and $\sin\theta$, by using Pythagoras' Theorem.

By definition, $\cos\theta = \dfrac{x}{r}$, $\sin\theta = \dfrac{y}{r}$,

$$\therefore \cos^2\theta + \sin^2\theta = \left(\frac{x}{r}\right)^2 + \left(\frac{y}{r}\right)^2$$

$$= \frac{x^2 + y^2}{r^2}.$$

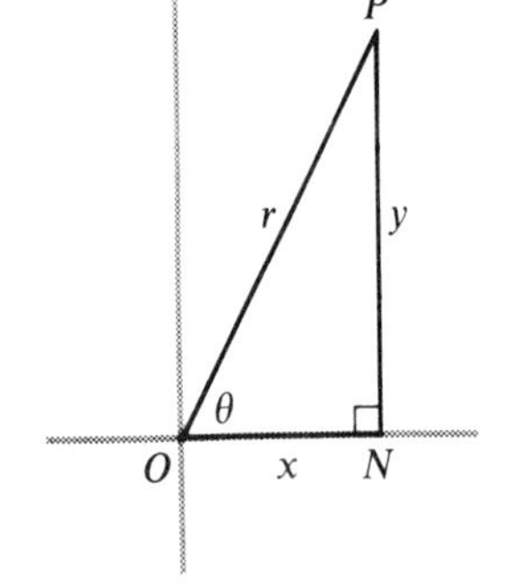

For all positions of P, $x^2 + y^2 = r^2$ by Pythagoras' Theorem in the triangle ONP.

$\therefore$ for all angles θ,

$$\cos^2\theta + \sin^2\theta = 1. \qquad (1)$$

This identity leads directly to two other identities which are true for all angles for which each side is defined.

Dividing each side of (1) by $\cos^2\theta$ gives, for $\cos\theta \neq 0$,

$$1 + \tan^2\theta = \sec^2\theta. \qquad (2)$$

Dividing each side of (1) by $\sin^2\theta$ gives, for $\sin\theta \neq 0$,

$$\cot^2\theta + 1 = \operatorname{cosec}^2\theta. \qquad (3)$$

Examples 4.3

1 Find θ given that $\sec\theta = -1.221$ and that $-180° < \theta < 180°$.

sec θ is not given on many calculators; the reciprocal key gives cos θ and the inverse cosine key gives one value of θ as 145.0°.

$\therefore \theta = \pm 145.0°$ to one decimal place.

2 Given that $\cos\theta = -\frac{3}{5}$ find the possible values of $\sin\theta$.

Since $\cos^2\theta + \sin^2\theta = 1$, $\sin^2\theta = 1 - \cos^2\theta$

$$= 1 - \frac{9}{25} = \frac{16}{25}$$

$$\therefore \sin\theta = \pm\frac{4}{5}$$

3 Solve for $-180° < \theta \leqslant 180°$ the equation $3\sin^2\theta = 5 - 5\cos\theta$, giving θ correct to one decimal place.

$3\sin^2\theta = 5 - 5\cos\theta$

$\therefore 3(1 - \cos^2\theta) = 5 - 5\cos\theta$, using $\cos^2\theta + \sin^2\theta = 1$

$\therefore 3\cos^2\theta - 5\cos\theta + 2 = 0$, a quadratic equation for $\cos\theta$

$\therefore (3\cos\theta - 2)(\cos\theta - 1) = 0$

$$\therefore \cos\theta = \frac{2}{3} \text{ or } 1$$

$\therefore \theta = \pm 48.2°$ or $0°$ (check by calculator)

4 Given that x, y and θ satisfy the equations $x = 3\cos\theta$, $y = 2\sin\theta$, obtain an equation in x and y only, by eliminating θ.

$x = 3\cos\theta$ gives $\cos\theta = \frac{x}{3}$, $y = 2\sin\theta$ gives $\sin\theta = \frac{y}{2}$

Since $\cos^2\theta + \sin^2\theta = 1$, $\left(\frac{x}{3}\right)^2 + \left(\frac{y}{2}\right)^2 = 1$,

or $\frac{x^2}{9} + \frac{y^2}{4} = 1$,

and this is the required equation.

5 Prove the identity $\cos^4\theta - \sin^4\theta = \cos^2\theta - \sin^2\theta$.

The left-hand side of the identity (which may be abbreviated to L.H.S.)

$= \cos^4\theta - \sin^4\theta$

$= (\cos^2\theta - \sin^2\theta)(\cos^2\theta + \sin^2\theta)$

$= \cos^2\theta - \sin^2\theta$

$=$ R.H.S.

$\therefore$ the identity has been proved.

Exercise 4.3A

Give all angles in the interval $-180° < \theta \leqslant 180°$ and to the nearest tenth of a degree when not exact.

1 Given that $\tan\theta = -\sqrt{3}$ and that $\cos\theta < 0$, find θ.

2 Given that $\sec\theta = -\sqrt{2}$ and that $\operatorname{cosec}\theta < 0$, find θ.

3 Given that $\sin\theta = \frac{5}{13}$, find the possible values of

a $\cos\theta$ **b** $\tan\theta$.

4 The points P and Q have polar coordinates $(2, 60°)$ and $(4, 120°)$ respectively. Write down the exact Cartesian coordinates of P and Q. Use the distance formula to calculate PQ.

In questions **5–16** solve the given equation.

5 $\sin\theta = 2\cos\theta$

6 $\sin^2\theta = \frac{1}{2}$

7 $\tan^2\theta = 3$

8 $2\sin\theta + 1 = \operatorname{cosec}\theta$

9 $2\cos\theta = 5 + 3\sec\theta$

10 $4\sin\theta = 3\operatorname{cosec}\theta$

11 $4\sin^2\theta = 4 - 3\cos\theta$

12 $4\cos^2\theta + 11\sin\theta = 10$

13 $6\sin^2\theta + \cos\theta = 4$

14 $5\sin^2\theta = 3\cos\theta + 3$

15 $2\tan^2\theta + 8 = 7\sec\theta$

16 $2\operatorname{cosec}^2\theta = \cot\theta + 12$

In questions **17–19** obtain an equation in x and y only, by eliminating θ.

17 $x = a\cos\theta$, $y = b\sin\theta$

18 $x = 3\sec\theta$, $y = 2\tan\theta$

19 $x = 4\operatorname{cosec}\theta$, $y = 3\cot\theta$

20 Solve $\tan 2\theta = \sqrt{3}$

21 Solve $\cos 2\theta = \frac{\sqrt{3}}{2}$

In questions **22–25** prove the given identity.

22 $\cos^2\theta - \sin^2\theta = 2\cos^2\theta - 1$

23 $\sec^2\theta + \cot^2\theta = \operatorname{cosec}^2\theta + \tan^2\theta$

24 $\sec^2\theta + \operatorname{cosec}^2\theta = \sec^2\theta \operatorname{cosec}^2\theta$

25 $\dfrac{1 - \tan^2\theta}{1 + \tan^2\theta} = 2\cos^2\theta - 1$

Exercise 4.3B

Give all angles in the interval $-180° < \theta \leqslant 180°$ and to the nearest tenth of a degree when not exact.

1 Given that $\sec\theta = 2$ and $\tan\theta < 0$, find θ.

2 Given that $\cot\theta = 0.678$, and that $\operatorname{cosec}\theta < 0$, find θ.

3 Given that $\tan\theta = -\frac{3}{4}$, find the possible values of $\sec\theta$.

In questions **4–11** solve the given equations.

4 $3 \sin^2\theta = \cos^2\theta$

5 $2 \cos \theta = \sec \theta$

6 $2 \tan \theta + 6 \cot \theta = 7$

7 $4 \cos \theta + 6 \sec \theta = 11$

8 $2 \cos^2\theta = 3 \sin \theta + 2$

9 $5 \sin^2\theta = 9 \cos \theta + 3$

10 $4 \cot^2\theta + 7 \operatorname{cosec} \theta + 2 = 0$

11 $2 \sec^2\theta + 5 \tan \theta = 5$

In questions **12–15** form an equation in x and y by eliminating θ.

12 $x = 4 \sec \theta$, $y = 3 \operatorname{cosec} \theta$

13 $x = 1 + \cos \theta$, $y = 2 + \sin \theta$

14 $x = 2 + 5 \sec \theta$, $y = 3 + 5 \tan \theta$

15 $x = \cos \theta + \sin \theta$, $y = \cos \theta - \sin \theta$

16 Solve $\tan 2\theta = -1$

17 Solve $\cos 2\theta = \dfrac{1}{\sqrt{2}}$

In questions **18–22** prove the given identity.

18 $\cos^2\theta - \sin^2\theta = 1 - 2 \sin^2\theta$

19 $1 + \tan^2\theta = \dfrac{1}{1 - \sin^2\theta}$

20 $\cos^2\theta \operatorname{cosec} \theta = \operatorname{cosec} \theta - \sin \theta$

21 $\operatorname{cosec}^4\theta - \cot^4\theta = \dfrac{1 + \cos^2\theta}{\sin^2\theta}$

22 $\cos^4\theta + \sin^4\theta = 1 - 2 \cos^2\theta \sin^2\theta$

4.4 Triangle relations

When working with a triangle ABC it is a standard notation to use a, b, c for the sides opposite the vertices A, B, C respectively.

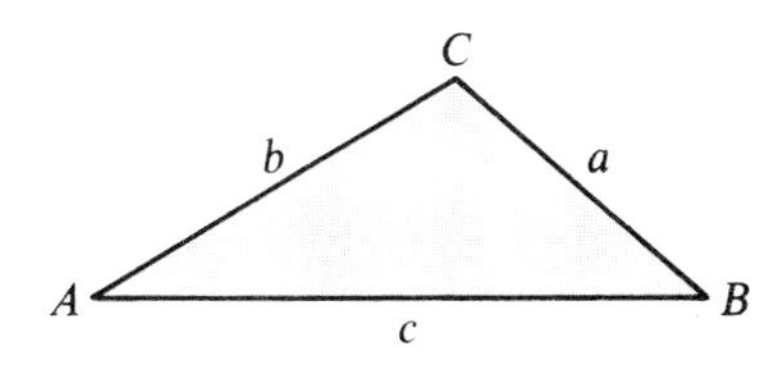

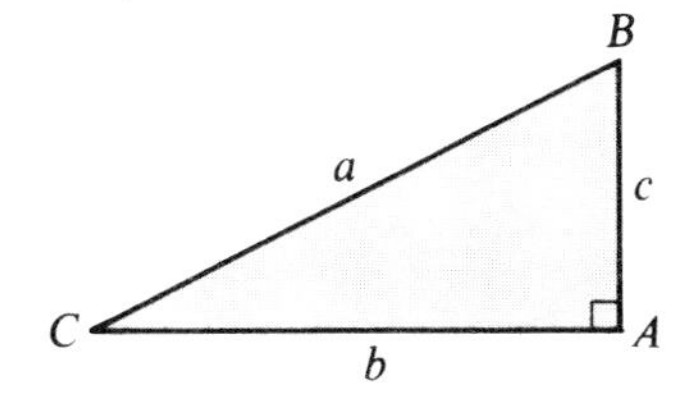

In the special case when one angle, say A, is 90°, the definitions of cos, sin and tan give

$$\cos C = \frac{b}{a}, \qquad \sin C = \frac{c}{a}, \qquad \tan C = \frac{c}{b}.$$

Also by Pythagoras' Theorem, $a^2 = b^2 + c^2$.

In the general case of a triangle with no right angle, there are two relations of special importance involving the sides and angles. These are called the *sine rule* and the *cosine rule*. The sine rule is the simpler and is considered first.

The sine rule

This rule states that, in any triangle ABC,

$$\frac{\sin A}{a} = \frac{\sin B}{b} = \frac{\sin C}{c}.$$

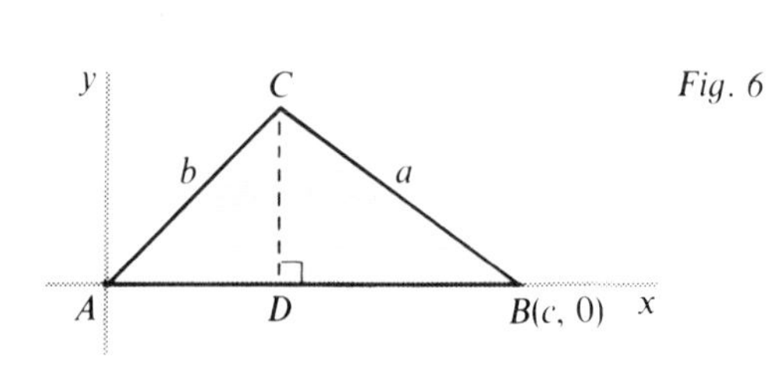

Fig. 6

Proof

Take axes as shown in the diagrams, with the origin at A, and B at $(c, 0)$. Then in each diagram the y-coordinate of C is $b \sin A$, and it is also $a \sin B$ from the right-angled triangle BCD.

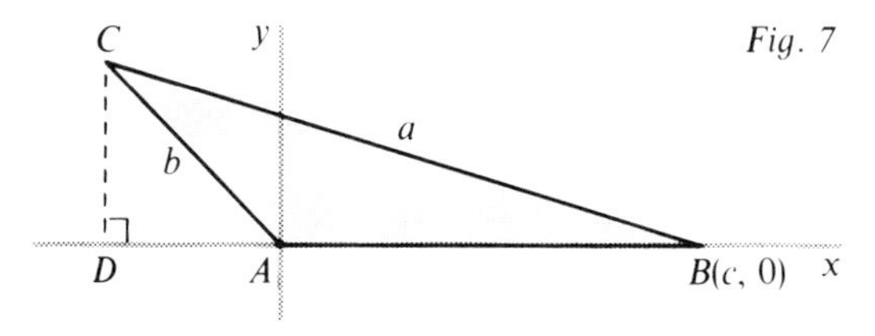

Fig. 7

$$\therefore b \sin A = a \sin B$$

or $$\frac{\sin A}{a} = \frac{\sin B}{b}$$

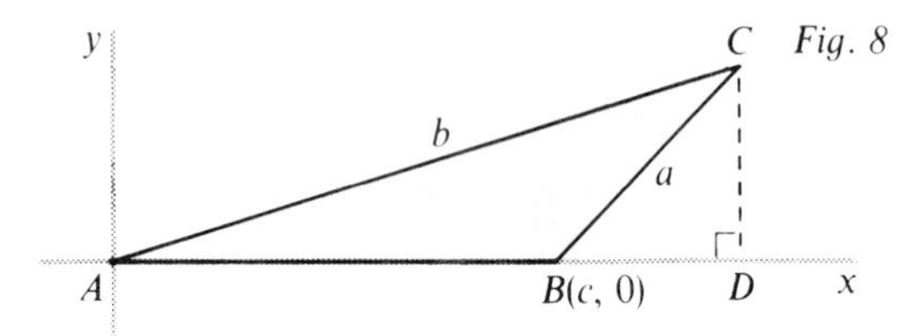

Fig. 8

Similarly $\dfrac{\sin B}{b} = \dfrac{\sin C}{c}$,

and the sine rule is proved.

The cosine rule

This rule states that, in any triangle ABC,

$$a^2 = b^2 + c^2 - 2bc \cos A.$$

Using Figs. 6, 7 and 8 as for the sine rule, C is the point $(b \cos A, b \sin A)$. In Figs. 6 and 7, $BD = c - b \cos A$; in Fig. 8, $BD = b \cos A - c$. So in each case $BD = |c - b \cos A|$.

Using Pythagoras' Theorem in the triangle BCD:

$$\begin{aligned} a^2 &= |c - b \cos A|^2 + (b \sin A)^2 \\ &= c^2 - 2bc \cos A + b^2 \cos^2 A + b^2 \sin^2 A \\ &= c^2 - 2bc \cos A + b^2(\cos^2 A + \sin^2 A) \\ &= c^2 - 2bc \cos A + b^2 \end{aligned}$$

$$\therefore a^2 = b^2 + c^2 - 2bc \cos A$$

and the cosine rule is proved.

The cosine rule may also be written in the forms

$$b^2 = c^2 + a^2 - 2ca \cos B$$

and $$c^2 = a^2 + b^2 - 2ab \cos C.$$

The formula may also be written with, for example, $\cos A$ as the subject.

It is important to see the pattern of the rule so that it may easily be applied in any triangle: the right-hand side involves two sides of the triangle and the angle between these sides; the left-hand side is the square of the remaining side, which is opposite the angle used.

The area of the triangle

Using AB as the base of the triangles in Figs. 6, 7 and 8, the height is the y-coordinate of C, which is $b \sin A$.

$\therefore$ the area of triangle ABC is $\frac{1}{2}c(b \sin A)$ or $\frac{1}{2}bc \sin A$.

The solution of triangles

This phrase is used to describe the calculation of the remaining sides and angles of a triangle, when sufficient data is provided to enable the triangle to be drawn. The following list summarises the possibilities.

Data	Method of solution
c, A, B	Calculate C and use the sine rule.
b, c, A	Use the cosine rule for a, then the sine rule.
a, b, c	Use the cosine rule for A, then the sine rule; or use the cosine rule only.
a, c, C	Use the sine rule to find $\sin C$, and hence possibly two values for C. In this case there may be two triangles with the given measurements. For this reason the case where two sides of the triangle and the non-included angle are given is called the ambiguous case.

Examples 4.4

Give all approximate answers correct to one d.p.

1 In the triangle ABC, $c = 4.2$, $A = 74°$, $B = 43°$. Calculate C, a and b.

$$C = 180° - (A + B) = 63°$$

By the sine rule, $\dfrac{a}{\sin A} = \dfrac{b}{\sin B} = \dfrac{c}{\sin C}$

$$\therefore \frac{a}{\sin 74°} = \frac{b}{\sin 43°} = \frac{4.2}{\sin 63°}$$

$$\therefore \quad a = \frac{4.2}{\sin 63°} \sin 74°$$

$$b = \frac{4.2}{\sin 63°} \sin 43°$$

$$\therefore a = 4.5,\ b = 3.2 \text{ to one d.p.}$$

2 In the triangle ABC, $b = 5.6$, $c = 2.4$, $A = 72°$. Calculate a, B, C and the area of the triangle.

By the cosine rule, $a^2 = b^2 + c^2 - 2bc \cos A$

$$= 5.6^2 + 2.4^2 - 2(5.6)(2.4) \cos 72°$$

$$\therefore a = 5.4 \text{ to 1 d.p.}$$

Since a is to be used again to find B and C, the displayed value of a should be stored in the calculator memory for later use.

By the sine rule,

$$\frac{\sin 72°}{a} = \frac{\sin B}{5.6} = \frac{\sin C}{2.4}$$

$$\therefore \sin B = \frac{\sin 72°}{a} 5.6, \quad \sin C = \frac{\sin 72°}{a} 2.4$$

$$\therefore B = 82.8° \text{ or } 97.2°, \quad C = 25.2° \text{ to 1 d.p.}$$

Since b is the longest side of the triangle, B could be obtuse but C could not; using $A + B + C = 180°$ shows that B is acute.

$$\therefore B = 82.8°, \quad C = 25.2°$$

The area of the triangle $= \frac{1}{2}bc \sin A = 6.4$.

3 In the triangle ABC, $a = 5.2$, $b = 6.6$, $c = 9.4$. Calculate the angles of the triangle.

To determine at once whether the triangle has an obtuse angle, calculate the largest angle first; this is C, since c is the longest side.

By the cosine rule, $\cos C = \dfrac{a^2 + b^2 - c^2}{2ab}$

$$= \frac{5.2^2 + 6.6^2 - 9.4^2}{2(5.2)(6.6)}$$

$$\therefore C = 105.0° \text{ to 1 d.p.}$$

This is C correct to one d.p. as required; the displayed C is used to obtain $\sin C$, which is then stored for later use.

Either: by the sine rule, $\sin A = \dfrac{\sin C}{9.4} 5.2$

$$\sin B = \frac{\sin C}{9.4} 6.6$$

$$\therefore A = 32.3°, B = 42.7° \text{ to 1 d.p.}$$

(Check: $A + B + C = 180°$)

Or: complete the solution using the cosine rule. This is a little more trouble but has the advantage that a mistake in the first stage is not carried through to the remainder of the work.

4 In the triangle ABC, $a = 4.3$, $c = 5.6$, $C = 75°$. Calculate A, B and b.

By the sine rule, $\dfrac{\sin A}{a} = \dfrac{\sin C}{c}$

$$\therefore \sin A = \frac{4.3 \sin 75°}{5.6}$$

$$\therefore A = 47.9° \text{ or } 132.1°$$

But if $A = 132.1°$ then $A + C > 180°$, so this is impossible.

$$\therefore A = 47.9° \text{ and } B = 57.1°$$

$$\therefore \text{by the sine rule, } b = \frac{5.6 \sin 57.1°}{\sin 75°}$$

$$\therefore b = 4.9 \text{ to 1 d.p.}$$

5 In the triangle ABC, $a = 3.6$, $b = 4.2$, $A = 34°$. Show that there are two triangles which satisfy these conditions and calculate B and C for each triangle.

By the sine rule, $\dfrac{\sin A}{a} = \dfrac{\sin B}{b}$

$$\therefore \sin B = \frac{4.2 \sin 34°}{3.6}$$

$$\therefore B = 40.7° \text{ or } 139.3°$$

$$\therefore A + B = 74.7° \text{ or } 173.3°$$

$$\therefore C = 105.3° \text{ or } 6.7°$$

So in this case there are two triangles which satisfy the conditions.
In one triangle, $B = 40.7°$ and $C = 105.3°$.
In the other triangle, $B = 139.3°$, $C = 6.7°$.

Exercise 4.4

Give answers correct to one d.p. unless otherwise stated.
In questions **1**–**8** solve the triangle ABC.

1 $a = 8.2$, $B = 64°$, $C = 36°$
2 $a = 6.4$, $b = 5.2$, $c = 4.5$
3 $b = 9.6$, $c = 7.3$, $A = 54°$
4 $b = 3.5$, $A = 110°$, $C = 25°$
5 $a = 2.4$, $b = 3.7$, $C = 105°$
6 $c = 7.4$, $A = 53°$, $B = 28°$
7 $a = 4.8$, $b = 3.4$, $c = 5.3$
8 $a = 9.2$, $c = 7.6$, $B = 56°$

9 Show that no triangle can be drawn in which $a = 6.2$, $c = 4.8$, $C = 75°$.

10 Given that $BC = 6.8$ cm, $AC = 9.2$ cm, $A = 30°$, show by calculation that two triangles ABC may be drawn and find the possible lengths of AB. Find also the area of each triangle. Construct the triangles accurately.

11 In the triangle ABC, $BC = 9$ cm, $CA = 12$ cm and the area is 28 cm^2. Find the possible angles at C and the possible lengths of AB.

12 A boy walking along a straight road sees a flagpole on a bearing of 048°. He walks 480 m along the road and then finds the bearing is 125°. Calculate the distance of the flagpole from the road, and the distance the boy had walked by the time the flagpole was due east of him. Give each answer to the nearest metre.

13 A circle with centre O passes through the points A, B and C. The radius of the circle is R. Prove that with the usual notation

$$\frac{a}{\sin A} = 2R.$$

Use this result to give an alternative proof of the sine rule.

Given that $BC = 4.2$ cm and that the angle BOC is 112°, calculate the radius of the circle through A, B and C. Find also the distance of BC from O.

14 In a parallelogram $ABCD$, $AB = 7.3$ cm, $AD = 4.6$ cm and the angle BAD is 72°. Calculate the lengths of the diagonals BD and AC, and the area of the parallelogram.

Miscellaneous Exercise 4

In questions **1**–**4** find the solutions of the equation between $-180°$ and $180°$, giving them to one decimal place.

1 $6 \sin^2\theta + 7 \cos \theta = 8$

2 $3 \sec^2\theta + 7 = 11 \tan \theta$

3 $\cos 2\theta = 0.567$

4 $\tan 2\theta = -2.234$

5 The function f is defined on the set of all angles θ for which $-90° < \theta < 90°$ by $f(\theta) = \tan \theta$. In each of the following, find $gf(\theta)$ and state the domain and range of gf.

a $g(x) = x^2 + 1$ for all x

b $g(x) = \dfrac{1}{x - 1}$ for $x \neq 1$

6 Use the factor theorem to express

$$2s^3 + 3s^2 - 3s - 2$$

as a product of three factors. Hence solve the equation

$$2 \sin^3\theta + 3 \sin^2\theta - 3 \sin \theta - 2 = 0$$

giving the solutions between $-180°$ and $180°$.

7 In the diagram, AB is a diameter of the circle with centre O and radius r; D is the foot of the perpendicular from B to OS. The angle BOS is θ. By applying the cosine rule to triangle AOD, or otherwise, prove that

$$AD^2 = r^2(1 + 3 \cos^2\theta).$$

For the case in which BD bisects the angle OBS, show that

$$AD = \frac{r}{2}\sqrt{7}.$$

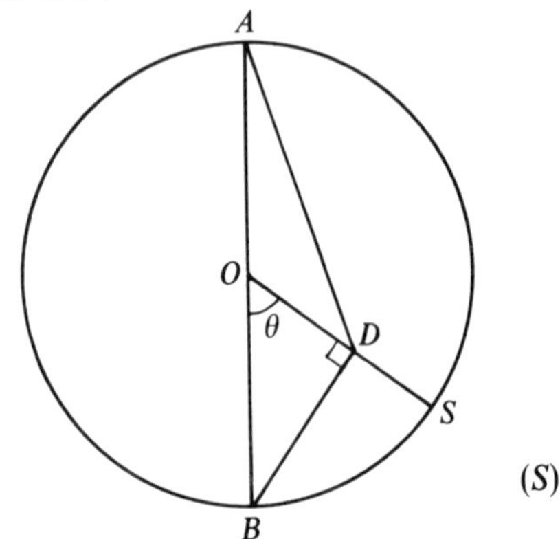

(S)

8 Three landmarks P, Q and R are on the same horizontal level. Landmark Q is 3 km and on a bearing of 328° from P, landmark R is 6 km and on a bearing of 191° from Q. Calculate the distance and the bearing of R from P, giving your answers in km to one decimal place and in degrees to the nearest degree. (*L*)

9 From the crossroads C a girl sees that the tower T is 2.3 km away on a bearing of 056° and the radio mast M is 4.5 km away on a bearing of 078°.

a State the angle MCT.

b Calculate the distance MT.

c Show that the angle CTM is about 138° and give the bearing of M from T.

d She now walks due East. Calculate how far she must walk until:
(i) she is due South of the mast
(ii) she is in line with the mast and the tower. (*SMP*)

10 A kite P and two points A, B on horizontal ground form a vertical plane as shown in the figure. $AB = 106$ m, $BP = 144$ m and the angle of elevation of P from B is 72°.

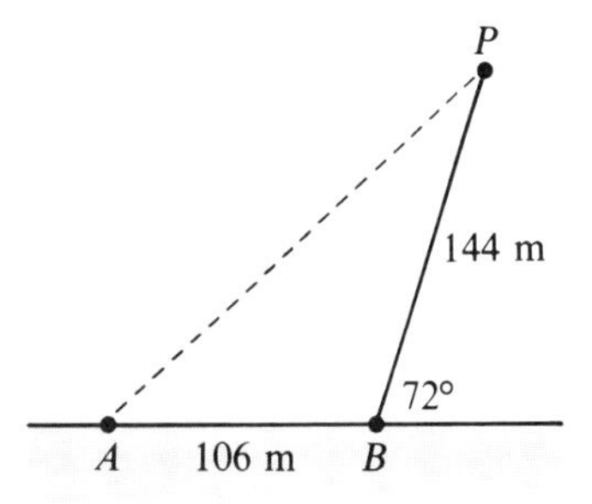

Calculate the following, giving all your answers correct to 2 significant figures:

a the height of P above the ground

b the distance AP

c angle PAB, the angle of elevation of P from A. (*SMP*)

11 Three forts A, B and C are situated in a flat desert region. A is 8 km due west of B, and C is 3 km due east of B. An oasis O is situated to the north of the line ABC and is 7 km from both A and C. Calculate

a the distance between O and B

b the bearing of O from B.

A mine M is situated to the south of ABC. The bearing of M from A is 135° and the bearing of M from C is 210°.

c Calculate the distance between M and B. (*L*)

Chapter 5

Rational and irrational numbers, surds, quadratic equations

5.1 Rational and irrational numbers

A student starting an advanced mathematics course is unlikely to have met any numbers other than *real* numbers, but will do so during the later part of the course. All the numbers in this book are real.

Every real number corresponds to a point on a line, the number line, which is a directed line through a point O. The number line is usually drawn from left to right; the part of the line on the left of O corresponds to negative numbers and the part on the right to positive numbers; the point O corresponds to zero. The real numbers are an *ordered* set, i.e. given any two unequal real numbers a and b, then either $a < b$ or $a > b$. If $a < b$, then the point corresponding to a lies on the left of the point corresponding to b on the number line.

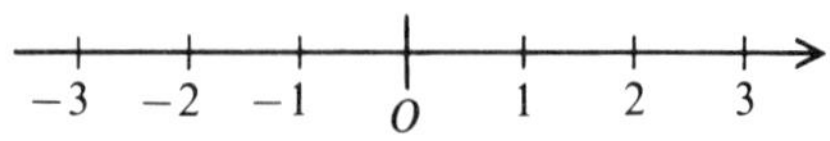

The symbol for the set of real numbers is $\mathbb{R}$. The set $\mathbb{R}$ contains the important subsets $\mathbb{N}$, $\mathbb{Z}$ and $\mathbb{Q}$. The set $\mathbb{N}$ is the set of natural numbers, $\{0, 1, 2, \ldots\}$. The set $\mathbb{Z}$ is the set of all integers, $\{0, \pm 1, \pm 2, \ldots\}$. The set $\mathbb{Q}$ is the set of rational numbers; a rational number is a number of the form $\frac{p}{q}$ where p and q are integers and $q \neq 0$. Since q can be 1, all the integers are also rational numbers, i.e. $\mathbb{Z} \subset \mathbb{Q}$. All real numbers which are not rational are called *irrational*; the irrational numbers are thus another subset of the real numbers, but there is no special symbol for them. Examples of irrational numbers are $\sqrt{2}, \sqrt{3}, \sqrt{5}, \sqrt{6}, \sqrt{7}, \ldots$. The number π is a particularly famous irrational number, of a more complicated type than the other examples given, since none of its powers is rational.

It is not difficult to prove that $\sqrt{2}$ is irrational. The following proof uses the method of 'reductio ad absurdum', i.e. the assumption that $\sqrt{2}$ is rational is shown to lead to a contradiction, or an 'absurdity'. 'Proof by contradiction' is an alternative name for this method of proof.

We wish to prove that $\sqrt{2}$ cannot be expressed in the form $\frac{p}{q}$, where p and q are integers. Suppose that $\sqrt{2}$ *can* be expressed in this form. Then we may assume that p and q have no common factors, since any such factors could be cancelled at the start. So we have $\frac{p}{q} = \sqrt{2}$ and p, q have no common factors. Squaring gives $p^2 = 2q^2$, so that p^2 is an even integer. Now the square of every odd number is odd, so p must be even; we may let p be $2k$, where k is an integer. Then $p^2 = 4k^2$. But $p^2 = 2q^2$.

$$\therefore 2q^2 = 4k^2 \text{ or } q^2 = 2k^2.$$

But this means that q^2 is even and so q is even.

So our supposition that $\sqrt{2}$ is rational has led to a contradiction; we set out with p and q having no common factor and then found that p and q have a common factor 2. Thus our supposition was false, and $\sqrt{2}$ is irrational.

All real numbers may be expressed in decimal form. The integers have only zeros on the right of the decimal point. All rational numbers have decimals which are either finite, e.g. $\frac{3}{4} = 0.75$, or are infinite and recurring, e.g. $\frac{1}{7} = 0.142857142857\ldots$. A study of the division process shows why this is so.

Conversely a finite decimal may easily be changed to fractional form, and a recurring decimal may be changed to fractional form by the method of Examples **3.4**, Q3. Thus an infinite non-recurring decimal corresponds to an irrational number; an example of such a decimal is $0.202002000200002\ldots$; the number of 0's before the next 2 increases by 1 at each stage, so the decimal cannot recur. An *approximation* to this number is $0.202 = \frac{202}{1000} = \frac{101}{500}$, a rational number.

Surds

A surd is a particularly simple type of irrational number. It is the square root (or cube root, etc.) of an integer which is not itself the exact square (or cube, etc.) of an integer.

Thus $\sqrt{2}$, $\sqrt{3}$, $\sqrt[3]{20}$ are surds, but $\sqrt{4}$, $\sqrt{9}$ and $\sqrt[3]{27}$ are not.

The following examples show how surds may be manipulated.

Examples 5.1

1 Express in a form without surds:
a $(\sqrt{3})^4$ **b** $(\sqrt{5}\sqrt{7})^2$ **c** $(\sqrt{35})^2$ **d** $(3 + \sqrt{5})(3 - \sqrt{5})$.

a since $(\sqrt{3})^2 = 3$, $(\sqrt{3})^4 = 3 \times 3 = 9$

b $(\sqrt{5}\sqrt{7})^2 = \sqrt{5}\sqrt{7}\sqrt{5}\sqrt{7} = \sqrt{5}\sqrt{5}\sqrt{7}\sqrt{7} = 5 \times 7 = 35$

c $(\sqrt{35})^2 = 35$ by definition of $\sqrt{35}$
Note that this is the same answer as **b**. In general $\sqrt{a}\sqrt{b} = \sqrt{(ab)}$.

d $(3 + \sqrt{5})(3 - \sqrt{5}) = 9 - 5 = 4$
The product of these two numbers is rational because the second is the *conjugate* of the first; in general for rational a, b the conjugate of $a + \sqrt{b}$ is $a - \sqrt{b}$.

2 Express $\sqrt{18}$ as a multiple of a smaller surd.

$$\sqrt{18} = \sqrt{(9 \times 2)} = \sqrt{9} \times \sqrt{2} = 3\sqrt{2}$$

3 Express $\dfrac{1}{3-\sqrt{5}}$ in a form in which the denominator is rational.

$$\frac{1}{3-\sqrt{5}} = \frac{3+\sqrt{5}}{(3-\sqrt{5})(3+\sqrt{5})} = \frac{3+\sqrt{5}}{4}$$

This process is described as 'rationalising the denominator'. Note that the numerator and the denominator were multiplied by the conjugate of the denominator.

4 Express $\dfrac{1}{\sqrt{5}} + \sqrt{20}$ in the form $a\sqrt{5}$, where a is rational.

$$\frac{1}{\sqrt{5}} + \sqrt{20} = \frac{\sqrt{5}}{\sqrt{5}\sqrt{5}} + \sqrt{(4 \times 5)}$$

$$= \frac{\sqrt{5}}{5} + 2\sqrt{5}$$

$$= \frac{11}{5}\sqrt{5}$$

Exercise 5.1A

1 Express the following in a form without surds.

a $(\sqrt{5})^6$ **b** $(\sqrt{3}\sqrt{7})^2$ **c** $(4+\sqrt{6})(4-\sqrt{6})$ **d** $\left(\dfrac{\sqrt{2}}{\sqrt{5}}\right)^2$

2 Express each of the following as a multiple of the smallest possible surd.

a $\sqrt{50}$ **b** $\sqrt{80}$ **c** $\sqrt{98}$ **d** $\sqrt{108}$ **e** $\sqrt{243}$

3 Rationalise the denominator in each of the following.

a $\dfrac{2}{3\sqrt{7}}$ **b** $\dfrac{3}{4-\sqrt{3}}$ **c** $\dfrac{\sqrt{2}}{3+\sqrt{2}}$ **d** $\dfrac{4}{5+2\sqrt{2}}$

Exercise 5.1B

1 Express in a form without surds.

a $(\sqrt{7}\sqrt{8})^2$ **b** $(5+2\sqrt{3})(5-2\sqrt{3})$ **c** $\left(\sqrt{\dfrac{7}{8}}\right)^2$

2 Express as a multiple of the smallest possible surd.

a $\sqrt{75}$ **b** $\sqrt{180}$ **c** $\sqrt{242}$ **d** $\sqrt{192}$

3 Rationalise the denominator in each of the following.

a $\dfrac{4}{3\sqrt{5}}$ **b** $\dfrac{2}{6-\sqrt{7}}$ **c** $\dfrac{3}{4-2\sqrt{3}}$ **d** $\dfrac{\sqrt{5}}{2+3\sqrt{5}}$

4 Find two unequal surds such that their product is rational.

5 Express in the form $a\sqrt{b}$, where a and b are rational, each of

a $\frac{2}{\sqrt{6}} + \sqrt{24}$ **b** $\frac{4}{\sqrt{7}} + \sqrt{63}$.

5.2 Quadratic equations

A quadratic equation is an equation of the form

$$ax^2 + bx + c = 0, \qquad a \neq 0.$$

Quadratic equations arise in a wide variety of contexts; they have been used in trigonometry in Chapter 4. The simplest method of solution is by using factors of the left-hand side, when factors with integral coefficients exist; this was the only method used in Chapter 4. Another method, which can be used in all cases, is the method of completing the square. This method depends on the identity

$$(a + b)^2 = a^2 + 2ab + b^2.$$

Examples 5.2

Use the method of completing the square to solve the following equations. Give the roots correct to 2 d.p.

1 $x^2 + 6x - 2 = 0$ **2** $x^2 - 8x - 6 = 0$ **3** $x^2 + 3x + 1 = 0$

4 $2x^2 + 5x - 4 = 0$ **5** $x^2 - 3x + 4 = 0$

1 $x^2 + 6x - 2 = 0$

The equation can be written $x^2 + 6x = 2$.

The terms on the left are the first 2 terms of $(x + 3)^2$, since

$$(x + 3)^2 = x^2 + 6x + 9$$

$\therefore$ adding 9 to $x^2 + 6x$ 'completes the square'.

Adding 9 to both sides of the equation gives

$$(x + 3)^2 = 11$$

$$\therefore x + 3 = \pm\sqrt{11}$$

$$x = \pm\sqrt{11} - 3$$

$$\therefore x = 0.32, -6.32, \text{ to 2 d.p.}$$

2 $x^2 - 8x - 6 = 0$

Rewriting: $x^2 - 8x = 6$

Completing the square by adding $\left(\frac{8}{2}\right)^2$ or 16 to both sides gives

$$(x - 4)^2 = 22$$

$$x - 4 = \pm\sqrt{22}$$

$$x = \pm\sqrt{22} + 4$$

$$\therefore x = 8.69, -0.69, \text{ to 2 d.p.}$$

3 $x^2 + 3x + 1 = 0$

Rewriting: $x^2 + 3x = -1$

Adding $\frac{9}{4}$: $\left(x + \frac{3}{2}\right)^2 = -1 + \frac{9}{4} = \frac{5}{4}$

$$\therefore x + \frac{3}{2} = \pm\frac{\sqrt{5}}{2}$$

$$\therefore x = \frac{\pm\sqrt{5} - 3}{2}$$

$$\therefore x = -2.62, -0.38, \text{ to 2 d.p.}$$

4 $2x^2 + 5x - 4 = 0$

Rewriting: $x^2 + \frac{5}{2}x = 2$

Adding $\frac{25}{16}$: $\left(x + \frac{5}{4}\right)^2 = 2 + \frac{25}{16} = \frac{57}{16}$

$$\therefore x + \frac{5}{4} = \pm\frac{\sqrt{57}}{4}$$

$$\therefore x = \frac{\pm\sqrt{57} - 5}{4}$$

$$\therefore x = 0.64, -3.14, \text{ to 2 d.p.}$$

5 $x^2 - 3x + 4 = 0$

Rewriting: $x^2 - 3x = -4$

Adding $\frac{9}{4}$: $\left(x - \frac{3}{2}\right)^2 = -4 + \frac{9}{4} = -\frac{7}{4}$

Since the right side is negative, no real x satisfies this.
$\therefore$ the equation has no real solution.

Exercise 5.2A

Use the method of completing the square to solve each of the following equations. Give the roots correct to 2 d.p.

1 $x^2 + 2x - 4 = 0$
2 $x^2 + 4x + 2 = 0$
3 $x^2 - 6x + 3 = 0$
4 $x^2 - 5x + 2 = 0$
5 $4x^2 - 8x + 1 = 0$
6 $3x^2 - 4x - 5 = 0$

Exercise 5.2B

Use the method of completing the square to solve, where possible, each of the following equations. Give the roots correct to 2 d.p.

1 $x^2 - 2x - 5 = 0$
2 $x^2 - 4x - 6 = 0$
3 $x^2 - 8x + 5 = 0$
4 $x^2 - x + 3 = 0$
5 $3x^2 + 6x + 2 = 0$
6 $4x^2 - 2x - 5 = 0$

5.3 The formula for the roots

The method of solving a quadratic equation by completing the square may be applied to the general quadratic equation to obtain a formula for the roots. This may then be quoted as an alternative to completing the square.

The general quadratic equation is

$$ax^2 + bx + c = 0, \qquad a \neq 0.$$

Rewriting: $$x^2 + \frac{b}{a}x = -\frac{c}{a}$$

Adding $\left(\frac{b}{2a}\right)^2$: $$\left(x + \frac{b}{2a}\right)^2 = -\frac{c}{a} + \frac{b^2}{4a^2}$$

$$= \frac{b^2 - 4ac}{4a^2}$$

$$\therefore x + \frac{b}{2a} = \frac{\pm\sqrt{(b^2 - 4ac)}}{2a}$$

$$\therefore x = \frac{\pm\sqrt{(b^2 - 4ac)} - b}{2a} \quad \text{or} \quad x = \frac{-b \pm \sqrt{(b^2 - 4ac)}}{2a}$$

This is the required formula for the roots. The second version is the traditional form, but the previous version is more convenient for calculator use.

This result should be remembered.

Examples 5.3

Use the formula to solve the following equations, where possible. Give the roots correct to 2 d.p.

1 $x^2 - 7x + 5 = 0$ **2** $3x^2 + 6x + 2 = 0$ **3** $2x^2 - 5x + 6 = 0$

1 $x^2 - 7x + 5 = 0$

Here $a = 1, \quad b = -7, \quad c = +5$

$$\therefore x = \frac{\pm\sqrt{(49 - 20)} + 7}{2} = \frac{\pm\sqrt{29} + 7}{2}$$

$$\therefore x = 6.19, 0.81, \text{ to 2 d.p.}$$

2 $3x^2 + 6x + 2 = 0$

$$x = \frac{\pm\sqrt{(36 - 24)} - 6}{6} = \frac{\pm\sqrt{12} - 6}{6}$$

$$\therefore x = -0.42, -1.58, \text{ to 2 d.p.}$$

3 $2x^2 - 5x + 6 = 0$

$$x = \frac{\pm\sqrt{(25 - 48)} + 5}{4} = \frac{\pm\sqrt{-23} + 5}{4}$$

Since -23 has no real square root, this equation has no real solutions.

Exercise 5.3

Solve the following equations, where possible; give the roots correct to two decimal places.

1 $x^2 - 4x - 6 = 0$

2 $2x^2 + 5x + 1 = 0$

3 $4x^2 - 3x - 5 = 0$

4 $5x^2 - 2x + 1 = 0$

5 $3x^2 + 4x - 5 = 0$

6 $6x^2 - 3x + 2 = 0$

7 $2x^2 + 7x - 3 = 0$

8 $7x^2 - 4x + 2 = 0$

9 $5x^2 + 3x - 5 = 0$

10 $4x^2 - x - 2 = 0$

5.4 The discriminant

The discriminant of the equation $ax^2 + bx + c = 0$ is the number $b^2 - 4ac$, which occurs in the formula for the roots. This number will be denoted by Δ. From the formula for the roots it follows that:

If $\Delta > 0$, i.e. if $b^2 > 4ac$, there are two real distinct roots.

If $\Delta = 0$, i.e. if $b^2 = 4ac$, there are two real equal roots.

If $\Delta < 0$, i.e. if $b^2 < 4ac$, there are no real roots.

Thus Δ discriminates between the three possible cases.

Also if $\Delta = q^2$, where q is rational, then the roots are rational, provided that a and b are rational.

Examples 5.4

1 Calculate the discriminant for each of the following equations. Hence state whether the roots are real. If the roots are real, state whether they are also rational.

a $2x^2 - 5x + 3 = 0$

b $3x^2 - 6x + 4 = 0$

c $5x^2 + 7x - 3 = 0$

d $6x^2 - 2x + 1 = 0$

a $\Delta = 25 - 24 = 1$ so the roots are real and rational

b $\Delta = 36 - 48 = -12$ so the roots are not real

c $\Delta = 49 + 60 = 109$ so the roots are real but not rational

d $\Delta = 4 - 24 = -20$ so the roots are not real

2 The equation $x^2 - 4x + k = 0$ has real unequal roots. Find the possible values of k.

Since the roots are real and unequal, $\Delta > 0$

$$\therefore 16 - 4k > 0$$

$$\therefore k < 4$$

$\therefore$ the possible values of k are all values less than 4.

This may acceptably be shortened to '$k < 4$'.

3 The equation $x^2 + px + 6 = 0$ has equal roots. Find the possible values of p and the corresponding roots.

Since the roots are equal, $\Delta = 0$

$$\therefore p^2 - 24 = 0$$

$$\therefore p = \pm\sqrt{24} = \pm 2\sqrt{6}.$$

The equation is now $x^2 \pm 2\sqrt{6}\,x + 6 = 0$

or $(x \pm \sqrt{6})^2 = 0$

$$\therefore x = -\sqrt{6} \text{ or } +\sqrt{6}.$$

When $p = 2\sqrt{6}$, root $= -\sqrt{6}$; when $p = -2\sqrt{6}$, root $= \sqrt{6}$.

Exercise 5.4A

1 Calculate Δ for each of the following equations. Hence state whether the roots are real. If the roots are real, state whether they are also rational.

a $3x^2 - 4x - 2 = 0$

b $4x^2 + 5x + 3 = 0$

c $5x^2 - 2x + 1 = 0$

d $6x^2 + 4x - 5 = 0$

e $2x^2 - 3x + 4 = 0$

f $12x^2 - 11x + 2 = 0$

g $9x^2 - 30x + 25 = 0$

2 The equation $x^2 + 6x + k = 0$ has real roots. Find the possible values of k.

3 The equation $x^2 + px + 3 = 0$ has equal roots. Find the possible values of p and the corresponding roots.

4 The equation $x^2 + px + 7 = 0$ has real roots. Find the possible values of p.

5 Show that the equation $x^2 + px + q = 0$ has real unequal roots for all negative values of q.

Exercise 5.4B

1 The equation $x^2 + 8x - k = 0$ has real roots. Find the possible values of k.

2 The equation $x^2 - sx + 5 = 0$ has equal roots. Find the possible values of s and the corresponding roots.

3 The equation $x^2 - sx + 10 = 0$ has real unequal roots. Find the possible values of s.

4 Find the values of k for which the line $y = k$ meets the graph of $y = x + \dfrac{1}{x}$. Find also the values of k for which the line is a tangent to the graph.

5.5 Symmetric properties of the roots of a quadratic equation

The roots of the general quadratic equation $ax^2 + bx + c = 0$ are usually denoted by α and β. We now prove that these roots are related to the coefficients in the equation by the symmetric relations

$$\alpha + \beta = -\frac{b}{a}, \qquad \alpha\beta = \frac{c}{a}.$$

Proof It is given that the equation $ax^2 + bx + c = 0$ has roots α, β.

$\therefore$ by the factor theorem $ax^2 + bx + c$ has factors $(x - \alpha)$ and $(x - \beta)$

$$\therefore ax^2 + bx + c = a(x - \alpha)(x - \beta)$$
$$= a[x^2 - (\alpha + \beta)x + \alpha\beta]$$

The factor a on the right ensures that the coefficients of x^2 in the two forms are equal. Equating the coefficients of x and the constant term gives

$$b = -a(\alpha + \beta),\ c = a\alpha\beta \quad \text{and so} \quad \alpha + \beta = -\frac{b}{a},\ \alpha\beta = \frac{c}{a}, \text{ as required.}$$

These two relations are together equivalent to the given equation, conveying the same information. They provide a useful check on the accuracy of a numerical solution. They can often be used to avoid a numerical solution.

The relations between the coefficients and the roots may be used in either order. Given the equation, the sum and product of the roots may be written down. Conversely, if the sum and product of the roots are known, the equation may be written down in the form

$$x^2 - (\text{sum of roots})x + (\text{product of roots}) = 0.$$

Exercise 5.5

1 Write down the sum and product of the roots of the following equations.

a $3x^2 - 5x + 4 = 0$ **b** $2x^2 + 6x - 3 = 0$ **c** $-4x^2 + 3x - 5 = 0$
d $7x^2 - 2x + 3 = 0$ **e** $8x^2 + 3x - 4 = 0$ **f** $5x^2 - 4x - 2 = 0$

2 Find a quadratic equation with integer coefficients such that the sum and product of the roots are respectively

a $7, 3$ **b** $-\frac{5}{2}, 4$ **c** $-\frac{4}{3}, \frac{2}{3}$ **d** $\frac{6}{7}, -\frac{2}{7}$.

5.6 Some uses of symmetric properties of roots

Examples 5.6

1 The equation $3x^2 - 6x - 4 = 0$ has roots α and β. Find a quadratic equation with integer coefficients and with roots 3α and 3β.

$$\alpha + \beta = \frac{6}{3} = 2,\ \alpha\beta = -\frac{4}{3}$$

Sum of new roots $= 3\alpha + 3\beta = 3(\alpha + \beta) = 6$
Product $= 3\alpha \,.\, 3\beta = 9\alpha\beta = -12$
$\therefore$ the equation is $x^2 - 6x - 12 = 0$.

2 The equation $2x^2 - 6x + 1 = 0$ has roots α and β. Find an equation with integer coefficients and with roots α^2 and β^2.

$$\alpha + \beta = 3, \ \alpha\beta = \frac{1}{2}$$

Sum of new roots $= \alpha^2 + \beta^2 = (\alpha + \beta)^2 - 2\alpha\beta = 9 - 1 = 8$

Product $= \alpha^2\beta^2 = (\alpha\beta)^2 = \frac{1}{4}$

$\therefore$ the equation is $x^2 - 8x + \frac{1}{4} = 0$ or $4x^2 - 32x + 1 = 0$.

3 The equation $3x^2 - 4x + 1 = 0$ has roots α and β. Find an equation with integer coefficients and roots α^3 and β^3.

$$\alpha + \beta = \frac{4}{3}, \ \alpha\beta = \frac{1}{3}$$

Sum of new roots $= \alpha^3 + \beta^3 = (\alpha + \beta)(\alpha^2 - \alpha\beta + \beta^2)$

$$= \frac{4}{3}[(\alpha + \beta)^2 - 3\alpha\beta]$$

$$= \frac{4}{3}\left[\frac{16}{9} - 1\right]$$

$$= \frac{28}{27}$$

Product $= \alpha^3\beta^3 = (\alpha\beta)^3 = \frac{1}{27}$

$\therefore$ the equation is $x^2 - \frac{28}{27}x + \frac{1}{27} = 0$ or $27x^2 - 28x + 1 = 0$.

Exercise 5.6A

1 The equation $3x^2 - 9x + 1 = 0$ has roots α and β. Find in each case a quadratic equation with integer coefficients and with roots

a $2\alpha, 2\beta$ **b** $\alpha - 2, \beta - 2$ **c** $\frac{3}{\alpha}, \frac{3}{\beta}$

d $\alpha + \frac{2}{\beta}, \beta + \frac{2}{\alpha}$ **e** α^2, β^2 **f** $\alpha(1 - \beta), \beta(1 - \alpha)$.

2 The equation $2x^2 - 4x - 3 = 0$ has roots α and β. Find a quadratic equation with integer coefficients and with roots α^3, β^3.

Exercise 5.6B

1 The equation $2x^2 - 7x + 4 = 0$ has roots α and β. Find a quadratic equation with integer coefficients and with roots

a $-4\alpha, -4\beta$ **b** $2\alpha + 3, 2\beta + 3$ **c** $\alpha - \frac{2}{\beta}, \beta - \frac{2}{\alpha}$ **d** $\frac{1}{\alpha^2}, \frac{1}{\beta^2}$.

2 The equation $x^2 - px + q = 0$ has roots α, β. Find a quadratic equation with roots α^4, β^4.

5.7 Two alternative methods for use in special cases

Examples 5.7

1 The equation $2x^2 - 3x - 4 = 0$ has roots α, β. Calculate
a $\alpha^3 + \beta^3$ **b** $\alpha^4 + \beta^4$.

From the given equation, $\alpha + \beta = \frac{3}{2}$, $\alpha\beta = -2$.

An alternative to using only these two facts is to use directly the fact that α and β each satisfy the given equation, so that

$$2\alpha^2 - 3\alpha - 4 = 0 \qquad (1)$$
$$2\beta^2 - 3\beta - 4 = 0. \qquad (2)$$

Adding (1) and (2) gives

$$2(\alpha^2 + \beta^2) - 3(\alpha + \beta) - 8 = 0$$
$$\therefore \alpha^2 + \beta^2 = \frac{3}{2}(\alpha + \beta) + 4 = \frac{25}{4}.$$

To find $\alpha^3 + \beta^3$, multiply (1) by α and (2) by β

$$2\alpha^3 - 3\alpha^2 - 4\alpha = 0 \qquad (3)$$
$$2\beta^3 - 3\beta^2 - 4\beta = 0. \qquad (4)$$

Adding (3) and (4) gives

$$2(\alpha^3 + \beta^3) - 3(\alpha^2 + \beta^2) - 4(\alpha + \beta) = 0.$$

Using the known values of $\alpha + \beta$ and $\alpha^2 + \beta^2$ this gives

$$\alpha^3 + \beta^3 = \frac{99}{8}.$$

To find $\alpha^4 + \beta^4$, multiply (3) by α and (4) by β and add:

$$\alpha^4 + \beta^4 = \frac{3}{2}(\alpha^3 + \beta^3) + 2(\alpha^2 + \beta^2) = \frac{497}{16}.$$

The method may be extended to find $\alpha^5 + \beta^5$, etc. in turn.

2 The equation $3x^2 - 6x - 4 = 0$ has roots α, β. Find a quadratic equation with roots 3α, 3β.

Replace $3x$ in the given equation by t; since this equation is satisfied when $x = \alpha$, i.e. when $3x = 3\alpha$, the new equation in t is satisfied when $t = 3\alpha$, and similarly when $t = 3\beta$.

Writing $3x = t$, or $x = \frac{t}{3}$, the equation becomes

$$3\frac{t^2}{9} - 6\frac{t}{3} - 4 = 0$$

or $\quad t^2 - 6t - 12 = 0$

or $\quad x^2 - 6x - 12 = 0$, using x as usual.

This example was worked by a different method as Examples **5.6**, Q1.

3 The equation $4x^2 + 7x - 3 = 0$ has roots α, β. Find a quadratic equation with roots $\alpha + 2$, $\beta + 2$.

Replace $x + 2$ in the equation by t, i.e. replace x by $t - 2$.
The equation becomes $4(t-2)^2 + 7(t-2) - 3 = 0$
or $4t^2 - 9t - 1 = 0$
or $4x^2 - 9x - 1 = 0$.

The method used in questions **2** and **3** can be tried when the new roots α' and β' are defined in the form $\alpha' = f(\alpha)$, $\beta' = f(\beta)$.

Exercise 5.7

1 Use the method of Examples **5.7**, Q1, for this question.
The equation $3x^2 - 6x + 2 = 0$ has roots α, β. Find a quadratic equation with integer coefficients and with roots α^3, β^3.

In questions **2** and **3**, use the method of Examples **5.7**, Q2 and Q3.

2 The equation $2x^2 - 3x - 5 = 0$ has roots α, β. Find a quadratic equation with integer coefficients and with roots 2α, 2β.

3 The quadratic equation $4x^2 - 5x - 2 = 0$ has roots α, β. Find a quadratic equation with integer coefficients and with roots

a $\alpha - 3$, $\beta - 3$ **b** $\frac{3}{\alpha}$, $\frac{3}{\beta}$.

4 The equation $x^2 - px + q = 0$ has roots α, β. Given that $S_n = \alpha^n + \beta^n$, prove that

$$S_{n+2} - pS_{n+1} + qS_n = 0.$$

Hence calculate S_3 in terms of p and q.

5.8 More examples on symmetric properties of roots

Examples 5.8

1 The equation $x^2 - px + 9 = 0$ has unequal negative roots. Find the possible values of p.

Since the roots are real and unequal, $\Delta > 0$
i.e. $p^2 - 36 > 0$ so $p^2 > 36$
$\therefore |p| > 6$.

Since the roots are negative, they have a negative sum and a positive product. The sum is p and the product is 9.
$\therefore p$ is negative; and also $|p| > 6$
$\therefore p < -6$

2 The equation $x^2 - px + 16 = 0$ has roots α, α^3. Find the possible values of p.

The product of the roots $= \alpha^4 = 16$ so $\alpha = \pm 2$.
The sum of the roots $= \alpha + \alpha^3 = p$.
$\therefore p = 2 + 8$ or $-2 - 8$
$\therefore p = \pm 10$

3 One root of the equation $x^2 - 12x + q = 0$ is the square of the other root. Find the possible values of q.

Let the roots be α, α^2, then $\alpha + \alpha^2 = 12$.
$\therefore \alpha^2 + \alpha - 12 = 0$
$\therefore (\alpha + 4)(\alpha - 3) = 0$
$\therefore \alpha = -4$ or 3
The product of the roots $= \alpha^3 = q$, $\therefore q = -64$ or 27

4 The equation $x^2 - 2rx + s = 0$ has roots $\alpha, \alpha + 2$. Find a relation between r and s.

$\alpha + (\alpha + 2) = 2r$ and $\alpha(\alpha + 2) = s$
$\therefore \alpha + 1 = r, \quad \alpha = r - 1, \alpha + 2 = r + 1$
$\therefore (r - 1)(r + 1) = s \quad$ or $\quad r^2 = s + 1$

Exercise 5.8

1 One root of the equation $x^2 - px + q = 0$ is twice the other root. Find a relation between p and q.

2 The roots of the equation $x^2 - px + q = 0$ differ by 3. Find a relation between p and q.

3 Find the values of k for which the roots of the equation $x^2 + 6x + k = 0$ are
a real and negative **b** of opposite signs.

4 The roots of the equation $x^2 - 8x + q = 0$ differ by $2s$. Find a relation between q and s.
Given also that the roots are positive, find the possible values of s.

5.9 Graphical solution of quadratic equations

The graphical method of solving quadratic equations has not yet been mentioned in this chapter; the student is likely to have met it in earlier work. One method of finding approximate solutions of the equation

$$ax^2 + bx + c = 0$$

for given values of a, b, c is to draw an accurate graph of $y = ax^2 + bx + c$. The solutions are then given by the x-coordinates of the points on the graph at which $y = 0$, i.e. of the points of intersection of the graph with the x-axis. If the graph crosses the x-axis, the equation has two unequal roots. If the graph touches the x-axis, the equation has two equal roots. If the graph has no point in common with the x-axis, the equation has no (real) roots.

An alternative graphical method for the solution of $ax^2 + bx + c = 0$ is to write the equation in the form

$$x^2 = -\frac{bx + c}{a}.$$

The roots of the equation can then be found as the x-coordinates of the points of intersection of the graphs of $y = x^2$ and $y = -\dfrac{bx + c}{a}$. If approximate solutions of several quadratic equations are required, this method saves time and labour, since the same graph of $y = x^2$ can be used with several linear graphs.

Exercise 5.9

1 Draw an accurate graph of $y = 2x^2 - 5x + 1$ for $-2 \leqslant x \leqslant 5$. Use the graph to find approximate solutions of the equations

a $2x^2 - 5x + 1 = 0$ **b** $2x^2 - 5x - 9 = 0$ **c** $2x^2 - 7x + 1 = 0$.

2 Draw an accurate graph of $y = x^2$ for $-3 \leqslant x \leqslant 3$. Use this graph, and suitable linear graphs, which should be clearly labelled, to find approximate solutions of the equations

a $x^2 - 2x - 1 = 0$ **b** $x^2 + x - 3 = 0$ **c** $2x^2 - 3x - 4 = 0$

d $3x^2 + 5x - 1 = 0$.

5.10 Simultaneous equations, one linear and one quadratic

When a line meets a curve, the coordinates of the points of intersection satisfy both the equation of the line and the equation of the curve, i.e. these coordinates are the solution of two simultaneous equations, one of which is linear. If the equation of the curve is of the second degree in x and y, it is 'quadratic'; only this case will be discussed here.

Examples 5.10

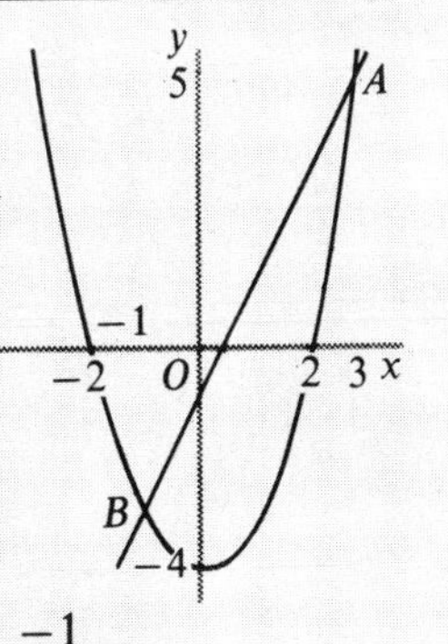

1 The line $y = 2x - 1$ meets the curve $y = x^2 - 4$ at the points A, B. Find the coordinates of A and B. Show the line and the curve in a sketch.

At A and B, $y = 2x - 1$ and $y = x^2 - 4$.

$\therefore$ the x-coordinates of A and B satisfy the equation

$2x - 1 = x^2 - 4$ or $x^2 - 2x - 3 = 0$

$(x - 3)(x + 1) = 0$

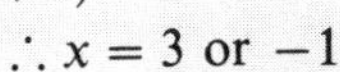

$\therefore x = 3$ or -1

From the linear equation, when $x = 3$, $y = 5$ and when $x = -1$, $y = -3$

$\therefore$ the points A and B are $(3, 5)$ and $(-1, -3)$, in either order.

Check: both these points satisfy the equation of the curve.

2 The line $2y = x - 4$ meets the circle $x^2 + y^2 = 4$ at the points A and B. Find the coordinates of A and B. Show the line and the circle in a sketch.

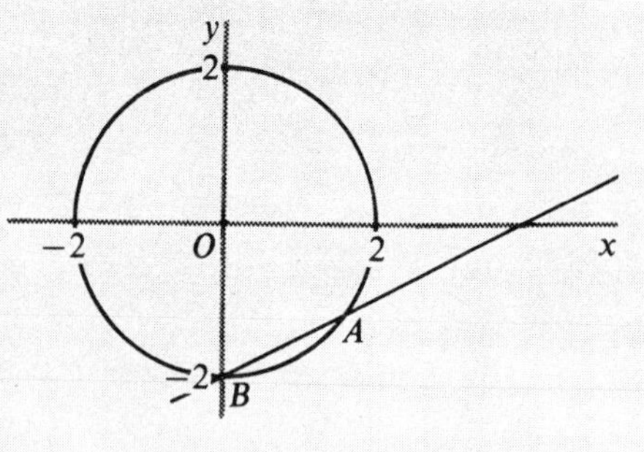

At A and B, $x = 2y + 4$ and $x^2 + y^2 = 4$.

$\therefore$ the coordinates of A and B satisfy the equation

$$(2y + 4)^2 + y^2 = 4 \quad \text{or} \quad 5y^2 + 16y + 12 = 0$$

$$(y + 2)(5y + 6) = 0$$

$$\therefore y = -2 \text{ or } -\frac{6}{5}$$

From the linear equation, A and B are $(0, -2)$ and $\left(\frac{8}{5}, -\frac{6}{5}\right)$, in either order.

Check: both these points lie on the circle.

The equation $x^2 + y^2 = 4$ states that the square of the distance of the point (x, y) from the origin is equal to 4; it is therefore the equation of a circle centre the origin and radius 2. The sketch is therefore as shown.

3 Find the values of m for which the line $y = m(x - 1)$ meets the curve $y = x^2 + 3$. Find also the equations of the tangents to the curve from the point $(1, 0)$.

At the points of intersection of the line and the curve, the x-coordinates satisfy the equation

$$x^2 + 3 = m(x - 1)$$

or $\quad x^2 - mx + 3 + m = 0.$

For the line to meet the curve, this equation must have real roots, so that $\Delta \geqslant 0$, i.e. $m^2 - 4(3 + m) \geqslant 0$

$$m^2 - 4m - 12 \geqslant 0$$

$$(m - 6)(m + 2) \geqslant 0$$

$$\therefore m \geqslant 6 \quad \text{or} \quad m \leqslant -2$$

$\therefore$ the line meets the curve for $m \geqslant 6$ and for $m \leqslant -2$.

For $m = 6$ and $m = -2$, $\Delta = 0$, and the equation for x has *equal* roots. In these cases the line touches the curve instead of crossing it, i.e. the corresponding lines are tangents to the curve. Since the line $y = m(x - 1)$ passes through $(1, 0)$ for all values of m, the tangents from $(1, 0)$ to the curve are $y = 6(x - 1)$ and $y = -2(x - 1)$.

The sketch shows the curve and some of the lines through the point (1, 0); L_1 and L_2 are tangents, L_3 and L_4 meet the curve twice, and L_5 (given by $m = 1$) does not meet the curve at all.

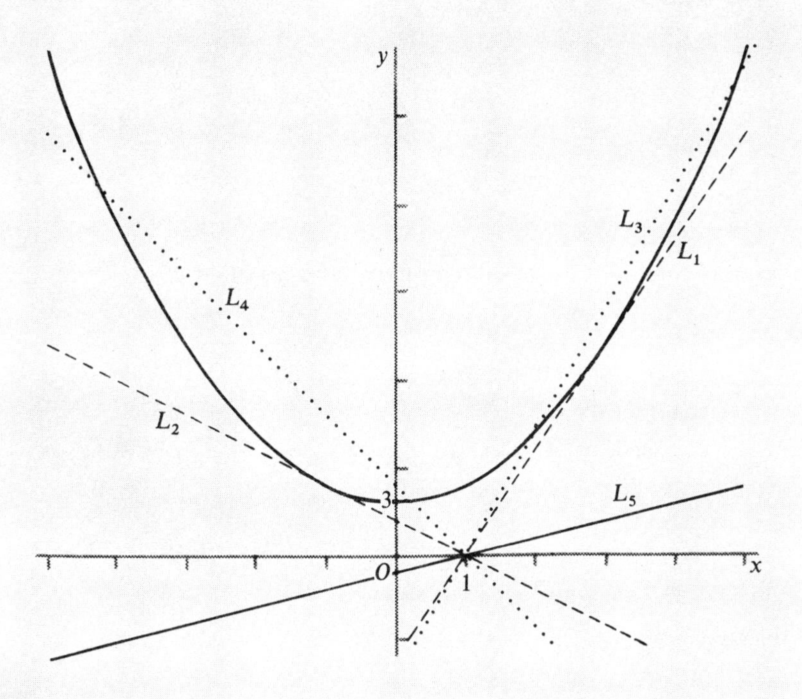

4 The line $y = 3(x - 1)$ meets the curve $y = x^2 - 4$ at A and B. Find the coordinates of the mid-point M of AB.

The x-coordinates of A and B satisfy the equation

$$x^2 - 4 = 3(x - 1)$$

or $\quad x^2 - 3x - 1 = 0.$

This equation can be solved by the formula, or by completing the square, to give the x-coordinates of A and B. From these the coordinates of M can be found. A quicker method is to write down the sum of the roots of the equation, which by inspection is 3.

The x-coordinate of $M = \dfrac{x_A + x_B}{2} = \dfrac{3}{2}$. Since M lies on $y = 3(x - 1)$, it follows that the y-coordinate of M is $3(x_M - 1) = 3\left(\dfrac{1}{2}\right) = \dfrac{3}{2}$.

$\therefore$ M is the point $\left(\dfrac{3}{2}, \dfrac{3}{2}\right)$.

Exercise 5.10A

In each of questions **1**–**3** find the points of intersection of the given line and the given curve.

1 $2y = x + 7$, $xy = 4$

2 $y + 3x = 5$, $2x^2 + 2xy + y^2 = 10$

3 $y + 2x = 1$, $2y^2 - x^2 = 1$

4 The line $y = 2x + 3$ meets the curve $5x^2 - y^2 = 1$ at A and B. Find the coordinates of the mid-point of AB.

Exercise 5.10B

In each of questions **1**–**3** find the points of intersection of the given line and the given curve.

1 $y = 3x - 5$, $x^2 + y^2 = 25$

2 $x + 2y = 3$, $xy = 1$

3 $x + y = 3$, $2x^2 + 3xy + 2y^2 = 16$

4 The line $y = 2(x - 1)$ meets the curve $y^2 = 4x$ at A and B. Find the coordinates of the mid-point of AB.

5 Find the values of m for which the line $y = m(x + 1)$ meets the curve $y^2 = 4x$. Find also the equations of the tangents to the curve from the point $(-1, 0)$. Show the curve and the tangents in a sketch.

Miscellaneous Exercise 5

1 Prove that the roots of the equation

$$(x - r)(x - s) = h^2$$

are real for all real values of r, s and h. Determine conditions which must be satisfied by r, s and h for the roots to be equal.

2 Given that a and b are rational, prove that the roots of $ax^2 - (a + b)x + b = 0$ are always rational.

Given that the roots of this equation are equal, find the relationship between a and b. (*S*)

3 Prove that the equation $x(x - 2p) = q(x - p)$ has real roots for all real values of p and q.

If $q = 3$, find a non-zero value for p so that the roots are rational. (*S*)

4 Find in surd form the roots of the equations

a $2x^2 - 6x + 3 = 0$ **b** $3x^2 - 6x + 2 = 0$.

Verify that the roots of **b** are the reciprocals of the roots of **a**.

5 Given that α and β are the roots of the equation $x^2 - px + q = 0$, find the equation, with coefficients in terms of p and q, whose roots are $\alpha^3\beta$ and $\alpha\beta^3$.

6 Given that the roots of the equation $x^2 - px + q = 0$ are α and β, express $(\alpha - 2\beta)(\beta - 2\alpha)$ in terms of p and q.

Hence, or otherwise, show that if one root of the equation is twice the other root, then $2p^2 = 9q$.

7 The equation $x^2 + 2x + k = 0$ has roots α, β.

The equation $x^2 - \left(k + \frac{1}{k}\right)x + 1 = 0$ has roots $\frac{\alpha}{\beta}, \frac{\beta}{\alpha}$.

Find the possible values of k.

8 Show that $\alpha^3 + \beta^3 = (\alpha + \beta)(\alpha^2 - \alpha\beta + \beta^2)$.

The roots of the equation $x^2 - px + q = 0$ are α, β, and it is given that $\alpha^3 + \beta^3 = 1$. Prove that $p^3 = 1 + 3pq$.

9 The roots of the equation $x^2 - px + 1 = 0$ are α and β. The roots of the equation $x^2 - 2px + 1 = 0$ are s and t. Without solving either equation show that the equation whose roots are $\alpha s + \beta t$ and $\alpha t + \beta s$ is

$$x^2 - 2p^2x + 5p^2 - 4 = 0.$$

Show also that if this last equation has equal roots, then either $\alpha = \beta$ or $s = t$.

10 The equation $x^2 - px + q = 0$ has roots α and β. Express in terms of p and q

(i) $\alpha^3 + \beta^3$ (ii) $(\alpha^2 - \beta)(\beta^2 - \alpha)$.

Deduce that if one root of the equation is the square of the other root, then

$$p^3 = 3pq + q^2 + q.$$

11 Solve the simultaneous equations

$$y + 2x = 3, \qquad x^2 + xy + y^2 = 3.$$

12 Find the coordinates of the points of intersection of the line $2y = x - 1$ and the curve $x^2 + xy + y^2 = 13$.

13 Find the coordinates of the points of intersection of the line $2x + y = 8$ and the curve $4x^2 + y^2 + 8x + 8y - 80 = 0$.

14 Given that x_1 and x_2 are the roots of $ax^2 + bx + c = 0$, state in terms of some or all of a, b, c

(i) the condition that $x_1 = x_2$ (ii) the value of $x_1 + x_2$.

a Find the values of m for which the line $y = mx$ is a tangent to the curve $y^2 = 3x - 1$.

b The line $y = 2x$ meets the curve $3y = x^2 - 10$ at the points $A(x_1, y_1)$ and $B(x_2, y_2)$.

(i) Obtain the quadratic equation whose roots are x_1 and x_2.

(ii) Without solving this equation, find the x-coordinate of the mid-point of AB. (*C*)

Chapter 6

Coordinate geometry 1: lines and circles

6.1 Introduction

The topic started in this chapter is the study of the properties of lines and curves by the use of coordinates in the x-y plane. The seventeenth-century French mathematician Descartes was the first to use coordinates in this way; the word 'Cartesian' for the system of coordinates is derived from his name.

In this book a 'line' is a *straight* line; curves are not lines.

The distance formula

This was proved in 4.1 and is given again here for convenience.

Given the points $P_1(x_1, y_1)$ and $P_2(x_2, y_2)$ then

$$P_1P_2 = \sqrt{[(x_2 - x_1)^2 + (y_2 - y_1)^2]}.$$

The mid-point formula

With the same notation for P_1 and P_2, let $M(X, Y)$ be the mid-point of the line-segment P_1P_2; the points Q and N are as shown in the diagram.

Then by similar triangles N is the mid-point of P_1Q and so x_1, X and x_2 are consecutive terms in an A.P.

$\therefore X$ is the arithmetic mean of x_1 and x_2

$$\therefore X = \frac{x_1 + x_2}{2} \text{ and similarly } Y = \frac{y_1 + y_2}{2}.$$

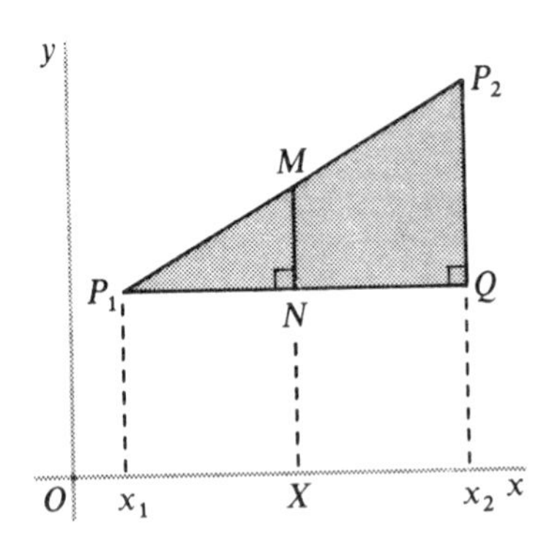

The gradient of a line in the x-y plane

The gradient measures the rate at which y changes as x changes; it is the increase in y for a unit increase in x. It may be written in various notations. With P_1 and P_2 as before:

$$\text{gradient} = \frac{y_2 - y_1}{x_2 - x_1} = \frac{y\text{-step}}{x\text{-step}}.$$

Since the increase in y may be negative for a unit increase in x, the gradient may be negative. It may also be zero, if an increase in x causes no change in y.

The gradient has the same value for any choice of the points P_1 and P_2 on the line.

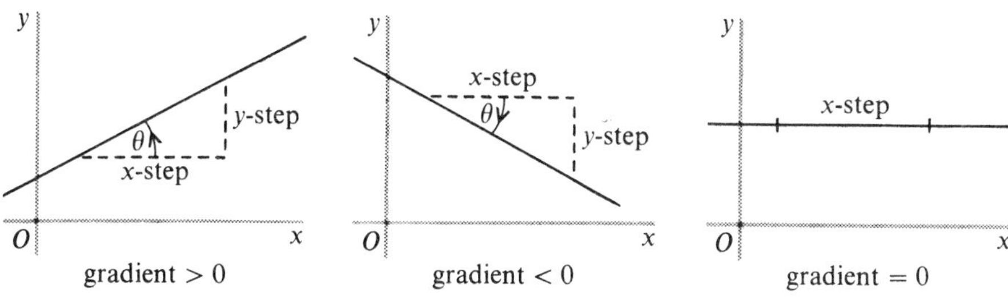

If the angle from the x-axis to the line is θ, the definition of the gradient may be written

$$\text{gradient} = \tan\theta.$$

Since a line is not in general drawn in a particular sense, the angle θ may be taken to lie between $-90°$ and $+90°$; it may then be found, for any given value of the gradient, by using the inverse tangent key on a calculator.

None of the above forms of the gradient has any meaning if the line is parallel to the y-axis, since the x-step between any two points is then zero; also $\theta = 90°$ and the tangent of $90°$ is not defined. In this case the gradient is not defined; the *direction* is given as parallel to the y-axis.

Examples 6.1

1 In each of the following cases, find

a the mid-point, M, of AB

b the length of AB, in its simplest surd form

c the gradient of AB.

(i) A is $(3, 7)$, B is $(5, 11)$

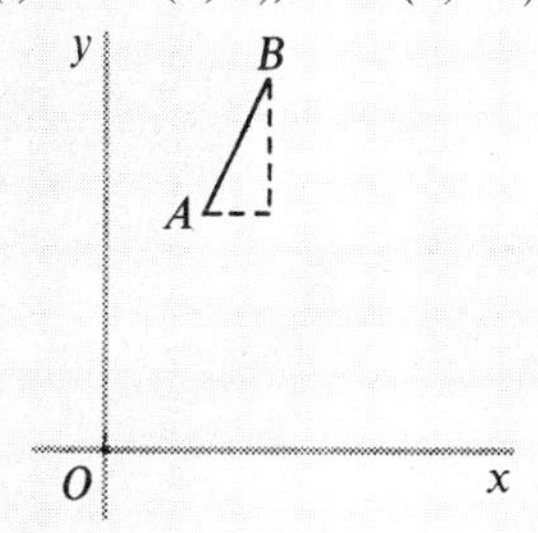

a M is $\left(\dfrac{3+5}{2}, \dfrac{7+11}{2}\right) = (4, 9)$

b $AB^2 = (5-3)^2 + (11-7)^2 = 20$
$AB = 2\sqrt{5}$

c gradient $= \dfrac{11-7}{5-3} = 2$

(ii) A is $(-4, 3)$, B is $(2, -1)$

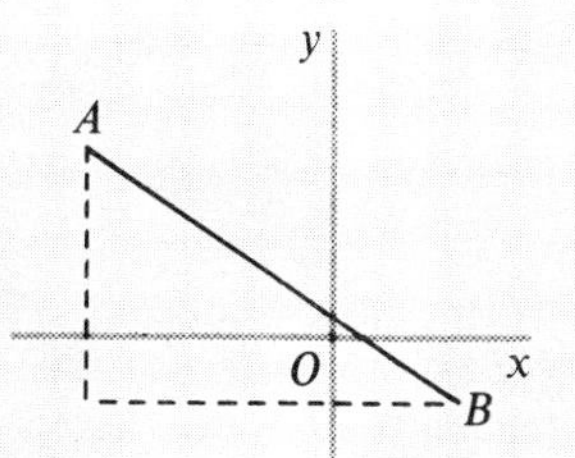

a M is $\left(\dfrac{-4+2}{2}, \dfrac{3-1}{2}\right) = (-1, 1)$

b $AB^2 = (2+4)^2 + (-1-3)^2 = 52$
$AB = 2\sqrt{13}$

c gradient $= \dfrac{-1-3}{2+4} = -\dfrac{2}{3}$

2 Given that A is (3, 2) and that B is the point such that the mid-point of AB is $M(6, 7)$, find B.

Method 1 Let B be the point (X, Y).

The x-coordinates of A, M and B are consecutive terms in an A.P. and so are the y-coordinates, i.e. 3, 6, X is an A.P. and so is 2, 7, Y.

$\therefore X = 9$ and $Y = 12$, so B is (9, 12).

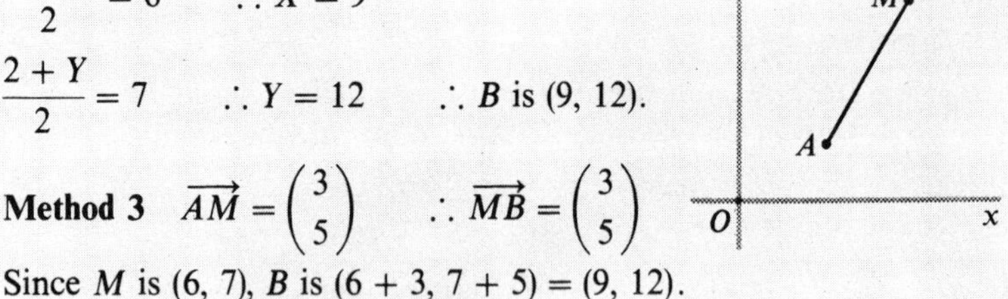

Method 2 Using the mid-point formula

$\dfrac{3 + X}{2} = 6 \qquad \therefore X = 9$

$\dfrac{2 + Y}{2} = 7 \qquad \therefore Y = 12 \qquad \therefore B$ is (9, 12).

Method 3 $\overrightarrow{AM} = \begin{pmatrix} 3 \\ 5 \end{pmatrix} \qquad \therefore \overrightarrow{MB} = \begin{pmatrix} 3 \\ 5 \end{pmatrix}$

Since M is (6, 7), B is $(6 + 3, 7 + 5) = (9, 12)$.

Exercise 6.1A

1 In each of the following cases, find

a the mid-point of AB

b the length of AB in surd form

c the gradient of AB

d the angle, to the nearest degree, from the x-axis to AB.

(i) A is (1, 9), B is (6, 12) (ii) A is (2, −5), B is (−3, −7)

(iii) A is (−7, 2), B is (5, 8)

2 Given that A is (7, 3), B is (9, 7), C is (12, 4), D is (4, 6), show that AB and CD bisect each other. Find also in surd form the length of AB and of CD.

3 Given that A is (6, 5) and that B is the point such that the mid-point M of AB is (9, 3), find B.

4 Show that the points A (4, 6), B (−2, −2) and C (5, −1) all lie on a circle centre D (1, 2). Verify that AB is a diameter. Find the coordinates of the point E such that CE is a diameter. Calculate the product of the gradients of AC and BC.

Exercise 6.1B

1 Given that A is (3, 7), B is (5, 4), find

a the mid-point of AB

b the length of AB in surd form

c the gradient of AB

d the angle, to the nearest degree, from the x-axis to AB.

2 Repeat question **1** given that A is (−2, −5), B is (6, −2).

3 Given that A is (4, 6), B is (3, 3), C is (6, 2), D is (7, 5), show that $ABCD$ is a rhombus.

4 Given that P is (3, 2), Q is (5, 7), R is (9, 4), find the coordinates of S so that $PQRS$ is a parallelogram.

6.2 Forms of the Cartesian equation of a line

The Cartesian equation of a line is an equation which is satisfied by the coordinates (x, y) of every point on the line. The equation of a line can always be written in the form $ax + by + c = 0$. Such an equation is called a *linear* equation.

The following summary describes various lines and gives their equations.

1 The line through the point $(a, 0)$ and parallel to the y-axis : $x = a$

2 The line through the point $(0, b)$ and parallel to the x-axis : $y = b$

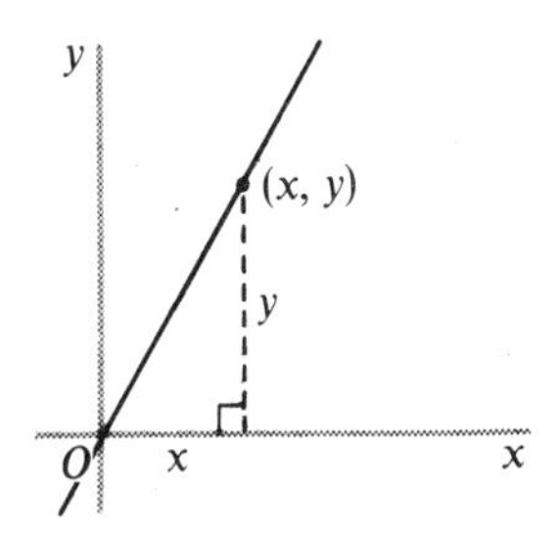

3 The line through the origin O, (0, 0), and of gradient m. At every point on the line except O, $\dfrac{y}{x} = m$ or $y = mx$, and (0, 0) satisfies this equation.

$\therefore$ the equation is $y = mx$.

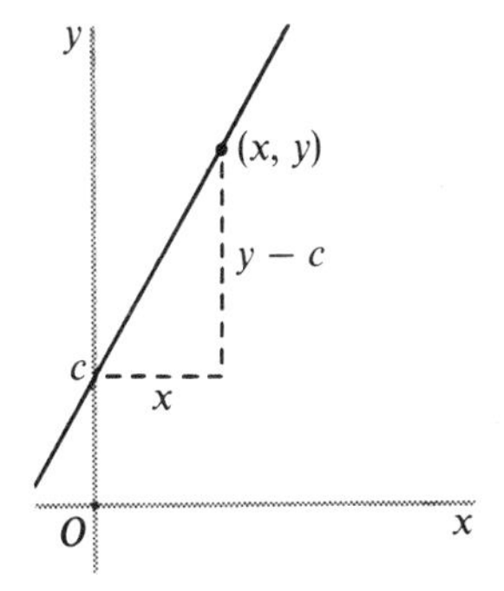

4 The line through the point $(0, c)$ and of gradient m. The equation is

$$y = mx + c.$$

It may be obtained from **3** by the translation $\begin{pmatrix} 0 \\ c \end{pmatrix}$, or obtained directly from the diagram.

This line is the graph of the linear function f given by $f(x) = mx + c$, and its equation has been met in Chapter 1.

Provided $b \neq 0$, the general linear equation $ax + by + c = 0$ may be written

$$y = -\frac{a}{b}x - \frac{c}{b}.$$

This is the equation of the line through the point $\left(0, -\dfrac{c}{b}\right)$ with gradient $-\dfrac{a}{b}$, and this is the graph of a linear function.

If $b = 0$, the general equation becomes $ax + c = 0$, and this, from **1**, gives a line parallel to the y-axis. Such a line is not the graph of any function, since y may have any value for one value of x.

5 The line through the point (h, k) and of gradient m. The equation is

$$y - k = m(x - h).$$

It may be obtained from **3** by the translation $\begin{pmatrix} h \\ k \end{pmatrix}$, or obtained directly from the diagram by the method used for **3**.

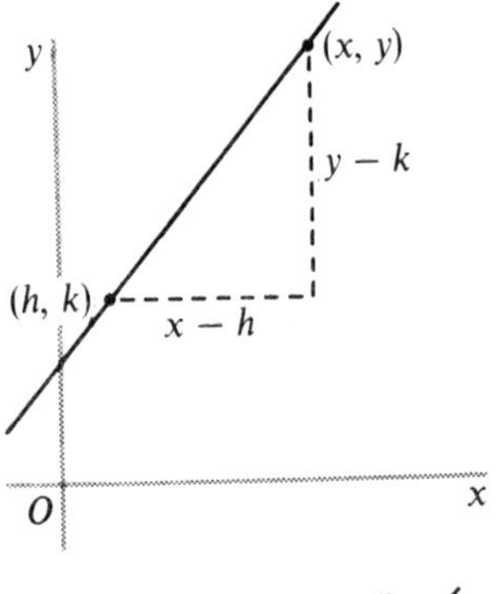

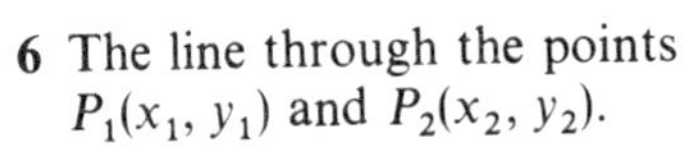

6 The line through the points $P_1(x_1, y_1)$ and $P_2(x_2, y_2)$.

The gradient is $\dfrac{y_2 - y_1}{x_2 - x_1}$ provided $x_1 \neq x_2$

$\therefore$ by **5** the equation, for $x_1 \neq x_2$, is

$$y - y_1 = \left(\frac{y_2 - y_1}{x_2 - x_1}\right)(x - x_1).$$

If $x_1 = x_2$, the equation is $x = x_1$.

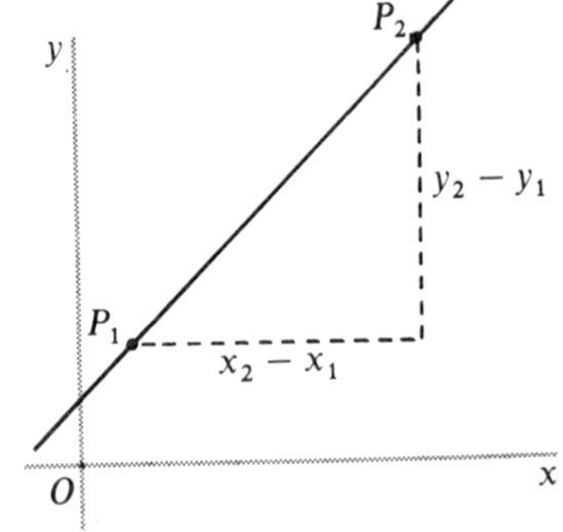

7 The line which meets the x-axis at $A(a, 0)$ and the y-axis at $B(0, b)$.

The gradient is $-\dfrac{b}{a}$ so by **4** the equation is

$$y = -\frac{b}{a}x + b,$$

which simplifies to $\dfrac{x}{a} + \dfrac{y}{b} = 1.$

This is called the intercept form.

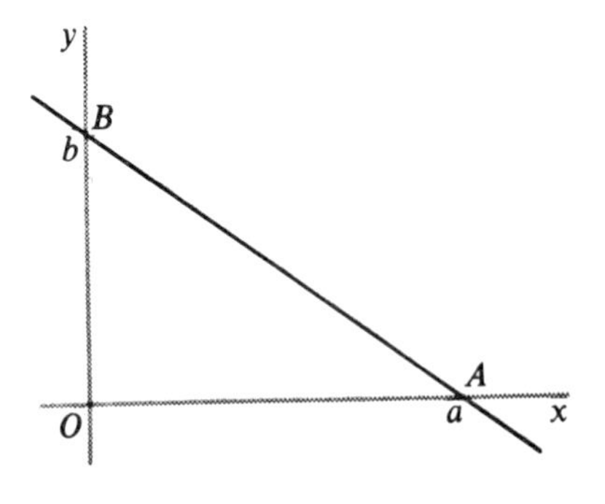

Note: The Cartesian equation of a line may be written in several forms; the terms may be arranged in different orders and they may each be multiplied or divided by any constant. It is customary to refer to any of these forms as 'the equation' of the line.

Parallel lines

Parallel lines have the same gradient. As the gradient of a line can be read directly from the equation of the line, it is easy to see if two lines are parallel.

Using the form $ax + by + c = 0$, the gradient is $-\dfrac{a}{b}$, so the lines $ax + by + c = 0$ and $ax + by + c' = 0$ are parallel. The equation of a line parallel to $ax + by + c = 0$ and also passing through the point (x_1, y_1) is $ax + by = ax_1 + by_1$.

Examples 6.2

1 Write down and simplify the equation of each of the following lines. In each case check that the given point satisfies the final equation.

a the line through (2, 3) with gradient 4

b the line through (−6, 1) with gradient $-\frac{3}{4}$

a Using form **5**, the equation is $y - 3 = 4(x - 2)$

or $y = 4x - 5$.

Check: $3 = 8 - 5$

b The equation is $y - 1 = -\frac{3}{4}(x + 6)$

$4(y - 1) = -3(x + 6)$ (clear the fraction first)

$4y + 3x = -14$ or $4y + 3x + 14 = 0$.

Check: $4 - 18 + 14 = 0$

2 Find the equation of the line through the points $P_1(4, -3)$ and $P_2(7, 2)$, giving it in simplified form.

Using **6**, the equation of the line is

$$y + 3 = \left(\frac{2 + 3}{7 - 4}\right)(x - 4)$$

or $3(y + 3) = 5(x - 4)$

or $3y - 5x + 29 = 0$. (Check)

3 Write down and simplify the equation of the line which passes through the points (3, 0) and (0, −5).

Using the intercept form, **7**, the equation is

$\frac{x}{3} - \frac{y}{5} = 1$ or $5x - 3y = 15$. (Check)

Exercise 6.2A

1 In each of the following cases determine whether the given point A lies on the given line.

a A (2, 5), $3x + 4y = 26$

b A (3, −4), $5x + 2y = 8$

c A (−6, −2), $2x - 5y + 2 = 0$

2 Write down, and simplify, the equation of each of the following lines. Check in each case that a given point satisfies the equation found.

a through (5, 3) with gradient 2

b through (4, −1) with gradient −3

c through (−2, 5) with gradient $\frac{4}{3}$

d through (2, 4) and (7, 8)

e through (6, −4) and (4, 1)

3 Write the equation $3x + 7y = 21$ in the intercept form.

4 Find the equation of the line parallel to the line $3x + 2y + 5 = 0$ and passing through the point $(4, -1)$.

Exercise 6.2B

1 Write down, and simplify, the equation of each of the following lines. Check in each case.

a through $(2, -3)$ with gradient $\frac{4}{5}$

b through $(-1, 5)$ with gradient $-\frac{2}{3}$

c through $(-2, 6)$ and $(3, 8)$

d through $(4, -1)$ and $(-2, 3)$

e through $(4, 2)$ and at $30°$ to the x-axis

f through $(4, -2)$ and at $-30°$ to the x-axis

2 Find the equation of the line parallel to the line $2x - 5y + 4 = 0$ and passing through the point $(3, 1)$.

3 Calculate to the nearest degree the angle from the x-axis

a to the line $3x - 4y = 7$ **b** to the line $6x + 5y = 10$.

4 Write down the equation of the line which is the reflection of the line $5x - 2y = 10$ in

a the x-axis **b** the y-axis **c** the line $y = x$.

Show the line and its reflections in three separate diagrams.

6.3 The parametric equations of a line

Consider the equations $x = 2 + t$, $y = 4 + 3t$, where t can take all values. Using $t = 0, 1, 2, 3$ gives the following table.

t	0	1	2	3
x	2	3	4	5
y	4	7	10	13

This table shows that as x increases by 1, y increases by 3, so that the points lie on a line of gradient 3. Since the line contains the point $(2, 4)$ its equation is

$$y - 4 = 3(x - 2) \quad \text{or} \quad y = 3x - 2.$$

This equation can be found directly from the given equations for x and y by eliminating t:

$$x = 2 + t \quad \text{so} \quad t = x - 2$$

$$y = 4 + 3t = 4 + 3(x - 2) \quad \text{or} \quad y = 3x - 2 \text{ as before.}$$

The number t in these equations is called a 'parameter', and the equations are called 'parametric equations'.

In general, the parametric equations

$$x = x_1 + tp, \quad y = y_1 + tq$$

where t takes all values and $p \neq 0$, represent the same line as the Cartesian equation

$$y - y_1 = \frac{q}{p}(x - x_1).$$

To form parametric equations for a line L given by a Cartesian equation, find the coordinates of any point on the line and the gradient of the line. If the point is (x_1, y_1) and the gradient is $\frac{q}{p}$ where p and q are integers, then a possible pair of parametric equations is $x = x_1 + tp, \quad y = y_1 + tq$. Note that the parametric equations for a line are not unique; any point on the line may be used as 'base point' (x_1, y_1), and any two numbers p and q such that the gradient is $\frac{q}{p}$ may be used.

The parameter t has a simple geometrical meaning; it is proportional to the displacement along the line from the base point $P_1(x_1, y_1)$ to the point $P(x, y)$. The distance P_1P is, by Pythagoras' theorem, $|t|\sqrt{(p^2 + q^2)}$. Note that $t > 0$ gives points on the line on one side of P_1, and $t < 0$ gives points on the other side of P_1.

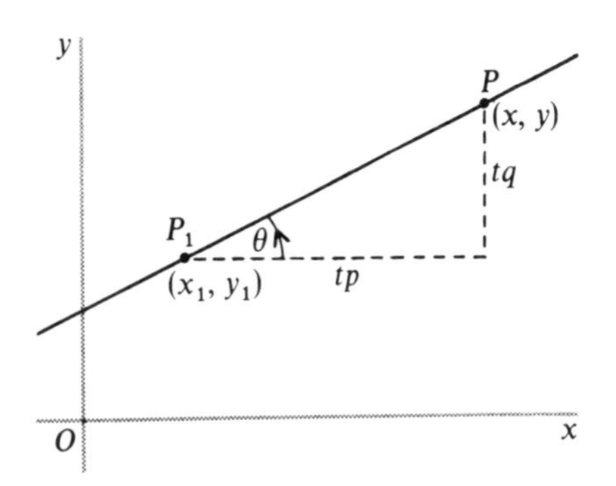

The point of intersection of two lines

The point of intersection of two lines given by their Cartesian equations is found by solving the equations as two simultaneous equations in x and y.

If each of the lines is given by a pair of parametric equations, then again two simultaneous equations are to be solved, this time for s and t, the parameters used. Note that it is essential to use different letters for the two parameters.

For example, let the lines be

$$L : x = 2 + 3s, \quad y = 4 - s$$

$$L' : x = 7 + t, \quad y = 9 - 2t.$$

At the point of intersection of L and L', the parameter values must be such that $2 + 3s = 7 + t$, so that the x-coordinates match, and also such that $4 - s = 9 - 2t$, so that the y-coordinates match. The values of s and t required are found by solving the simultaneous equations

$$2 + 3s = 7 + t \quad \text{or} \quad 3s - t = 5$$

$$4 - s = 9 - 2t \quad \text{or} \quad s - 2t = -5$$

and the solution is $s = 3$, $t = 4$. The point of intersection is therefore (11, 1).

The angle between two lines

The angle between two lines clearly depends only on their gradients; to simplify the diagram let the lines both pass through O. Let L be $y = mx$, and L' be $y = m'x$, and let the angles made by L and L' with the x-axis be θ and θ' respectively. Then

$$m = \tan\theta, \quad m' = \tan\theta'$$

and θ and θ' may be found by calculator to the required degree of accuracy. One of the angles between the lines is $\theta' - \theta$.

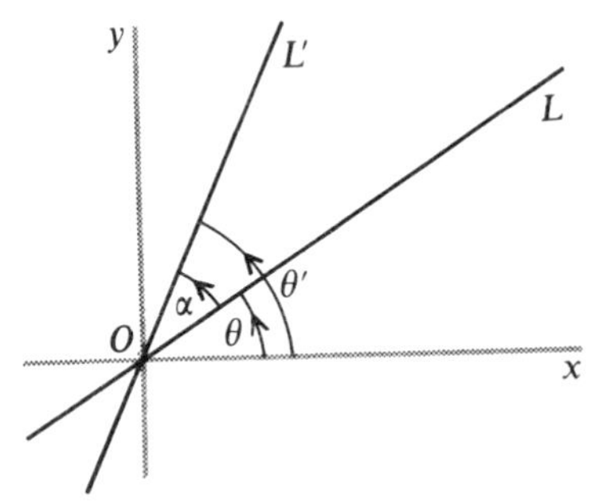

If the exact value of $\tan(\theta' - \theta)$ is required, it may be found by the following method, provided $\theta' - \theta$ is not 90°. The addition theorem for tangents is needed; this is proved in **10.1**.

$$\tan(\theta' - \theta) = \frac{\tan\theta' - \tan\theta}{1 + \tan\theta' \tan\theta} = \frac{m' - m}{1 + mm'}$$

If $mm' \neq -1$, this formula determines $\theta' - \theta$.

Perpendicular lines

If L and L' are perpendicular, then $\theta' = \theta + 90°$, and it was shown in **4.2** that $\tan(\theta + 90°) = -\dfrac{1}{\tan\theta}$, i.e. $m' = -\dfrac{1}{m}$ or $mm' = -1$. Conversely, if $mm' = -1$, then $m' = \tan(\theta + 90°)$ so $\theta' = \theta \pm 90°$ and the lines are perpendicular. This gives the important result:

> If two lines are perpendicular, then the product of their gradients is -1. Conversely, if the product of the gradients of two lines is -1, then the lines are perpendicular.

The length of the perpendicular from a point to a line

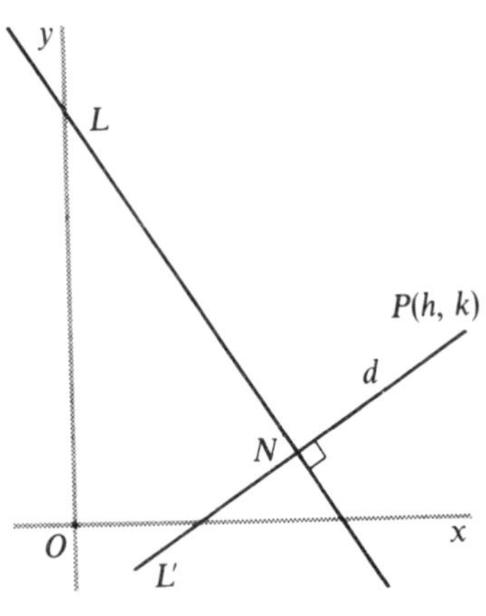

Given the line $L : ax + by + c = 0$ and the point $P(h, k)$, then the length d of the perpendicular from P to L is given by the formula

$$d = \left| \frac{ah + bk + c}{\sqrt{(a^2 + b^2)}} \right|.$$

Proof: In the diagram the foot of the perpendicular from P to L is N (X, Y), and the line PN is L'.

The gradient of L is $-\dfrac{a}{b}$.

$\therefore$ the gradient of L' is $\dfrac{b}{a}$, using $mm' = -1$.

Also $P(h, k)$ is on L'.

$\therefore L'$ is given by the parametric equations

$$x = h + at, \quad y = k + bt.$$

Since $N(X, Y)$ is on L', there is some value of t for which

$$X = h + at, \quad Y = k + bt \quad \text{and} \quad PN = |t|\sqrt{(a^2 + b^2)}.$$

Also $N(X, Y)$ is on L $\quad \therefore aX + bY + c = 0$

i.e. $a(h + at) + b(k + bt) + c = 0$

$$\therefore t = -\frac{ah + bk + c}{a^2 + b^2}.$$

Substituting for $|t|$ in the expression for PN gives

$$d = PN = \left|\frac{ah + bk + c}{\sqrt{(a^2 + b^2)}}\right|, \text{ the required result.}$$

If P lies on L, then $ah + bk + c = 0$. If not, the sign of $ah + bk + c$ depends on the side of the line on which P lies; all points on one side of L give a positive sign, all points on the other side give a negative sign. This gives a simple test to determine whether two points are on the same or opposite sides of a line, and in particular whether a given point is on the same side of L as is the origin O.

Note: A vector proof of the formula for d is given in Book 2.

Examples 6.3

1 Determine whether the point (9, 14) lies on the line given by the parametric equations

$$x = 1 + 2t, \quad y = 2 + 3t.$$

The given point lies on the line if the same value of t gives $x = 9$ and $y = 14$; by inspection, $t = 4$ gives the required values, so the point lies on the line.

2 Show that the parametric equations

$$x = 3 + 4t, \quad y = 2 - 5t$$

represent the same line as the parametric equations

$$x = 7 - 4s, \quad y = -3 + 5s.$$

Each line has gradient $-\frac{5}{4}$.

Using $t = 1$ in the first pair of equations gives the point $(7, -3)$, which is given by $s = 0$ in the second pair; $\therefore$ the lines are parallel and have a common point, and so they are the same line.

3 Find the acute angle α between the lines $L : 4x + 3y = 1$ and $L' : 5x - 2y = 4$, giving it to the nearest degree.

The gradient of L is $m = -\frac{4}{3}$, the gradient of L' is $m' = \frac{5}{2}$

$\therefore$ with the notation of **6.3**, $\theta = -53.1°$, $\theta' = 68.2°$

$\therefore$ one of the angles between L and L' is $68.2° + 53.1° = 121.3°$

$\therefore$ the acute angle between the lines is 59° to the nearest degree.

Or using the formula of **6.3**, with $\theta' - \theta = \alpha$,

$$\tan \alpha = \left|\frac{m' - m}{1 + mm'}\right| = \left|\frac{\frac{5}{2} + \frac{4}{3}}{1 - \frac{4}{3} \cdot \frac{5}{2}}\right| = \left|\frac{15 + 8}{6 - 20}\right| = \frac{23}{14}$$

$\therefore \alpha = 59°$, to the nearest degree.

4 Find the equation of the line L' which passes through $P_1(x_1, y_1)$ and is perpendicular to the line $L : ax + by + c = 0$.

The gradient of L is $-\frac{a}{b}$, $\therefore$ the gradient of L' is $\frac{b}{a}$, using $mm' = -1$.

$\therefore$ the equation of L' is $y - y_1 = \frac{b}{a}(x - x_1)$

or $\quad ay - bx = ay_1 - bx_1$.

5 Given that the line L has the equation $2x + 3y + 3 = 0$, find the distance of each of the points $A(4, 5)$ and $B(-6, 2)$ from L. State with reasons whether the point of intersection of AB and L lies between A and B.

The distance of a point from a line means the *shortest* distance, which is the length of the perpendicular from the point to the line.

Using the formula $d = \left|\frac{ah + bk + c}{\sqrt{(a^2 + b^2)}}\right|$,

the distance of A from L is $\left|\frac{8 + 15 + 3}{\sqrt{(4 + 9)}}\right| = \frac{26}{\sqrt{13}} = 2\sqrt{13}$

the distance of B from L is $\left|\frac{-12 + 6 + 3}{\sqrt{13}}\right| = \left|\frac{-3}{\sqrt{13}}\right| = \frac{3}{\sqrt{13}}$.

Since '$ah + bk + c$' is positive at A and negative at B, it follows that A and B lie on opposite sides of L and therefore the point of intersection of AB and L lies between A and B.

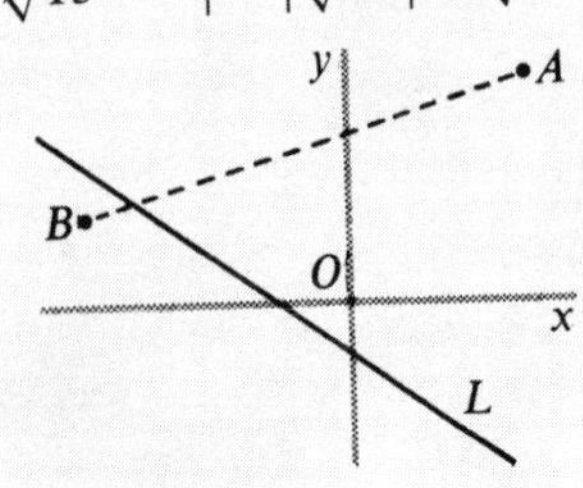

6 The lines L and L' have the equations $x = 4$ and $3x + 4y + 12 = 0$ respectively. Find the equations of the lines which bisect the angles between L and L'. Illustrate with a sketch.

Each point on a line which bisects an angle between L and L' is equidistant from L and L'. Let $P(X, Y)$ be such a point.

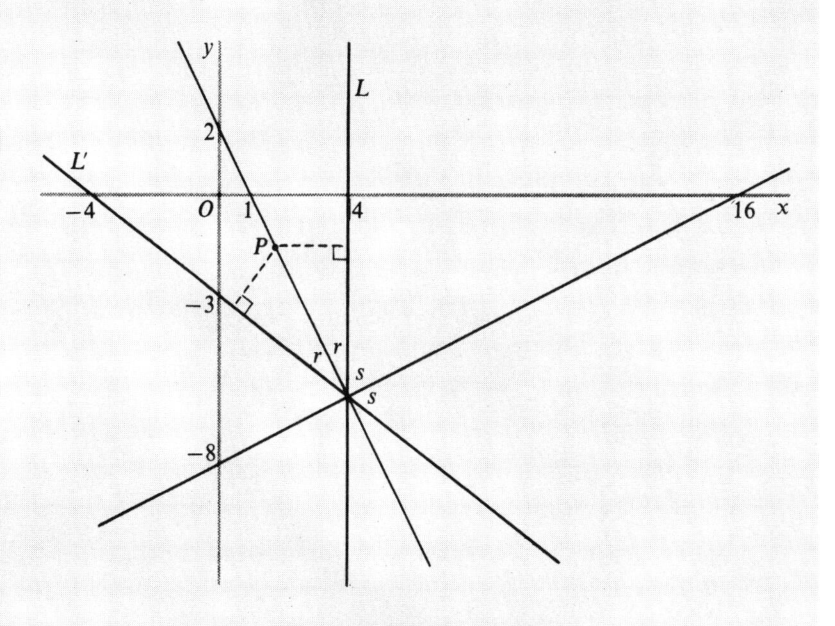

The distance of P from L is $|X - 4|$; the distance of P from L' is

$$\left|\frac{3X + 4Y + 12}{5}\right|,$$

and these distances are equal.

$$\therefore X - 4 = \pm\frac{(3X + 4Y + 12)}{5}.$$

Using the + sign, $5(X - 4) = 3X + 4Y + 12$

Using the − sign, $5(X - 4) = -(3X + 4Y + 12)$

$\therefore$ either $2X - 4Y = 32$ or $8X + 4Y = 8$

which simplify to $X - 2Y = 16$ and $2X + Y = 2$.

$\therefore$ the point $P(X, Y)$ lies on one of the lines

$$x - 2y = 16 \quad \text{and} \quad 2x + y = 2.$$

These are the required equations.

The two bisectors meet at right angles; as a check, the lines given by the above equations have gradients $\frac{1}{2}$ and -2, with a product of -1.

Exercise 6.3A

1 Find the Cartesian equation of the line given by the parametric equations

$$x = 4 + 3t, \quad y = 1 + 2t.$$

State the gradient of the line.

2 Show that the point $(7, -1)$ lies on each of the lines

$$L : x = 5 + s, \quad y = 3 - 2s \qquad L' : x = 4 + 3t, \quad y = 4 - 5t.$$

3 Find the point of intersection of the lines

$$L : x = 5 + 2s, \quad y = 4 - s \qquad L' : x = 2 + 3t, \quad y = \frac{1}{2} + t.$$

4 Find to the nearest degree the acute angle between the lines

$$L : 3x + 2y = 1 \qquad L' : 4x + 5y = -1.$$

Find also their point of intersection.

5 Find in each case the equation of the line L' through A and at right angles to the line L.

a $A(1, 3)$, $L : 2x + 5y = 9$ **b** $A(-2, 5)$, $L : 3x - 4y = 8$

c $A(7, 4)$, $L : 6x + y = 12$

6 Given the points $A(7, 2)$ and $B(3, 4)$, find the equation of the perpendicular bisector of AB.

7 Find the length of the perpendicular from $P(2, 5)$ to the line $3x + 4y = 12$. State whether the point P is on the same side of the line as the point O, and check in a sketch.

Exercise 6.3B

1 Show that the parametric equations

$$x = 6 + 2t, \quad y = 8 - 3t$$

represent the same line as the parametric equations

$$x = 10 - 2s, \quad y = 2 + 3s.$$

2 Find a pair of parametric equations for the line $3x - 4y + 12 = 0$.

3 Find to the nearest degree the acute angle between the lines L and L'.

a $L : 4x + 3y = 20$ $\quad L' : 2x - y = 6$

b $L : 3x - 2y + 4 = 0$ $\quad L' : 5x + 3y + 6 = 0$

4 Find the point of intersection of the lines

$$L : x = 4 + 3s, \quad y = 5 - 2s \qquad L' : x = 3 - 5t, \quad y = 1 + 8t.$$

5 Find in each case the equation of the line L' through A and perpendicular to L.

a $A(2, -3)$, $L : 4x + 3y = 10$ **b** $A(-4, -5)$, $L : 5x - 2y = 6$

6 The points A (2, 7) and C (4, 3) are opposite vertices of a rhombus $ABCD$. Find the equation of the line BD.

Given that the x-coordinate of B is 1, find the y-coordinate of B and calculate the coordinates of D. Prove that in this case the rhombus is a square.

7 The lines L and L' have the equations $y = 3$ and $5x + 12y = 9$ respectively. Find the equations of the lines which bisect the angles between L and L'. Illustrate with a sketch.

6.4 Circles with centre at the origin

Given that a circle has centre O (0, 0) and radius a, and that P (x, y) is any point on the circle, then $OP = a$ and so

$$x^2 + y^2 = a^2.$$

This is the Cartesian equation of the circle.

The parametric equations

$$x = a \cos \theta, \quad y = a \sin \theta,$$
$$\text{for } -180° < \theta \leqslant 180°,$$

give the same circle; the angle θ is the angle from the x-axis to OP.

An important geometrical property of circles is that the tangent at any point P on a circle is at right angles to the radius through P. This means that the length of the perpendicular from the centre of a circle to the tangent is equal to the radius, and also that the gradient of the tangent may be found by using the gradient of the radius.

For curves other than the circle, calculus is needed to find the gradient of a tangent.

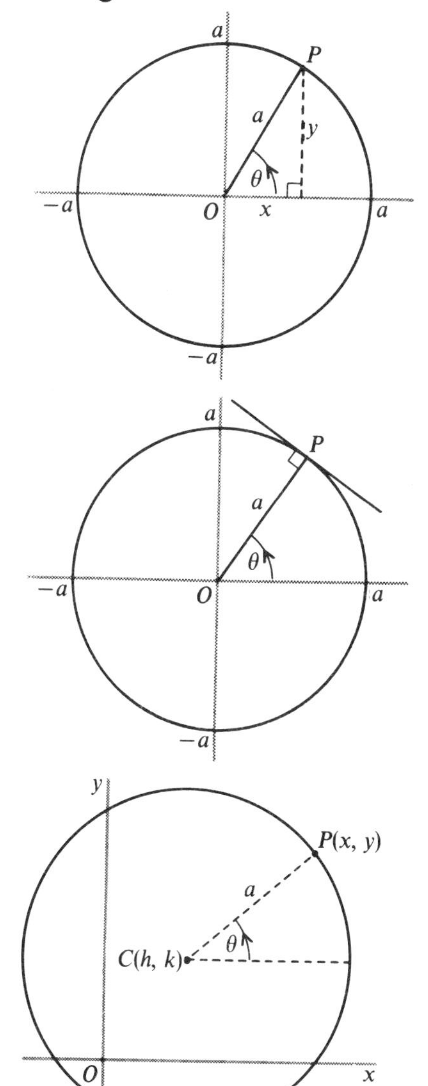

The general circle

Given that a circle has centre $C(h, k)$ and radius a, and that $P(x, y)$ is any point on the circle, then $CP = a$, and the distance formula gives

$$(x - h)^2 + (y - k)^2 = a^2. \qquad (1)$$

This is the equation of the circle. The translation $\begin{pmatrix} h \\ k \end{pmatrix}$ maps the circle centre O and radius a to this circle.

Parametric equations for this circle are

$$x = h + a\cos\theta,\ y = k + a\sin\theta,\ -180° < \theta \leqslant 180°.$$

The Cartesian equation may be written in the form

$$x^2 + y^2 - 2hx - 2ky + h^2 + k^2 - a^2 = 0.$$

This is an equation of the second degree in x and y with the special properties that the coefficients of x^2 and y^2 are equal and there is no term in xy. The general equation with these properties may be written in the form

$$x^2 + y^2 + 2gx + 2fy + c = 0. \qquad (2)$$

By the process of completing the square this becomes

$$(x + g)^2 + (y + f)^2 = g^2 + f^2 - c. \qquad (3)$$

Comparison of (3) with (1) shows that (2) is the equation of a circle with centre $(-g, -f)$ and radius $\sqrt{(g^2 + f^2 - c)}$, provided that $g^2 + f^2 > c$. If $g^2 + f^2 = c$, the only point which satisfies equation (3) is the point $(-g, -f)$. If $g^2 + f^2 < c$, no point satisfies (3).

Examples 6.4

1 A circle has centre $C(2, 3)$ and radius 5.

a Find the equation of the tangent at the point $A(5, 7)$ on the circle.

b Show that the line $3x - 4y + 31 = 0$ is a tangent to the circle.

a The tangent at A is at right angles to the radius CA

$$m(CA) = \frac{7-3}{5-2} = \frac{4}{3}$$

$$\therefore\ m(\text{tangent}) = -\frac{3}{4} \qquad (\text{using } mm' = -1)$$

$\therefore$ the equation of the tangent at A is

$$y - 7 = -\frac{3}{4}(x - 5)$$

or $\quad 4y + 3x = 43. \qquad$ (Check: A is on this)

b Several methods are available. Since the point of contact is not required, the simplest method is to use the length of the perpendicular from C to the given line.

The perpendicular from $C(2, 3)$ to $3x - 4y + 31 = 0$ is given by

$$d = \left|\frac{ah + bk + c}{\sqrt{(a^2 + b^2)}}\right| = \frac{6 - 12 + 31}{5} = 5.$$

Since the radius is also 5, the line is a tangent.

2 A circle has centre $C(3, 4)$ and radius 2. The point $A(4, 3)$ is the mid-point of a chord of the circle. Find the equation of this chord.

The line CA is at right angles to the chord through A, by the symmetry of the circle.

$m(CA) = -1$,

$\therefore m(\text{chord}) = 1$

$\therefore$ the equation of the line is

$$y - 3 = x - 4$$

or $\quad y = x - 1.$

(Check)

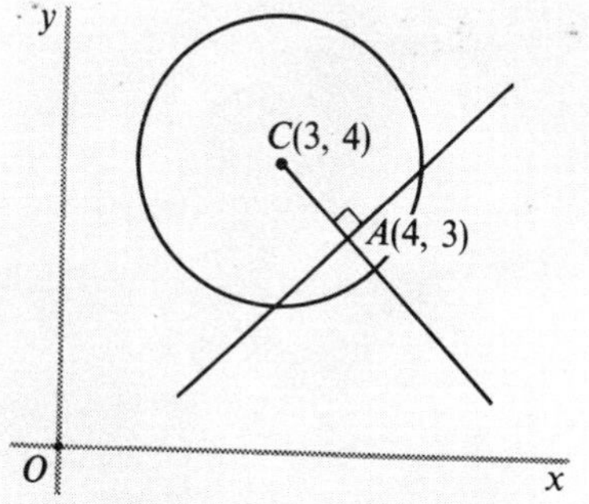

3 The points $P_1(x_1, y_1)$ and $P_2(x_2, y_2)$ are opposite ends of a diameter of a circle. Find the equation of the circle.

The 'obvious' approach is to use the mid-point of P_1P_2 as the centre, and the distance from this point to P_1 as the radius, and use the standard method. The following method simplifies the algebra.

Let $P(x, y)$ be any point on the circle other than P_1 or P_2.

Since the angle in a semi-circle is a right angle, P_1P is at right angles to P_2P; $\therefore$ the product of their gradients is -1.

$$\therefore \left(\frac{y - y_1}{x - x_1}\right) \cdot \left(\frac{y - y_2}{x - x_2}\right) = -1$$

or $(x - x_1)(x - x_2) + (y - y_1)(y - y_2) = 0.$

This equation has been shown to be satisfied by the coordinates of any point on the circle except P_1 and P_2. But by inspection the equation is also satisfied by $x = x_1$, $y = y_1$ and by $x = x_2$, $y = y_2$. This is therefore the equation of the circle. It may be expressed in standard form if required by removing brackets and rearranging.

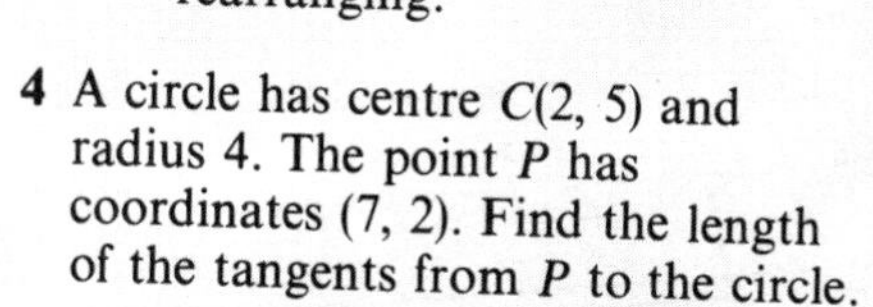

4 A circle has centre $C(2, 5)$ and radius 4. The point P has coordinates $(7, 2)$. Find the length of the tangents from P to the circle.

Let one of the tangents touch the circle at A.

Then applying Pythagoras' theorem to the triangle APC gives

$$AP^2 = CP^2 - CA^2$$

$\therefore AP^2 = 25 + 9 - 16 = 18$

$\therefore$ the length of the tangents is $\sqrt{18}$.

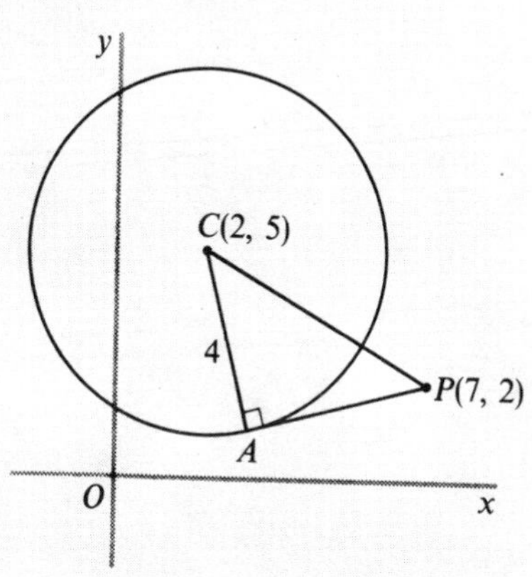

5 Find the centre C and the radius of the circle given by the equation

$$x^2 + y^2 - 8x + 10y + 28 = 0.$$

Show that the line $L : 2x + 3y = 6$ is a tangent to the circle and find the coordinates of the point of contact.

The equation of the circle may be written

$$(x - 4)^2 + (y + 5)^2 = 13$$

$\therefore$ the centre is $C(4, -5)$ and the radius is $\sqrt{13}$.

For the second part, since the coordinates of the point of contact are required, to use the length of the perpendicular from the centre to L is not helpful. Three other methods will be given:

Method 1 Find the equation of the line L' through C at right angles to L, and find the point of intersection D of L and L'. If the length of CD is equal to the radius, then L is a tangent and the point of contact is D.

The gradient of L is $-\frac{2}{3}$, $\quad\therefore$ the gradient of L' is $\frac{3}{2}$.

$\therefore$ the equation of L' is

$$y + 5 = \frac{3}{2}(x - 4) \qquad \text{or} \qquad 3x - 2y = 22.$$

The point of intersection D of L and L' is found by solving their equations simultaneously, and is $(6, -2)$.

$\therefore CD^2 = (6 - 4)^2 + (-2 + 5)^2 = 13$

$\therefore CD = \sqrt{13} =$ the radius of the circle.

$\therefore$ the line L is a tangent and the point of contact is $(6, -2)$.

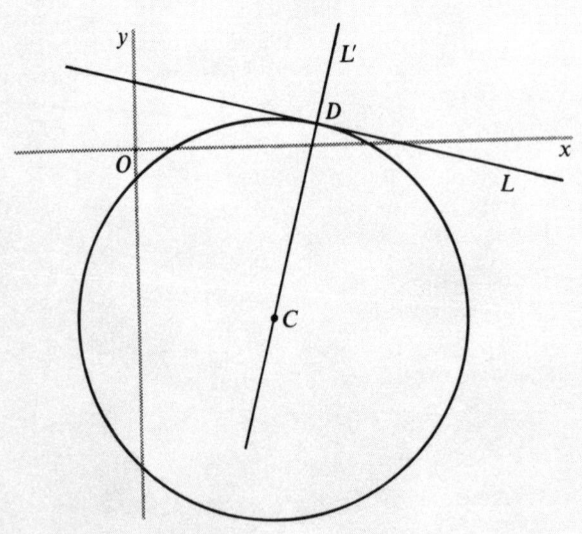

Method 2 Solve the equation of L and the equation of the circle as a pair of simultaneous equations. Since L is to be shown to be a tangent, these equations should have just one solution, and this solution gives the coordinates of the point of contact.

The equation of L is $2x + 3y = 6$ or $y = \dfrac{6 - 2x}{3}$.

The equation of the circle is $x^2 + y^2 - 8x + 10y + 28 = 0$.

Substituting for y in the equation of the circle:

$$x^2 + \frac{(6 - 2x)^2}{9} - 8x + 10\frac{(6 - 2x)}{3} + 28 = 0$$

$$9x^2 + 36 - 24x + 4x^2 - 72x + 30(6 - 2x) + 252 = 0$$

$$13x^2 - 156x + 468 = 0$$

$$x^2 - 12x + 36 = 0 \quad \text{or} \quad (x - 6)^2 = 0$$

$$\therefore x = 6$$

Since there is only one solution for x, L is a tangent. Using the equation of L, when $x = 6$, $y = -2$, so the point of contact is $(6, -2)$.

The disadvantage of this method is that the algebra is often laborious. Method 1 is simpler here, but its use is limited to cases where the curve is a circle. Method 2 may be applied to other curves given by equations of the second degree.

Method 3 This uses the same idea as Method 2, but the algebra is simplified by using parametric equations for L. Since by inspection $(3, 0)$ lies on L and the gradient is $-\frac{2}{3}$, a pair of parametric equations is $x = 3 - 3t$, $y = 2t$. Substituting in the equation of the circle, and using $x = 3(1 - t)$, gives

$$9(1 - t)^2 + 4t^2 - 24(1 - t) + 20t + 28 = 0$$

$$9(1 - 2t + t^2) + 4t^2 - 24 + 24t + 20t + 28 = 0$$

$$13t^2 + 26t + 13 = 0$$

$$t^2 + 2t + 1 = 0 \quad \text{or} \quad (t + 1)^2 = 0$$

$$\therefore t = -1$$

Since there is only one solution, L is a tangent and the point of contact, from the parametric equations, is $(6, -2)$.

Exercise 6.4A

1 Find the equation of the tangent at the point $A(3, 2)$ on the circle given by the equation $x^2 + y^2 = 13$.

2 Find the equation of the tangent at the point $P(x_1, y_1)$ on the circle given by the equation $x^2 + y^2 = a^2$.

3 Find the equation of each of the circles.

a centre (3, 1), radius 2 **b** centre (−2, 5), radius $\sqrt{3}$

4 Determine which of the following equations represents a circle. State the centre and radius of each circle.

a $x^2 + y^2 - 6x + 4y + 2 = 0$ **b** $x^2 + y^2 + 8x - 2y + 16 = 0$
c $2x^2 + 2y^2 + 10x - 3y + 17 = 0$ **d** $3x^2 + 3y^2 + 12x - 8y = 0$

5 A circle of radius 5 passes through the points $A(1, 2)$ and $B(9, 2)$. Find the mid-point of AB and the two possible positions of the centre of the circle.

6 A circle has centre $C(4, 2)$ and radius 5.
a Find the equation of the tangent at $A(7, 6)$.
b Show that the line $3x - 4y + 21 = 0$ is a tangent to the circle.

7 A circle has centre $C(1, 2)$ and radius $\sqrt{6}$. Find the length of the tangents from $P(4, 5)$ to the circle.

Exercise 6.4B

1 Find the equation of the tangent at the point $A(2, 2\sqrt{3})$ on the circle given by the parametric equations $x = 4\cos\theta$, $y = 4\sin\theta$.

2 Find the equation of the tangent at the point $(a\cos\phi, a\sin\phi)$ on the circle given by the parametric equations $x = a\cos\theta$, $y = a\sin\theta$.

3 A circle has centre $C(6, 3)$ and radius 4. Find the coordinates of the foot of the perpendicular from C to the line $L : 2x - 4y + 5 = 0$. Hence show that L intersects the circle.

4 A circle passes through the points $A(2, 5)$, $B(6, 5)$ and $C(8, 7)$. Find the equation of the perpendicular bisector of AB and of BC. Hence find the centre and the radius of the circle. Write down and simplify the equation of the circle.

5 Show that the line $L : 2x + 3y = 27$ is a tangent to the circle with centre (4, 2) and radius $\sqrt{13}$. Find the coordinates of the point of contact.

6 A circle has centre (2, 3) and radius $\sqrt{10}$. The line L has the parametric equations $x = -1 + 2t$, $y = 7 - t$. Show that L meets the circle in two distinct points and find the coordinates of these points.

7 A circle is given by the equation $x^2 + y^2 + 2gx + 2fy + c = 0$. The point P has coordinates (x_1, y_1) and T is the point of contact of a tangent from P to the circle. Prove that

$$PT^2 = x_1^2 + y_1^2 + 2gx_1 + 2fy_1 + c.$$

8 A circle is given by the equation $x^2 + y^2 + 2gx + 2fy + c = 0$. The point P lies on the circle and has coordinates (x_1, y_1). Show that the equation of the tangent to the circle at P may be written in the form

$$xx_1 + yy_1 + g(x + x_1) + f(y + y_1) + c = 0.$$

Miscellaneous Exercise 6

1 A, B and C are the points (5, 8), (−2, 1) and (6, −1) respectively and M is the mid-point of AC.

a Calculate the coordinates of M and the equation of BM.

b If the perpendicular from C to AB meets BM in T, find the coordinates of T. (*S*)

2 A rhombus $ABCD$ is such that the coordinates of A and C are (0, 4) and (8, 0) respectively. Show that the equation of the diagonal BD is $y = 2x - 6$.

The side AB has gradient −2. Find the coordinates of B and the coordinates of D.

Show that the rhombus has an area of 30 square units. (*JMB*)

3 $ABCD$ is a rectangle in which the coordinates of A and C are (0, 4) and (11, 1) respectively and the gradient of the side AB is −5.

(i) Find the equations of the sides AB and BC.

(ii) Show that the coordinates of B are (1, −1).

(iii) Calculate the area of the rectangle.

(iv) Find the coordinates of the point on the y-axis which is equidistant from A and D. (*JMB*)

4 The points $A(1, 2)$, $B(7, -1)$ and $C(-1, -2)$ are three of the vertices of the parallelogram $ABCD$. Find the coordinates of D.

Prove that the angle BAC is a right angle, and calculate the area of $ABCD$. Hence or otherwise find the length of the perpendicular from A to BC, leaving the answer in surd form.

5 The line whose equation is $7y = 3x - 6$ meets the x-axis at A. The line whose equation is $3y = 18 - x$ meets the y-axis at B. The two lines intersect at the point C.

(i) Calculate the coordinates of A, B and C.

(ii) Show that OC is perpendicular to AB.

(iii) Calculate the area of the triangle OBC. Given that OC and AB meet at D, deduce that $DB = \dfrac{9\sqrt{10}}{5}$.

(iv) Find the coordinates of the point P such that $ABPC$ is a parallelogram.

6 A, B and C are the points (−1, 1), (1, 2) and (4, 1) respectively. AP is a diameter of a circle, centre B.

a State the equation of the circle.

b Prove that CP is a tangent to the circle.

c D is the point (0, −1). Prove that CD is the other tangent to the circle from C. (*S*)

7 Find the equation of the circle, centre $(9, -1)$, which passes through the point A $(3, 8)$. Obtain the equation of the tangent to this circle at A and prove that this tangent passes through the centre of the circle with equation $x^2 + y^2 + 6x - 8y + 12 = 0$. (*S*)

8 A circle has equation $x^2 + y^2 - 2x - 10y + 18 = 0$.

a State the coordinates of C, the centre of the circle.

b Establish the equation of the chord with mid-point P $(2, 6)$.

c Show that the line with equation $x + y = 10$ is a tangent to the circle and find the coordinates of D, the point of contact.

d Verify that C, D and P are collinear. (*S*)

9 A and B are the points $(2, 2)$ and $(4, 8)$ respectively.

a Find the equation of the perpendicular bisector of AB.

b Given that C, a point in the first quadrant equidistant from both axes, is the centre of a circle passing through A and B, find
(i) the coordinates of C
(ii) the equation of the circle.

c Prove that the line $7x - y - 2 = 0$ is a tangent to this circle and state the coordinates of the point of contact. (*S*)

10 Find the coordinates of the centre, C, and the radius of the circle whose equation is

$$x^2 + y^2 - 2x - 4y - 3 = 0.$$

The tangent to the circle at the point $A(3, 4)$ on its circumference is drawn.
(i) Find the equation of the tangent at A.
(ii) Prove that the point $P(7, 0)$ lies on the tangent.
(iii) Find the equation of the circle which passes through the points C, A and P. (*S*)

11 The equation of a circle is $x^2 + y^2 - 3x - 4 = 0$.
Find
(i) the coordinates of its centre
(ii) its radius
(iii) the coordinates of the points at which it cuts the axes.

Show that the line whose equation is $3x + 4y = 17$ touches the circle and find the coordinates of its point of contact.

Show also that this line and the tangent to the circle at the point $(3, -2)$ intersect at a point on the x-axis and find its coordinates. (*JMB*)

12 The points A and B have coordinates $(2, 3)$ and $(-3, 1)$ respectively.
A point P moves in such a way that AP and BP are perpendicular. Show that the locus of P is a circle and for this circle find
(i) its equation
(ii) the coordinates of its centre
(iii) its radius.

State why the tangents to the circle at A and B are parallel.

The perpendicular from A to the x-axis meets the circle again at C. Find
(iv) the coordinates of C
(v) the equation of the tangent at C
(vi) the acute angle between the tangents at B and C. (*JMB*)

13 A circle has its centre at the point C (2, 1) and touches the line $3x + 4y - 60 = 0$. Find the radius of the circle and the coordinates of the point of contact P of the circle with the given line.

Given that the line meets the x-axis at A, show that CA is a diameter of the circle through C, P and A. For this second circle, find its equation and the equation of the tangent at P.

14 Write down the perpendicular distance from the point (a, a) to the line $4x - 3y + 4 = 0$. The circle, with centre (a, a) and radius a, touches the line $4x - 3y + 4 = 0$ at the point P. Find a, and the equation of the normal to the circle at P. Show that P is the point $\left(\frac{1}{5}, \frac{8}{5}\right)$.

Show that the equation of the circle which has centre P and which passes through the origin is

$$5(x^2 + y^2) - 2x - 16y = 0.$$ (*L*)

Chapter 7

Indices; exponential and logarithmic functions

7.1 Indices: the index laws

The student has for some years been familiar with the meaning of the notation a^2, a^3, etc, where each of the numbers 2, 3, etc is an *index*. The student will also have met the use of negative integers as indices, for example in standard form, where 4.73×10^{-2} means 0.0473. This section extends the use of indices to positive and negative rational numbers.

The definition of a^n, where n is a positive integer, is that

$$a^n = a \times a \times a \times \ldots \times a$$

where the right-hand side is the product of n a's. This definition has no meaning if n is not a positive integer. The extension of the definition of a^x to all rational x is chosen so that the index laws which hold for positive integral indices still hold. These laws state that for positive integers m and n:

1 $a^m \times a^n = a^{m+n}$

2 $\dfrac{a^m}{a^n} = a^{m-n}$ for $m > n$

3 $(a^m)^n = a^{mn}$.

The extended definition of a^x for all rational x is given below; p, q and n are positive integers and $a > 0$:

$$a^{\frac{1}{q}} = \sqrt[q]{a} = \text{the positive } q\text{th root of } a$$

$$a^{\frac{p}{q}} = \left(a^{\frac{1}{q}}\right)^p = (a^p)^{\frac{1}{q}}$$

$$a^{-\frac{p}{q}} = \frac{1}{\left(a^{\frac{p}{q}}\right)}$$

$$a^0 = 1.$$

This completes the definition of a^x for all rational x.

The index laws may now be stated in the more general form:

for all rational b and c, and $a > 0$,

1 $a^b \times a^c = a^{b+c}$

2 $\dfrac{a^b}{a^c} = a^{b-c}$

3 $(a^b)^c = a^{bc}$.

The definition of a^x for irrational x

This will be discussed more fully in Book 2. For the present, consider the case $x = \sqrt{2}$. It was shown in **5.1** that $\sqrt{2}$ is irrational. To four decimal places, $\sqrt{2}$ is 1.4142, so the rational numbers 1.4, 1.41, 1.414, 1.4142 give successive approximations, each one better than the previous one, to $\sqrt{2}$, and this set of approximations can be continued as far as we like. Therefore $10^{1.4}$, $10^{1.41}$, $10^{1.414}$, $10^{1.4142}$, ... give successive approximations to $10^{\sqrt{2}}$, and the limit to which these numbers converge is $10^{\sqrt{2}}$.

From now on, we will regard a^x as defined for all x. It will be assumed that the index laws hold for all x, and that a^x takes all positive values.

Examples 7.1

1 Simplify to an integer or fraction:

a $16^{\frac{1}{2}}$ **b** 3^{-2} **c** $9^{\frac{3}{2}}$ **d** $8^{-\frac{2}{3}}$.

a $16^{\frac{1}{2}} = \sqrt{16} = 4$

b $3^{-2} = \frac{1}{3^2} = \frac{1}{9}$

c $9^{\frac{3}{2}} = \left(9^{\frac{1}{2}}\right)^3 = 3^3 = 27$

d $8^{-\frac{2}{3}} = \frac{1}{8^{\frac{2}{3}}} = \frac{1}{\left(8^{\frac{1}{3}}\right)^2} = \frac{1}{2^2} = \frac{1}{4}$

Exercise 7.1

Simplify to an integer or fraction.

1 5^{-1}

2 $64^{\frac{1}{2}}$

3 $25^{\frac{3}{2}}$

4 $32^{\frac{2}{5}}$

5 $27^{\frac{2}{3}}$

6 $49^{-\frac{1}{2}}$

7 $81^{\frac{3}{4}}$

8 $8^{\frac{2}{3}}$

9 $\left(\frac{9}{4}\right)^{-\frac{1}{2}}$

10 $169^{\frac{1}{2}}$

11 $128^{\frac{5}{7}}$

12 10^{-2}

13 $36^{-\frac{1}{2}}$

14 $0.16^{\frac{1}{2}}$

15 $100^{-\frac{3}{2}}$

16 $64^{\frac{5}{6}}$

17 $\left(\frac{144}{49}\right)^{-\frac{1}{2}}$

18 $\left(\frac{4}{9}\right)^{\frac{3}{2}}$

19 $\left(\frac{27}{8}\right)^{-\frac{2}{3}}$

20 $10\,000^{\frac{3}{4}}$

21 $256^{\frac{5}{8}}$

7.2 Exponential functions

The function f which is defined for the domain $\mathbb{R}$ by

$$f(x) = a^x, \quad a > 0$$

is an exponential function; the word 'exponent' is an alternative name for the index x. Using $a = 2$, $a = 10$, etc, gives different exponential functions. The range of every exponential function with domain $\mathbb{R}$ is the set of positive numbers. A particularly important case uses $a = e$, where e is an irrational constant, whose value correct to three decimal places is 2.718; this case is called *the* exponential function, and it will be discussed in Book 2.

Consider first the case $a = 2$, so that $f(x) = 2^x$, $x \in \mathbb{R}$.
Let $y = 2^x$; the graph of y for $-3 \leqslant x \leqslant 3$ is shown in Fig. 1.

Fig. 1

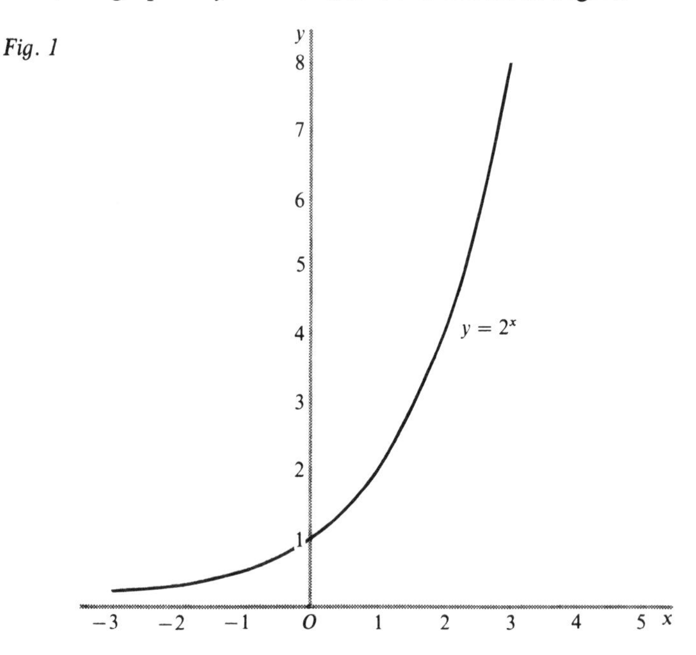

An important feature of the graph is that each value of y is the image of only one value of x, i.e. the function is one-one, and therefore has an inverse function.

The graph of $y = a^x$ for $a > 1$ has the same general shape as that of $y = 2^x$; the larger the value of a the more steeply the graph rises as x increases.

Examples 7.2

1 The functions f and g are defined on the domain $\mathbb{R}$ by

$f(x) = 3^x, \qquad g(x) = x - 2.$

a Find $fg(x)$ and give the domain and range of fg.

b Find $gf(x)$ and give the domain and range of gf.

a $fg(x) = f(x - 2) = 3^{x-2}$

The domain of fg is $\mathbb{R}$, since the domain of g is $\mathbb{R}$ and so is the range, i.e. $g(x)$ is in the domain of f for all x in $\mathbb{R}$. The range of fg is the set of all positive numbers.

b $gf(x) = g(3^x) = 3^x - 2$

The domain of gf is $\mathbb{R}$, since the domain of f is $\mathbb{R}$ and $f(x)$ is in the domain of g for all x in $\mathbb{R}$.

Since 3^x takes all positive values, the range of gf is the set of all numbers greater than -2, i.e. $\{y : y > -2\}$.

Exercise 7.2A

1 Draw an accurate graph of $y = 3^x$ for $-1 \leqslant x \leqslant 3$.

Draw a tangent at each of the points on the curve given by $x = 0, 1, 2, 2.5$; estimate the gradient, g, of each tangent, correct to one decimal place. Copy and complete the following table, and comment on your results.

x	0	1	2	2.5
y				
g				
$\frac{g}{y}$				

2 *Sketch* the graph of $y = 3^{-x}$ for $-3 \leqslant x \leqslant 1$.

3 The functions f and g are defined on the domain $\mathbb{R}$ by

$$f(x) = 2^x, \qquad g(x) = 2x + 2.$$

Find $gf(x)$ and state the domain and range of gf.

4 Given that, for non-zero x, $f(x) = 2^x$ and $g(x) = \frac{1}{x}$, solve the equation $fg(x) = f(x)$.

Exercise 7.2B

1 Answer Exercise 7.2A, Q1, replacing 3^x by e^x and using a calculator to make the table of values of y.

2 *Sketch* the graph of $y = e^{-x}$ for $-3 \leqslant x \leqslant 1$.

3 The functions f and g are defined on the domain $\mathbb{R}$ by

$$f(x) = 4^x, \qquad g(x) = \frac{x}{2}.$$

a Find $fg(x)$ and state the domain and range of fg.

b Find $gf(x)$ and state the domain and range of gf.

4 The functions f and g are defined on the domain $\mathbb{R}$ by

$$f(x) = 3^x, \qquad g(x) = x^2.$$

Given that g^2f means ggf, g^3f means gg^2f, and so on, find $g^2f(x)$, $g^3f(x)$ and $g^6f(x)$.

7.3 Logarithmic functions

The function f defined on ℝ by $f(x) = 2^x$ was discussed in **7.2**. It was noted that f is a one-one function and therefore has an inverse function. To obtain the inverse of f, the subject of the formula $y = 2^x$ must be changed from y to x. A new notation is needed here to change the subject; it is called 'logarithmic notation'. Using this notation

$$y = 2^x \text{ can be written } x = \log_2 y;$$

this is an abbreviation for 'x is the logarithm to base 2 of y'. In this notation $f^{-1}(y) = \log_2 y$. It follows that

$$\text{if } f(x) = 2^x \text{ then } f^{-1}(x) = \log_2 x.$$

In general, $y = a^x$ can be written $x = \log_a y$, for $a > 0$. The pattern of the relation between y, a and x should be carefully studied in each of these forms; in words:

'x is the logarithm of y to the base a' means that 'x is the index to which the base a must be raised to give y.'

If $f(x) = a^x$, then $f^{-1}(x) = \log_a x$.

This result should be remembered.

Examples of the use of logarithmic notation are:

$$32 = 2^5, \quad \log_2 32 = 5; \qquad 1000 = 10^3, \quad \log_{10} 1000 = 3;$$

$$2 = 8^{\frac{1}{3}}, \quad \log_8 2 = \frac{1}{3}; \qquad 81 = 27^{\frac{4}{3}}, \quad \log_{27} 81 = \frac{4}{3}.$$

The only logarithms in general use are 'common logs', with base 10, and 'natural logs', with base e. The notation $\log x$ or $\lg x$ is often used for $\log_{10} x$, and $\ln x$ is used for $\log_e x$. Both of these are given on many calculators. Use of the two keys log (or lg) and 10^x in succession, in either order, will restore any positive number to itself, or approximately so, because of the inverse relation between the two. Similarly, use of the keys ln and e^x in succession have no effect on a number.

Algebraically these facts may be written

$$x = \log_{10}(10^x) \quad \text{and} \quad x = 10^{\log_{10} x},$$
$$x = \log_e(e^x) \quad \text{and} \quad x = e^{\log_e x}.$$

Some calculators do not have keys for 10^x or e^x; instead they have an inverse key which reverses the effect of the log and ln keys.

Logarithms to base e will be discussed in Book 2.

The graph of a log function may be drawn by reflecting the graph of the corresponding exponential function in the line $y = x$, as in the case of all inverse functions, provided that the scales are the same on both the axes. This is most easily done in the case of $f(x) = 2^x$ and $f^{-1}(x) = \log_2 x$. These graphs are shown in Fig. 2. The domain and range of f^{-1} are obtained by interchanging the domain and range of f, so the domain of f^{-1} is the set of positive numbers and the range is ℝ.

Fig. 2

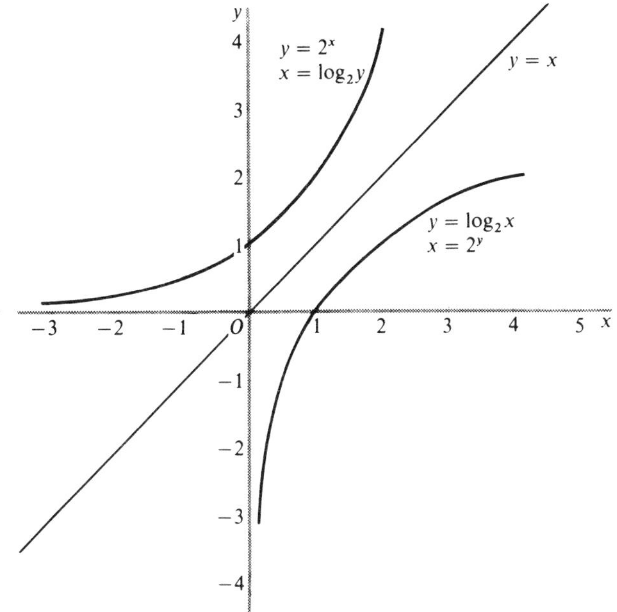

Examples 7.3

1 Write in a form using a logarithm:

a $3^4 = 81$ **b** $7^{-2} = \frac{1}{49}$ **c** $25^{\frac{1}{2}} = 5$ **d** $r^s = t$.

The index in each case is the log; the number raised to this index is the base.

a $4 = \log_3 81$ **b** $-2 = \log_7\left(\frac{1}{49}\right)$ **c** $\frac{1}{2} = \log_{25} 5$ **d** $s = \log_r t$

2 Write without using a logarithm:

a $\log_2 8 = 3$ **b** $\log_{10} 100 = 2$ **c** $\log_{16} 2 = \frac{1}{4}$ **d** $\log_b c = f$.

The log is the index to which the base must be raised.

a $2^3 = 8$ **b** $10^2 = 100$ **c** $16^{\frac{1}{4}} = 2$ **d** $b^f = c$

3 Simplify:

a $\log_2 128$ **b** $\log_6 36\sqrt{6}$ **c** $\log_p\left(\frac{1}{p^{\frac{3}{2}}}\right)$.

a $\log_2 128 = \log_2(2^7) = 7$

b $\log_6 36\sqrt{6} = \log_6\left(6^2 \times 6^{\frac{1}{2}}\right) = \log_6 6^{2.5} = 2.5$

c $\log_p\left(\frac{1}{p^{\frac{3}{2}}}\right) = \log_p\left(p^{-\frac{3}{2}}\right) = -\frac{3}{2}$

Exercise 7.3A

1 Write in a form using a logarithm.

a $5^3 = 125$ **b** $2^{-3} = \frac{1}{8}$ **c** $4^{\frac{5}{2}} = 32$ **d** $3^{-3} = \frac{1}{27}$

2 Write without using a logarithm.

a $\log_5 \frac{1}{25} = -2$ **b** $\log_8 2 = \frac{1}{3}$ **c** $\log_{100} 10 = \frac{1}{2}$ **d** $\log_c d = a$

3 Simplify the following.

a $\log_4 64$ **b** $\log_2 \frac{1}{256}$ **c** $\log_3 81\sqrt{3}$

d $\log_2 \sqrt{32}$ **e** $\log_{10} 100^{\frac{1}{3}}$ **f** $\log_b 1$

g $\log_8 4$ **h** $\log_{10} \frac{1}{10}$ **i** $\log_b b^c$

Exercise 7.3B

1 Write in a form using a logarithm.

a $7^3 = 343$ **b** $6^{-2} = \frac{1}{36}$ **c** $9^{\frac{3}{2}} = 27$ **d** $p^q = r$ **e** $\frac{1}{r^s} = t$

2 Write without using a logarithm.

a $\log_{27} 9 = \frac{2}{3}$ **b** $\log_5 625 = 4$ **c** $\log_9 2187 = 3.5$ **d** $\log_b \frac{1}{\sqrt{a}} = c$

3 Simplify the following.

a $\log_{10} 0.001$ **b** $\log_5 25\sqrt{5}$ **c** $\log_2 8\sqrt{2}$ **d** $\log_3 6561$ **e** $\log_2 \frac{1}{32}$

7.4 Properties of logarithms

Since a logarithm is an index, the index laws can be rewritten in terms of logarithms. The first three laws for logarithms are:

Law 1 The multiplication law: $\log_a pq = \log_a p + \log_a q$

Law 2 The division law: $\log_a \frac{p}{q} = \log_a p - \log_a q$

Law 3 The power law: $\log_a p^q = q \log_a p$.

To prove the multiplication law, let

$$\log_a p = r, \quad \log_a q = s.$$

Then $\quad p = a^r, \quad q = a^s.$

$\therefore pq = a^r \cdot a^s = a^{r+s}$, by the first index law.

$\therefore \log_a pq = r + s$

i.e. $\quad \log_a pq = \log_a p + \log_a q.$

Laws 2 and 3 can be proved in a similar way by using the 2nd and 3rd index laws.

Change of base

It is sometimes necessary to change a log from one base to another.

Law 4 The change of base law: $\log_a x = \dfrac{\log_b x}{\log_b a}$

To prove this, let $\log_a x = y$ then $a^y = x$.

Taking logs to base b and using Law 3 gives

$$y \log_b a = \log_b x$$

$$\therefore\ y = \frac{\log_b x}{\log_b a} \text{ as required.}$$

In particular, the case $x = b$ gives $\log_a b = \dfrac{1}{\log_b a}$.

Examples 7.4

A base is given only in questions where it affects the answers.

1 Express in terms of $\log p$, $\log q$ and $\log r$:

a $\log pqr$ **b** $\log \dfrac{pq}{r}$ **c** $\log p^2q^3r^4$.

a $\log pqr = \log p + \log q + \log r$, by two applications of Law 1.

b $\log \dfrac{pq}{r} = \log pq - \log r$, by Law 2
$= \log p + \log q - \log r$, by Law 1.

c $\log p^2q^3r^4 = \log p^2 + \log q^3 + \log r^4$, by Law 1
$= 2 \log p + 3 \log q + 4 \log r$, by Law 3.

2 Express as a single logarithm in its simplest form:

a $\log 5 + \log 3 - \log 2$ **b** $4 \log 6 - 3 \log 2$ **c** $2 \log_{10} 4 - \frac{1}{2} \log_{10} 16 + 1$.

a $\log 5 + \log 3 - \log 2 = \log \dfrac{5.3}{2}$
$= \log \dfrac{15}{2}$, by Laws 1 and 2

b $4 \log 6 - 3 \log 2 = \log 6^4 - \log 2^3$, by Law 3
$= \log \dfrac{6^4}{2^3}$, by Law 2
$= \log 162$

c $2 \log_{10} 4 - \dfrac{1}{2} \log_{10} 16 + 1$
$= \log_{10} 4^2 - \log_{10} 16^{\frac{1}{2}} + \log_{10} 10$, by Law 3
$= \log_{10} \dfrac{16.10}{4}$, by Laws 1 and 2
$= \log_{10} 40$

3 Solve the equation $3^x = 8$, giving x to four significant figures.

The solution of this equation can be written as $\log_3 8$, but logs to base 3 are not commonly used. The solution could be found by applying Law 4 to $\log_3 8$, but use of Law 3 at the start is more direct.

The equation is $3^x = 8$

$\therefore x \log_{10} 3 = \log_{10} 8$, by Law 3

$$x = \frac{\log_{10} 8}{\log_{10} 3} = 1.893 \text{ to 4 s.f.}$$

(Check by calculator: $3^{1.893} = 8.002$)

4 In a geometric series the first term is 4 and the common ratio is $\frac{1}{3}$. Find the sum to infinity. Calculate the least value of n for which the sum of n terms differs from the sum to infinity by less than 10^{-8}.

In the usual notation $a = 4$, $r = \frac{1}{3}$; the sum to infinity $= S$

$$S = \frac{a}{1-r} = 6$$

$$S_n = \frac{a}{1-r}(1 - r^n) = 6\left(1 - \frac{1}{3^n}\right)$$

$$\therefore S - S_n = \frac{6}{3^n}$$

We have to find n so that $\frac{6}{3^n} < \frac{1}{10^8}$ or $3^n > 6(10^8)$

$\therefore n \log_{10} 3 > \log_{10} 6 + 8$

$n > 18.4$

$\therefore$ the least value of n is 19.

Exercise 7.4A

A base is given only in questions where it affects the answer.

1 Express the following in terms of $\log r$, $\log s$ and $\log t$.

a $\log rs$ **b** $\log \frac{s}{t}$ **c** $\log r^2$ **d** $\log \sqrt{(st)}$

e $\log \frac{1}{t^3}$ **f** $\log_{10}(100r^3)$ **g** $\log \left(r^{\frac{1}{2}}s^{\frac{1}{3}}\right)$ **h** $\log \sqrt{(r^3 s^5)}$

2 Express as a single logarithm in its simplest form.

a $\log 7 + 2 \log 3$ **b** $3 \log 5 + 4 \log 2$

c $\log 6 + \log 5 - \log 2$ **d** $2 \log_{10} 6 - 3 \log_{10} 2 + 2$

e $\log_2 p + 2 \log_2 q + 3$ **f** $2 \log_3 r + 3 \log_3 s - 4 \log_3 t - 2$

g $\frac{1}{2} \log p + \frac{1}{3} \log q^2$

3 Solve the following equations, giving x to four significant figures.

a $2^x = 7$ **b** $5^x = 10$ **c** $4^x = 3.2$ **d** $\left(\frac{1}{3}\right)^x = 4.5$

4 In a geometric sequence the first term is 2 and the common ratio is 3. Find the least value of n for which the nth term of the sequence is greater than 10^8. Check by calculating the corresponding term, giving it in standard form to 3 significant figures.

5 A solution contains x bacteria at time t hours after noon, and $x = 260(2^t)$. Find the number of bacteria in the solution at 3 p.m. Find also the time to the nearest minute at which the number of bacteria is 3000.

6 Given that $f(x) = \log_{10}x$ and $g(x) = x^3$, find

a $fg(x)$ **b** $(fg)^{-1}(x)$ **c** $gf(x)$ **d** $(gf)^{-1}(x)$.

Exercise 7.4B

1 Express the following in terms of $\log a$, $\log b$ and $\log c$.

a $\log abc$ **b** $\log \frac{bc}{a}$ **c** $\log a^2b^3c^4$

d $\log \sqrt{(a^3)}$ **e** $\log \frac{1}{b^3c^2}$ **f** $\log a^b b^a c^{ab}$

2 Express as a single logarithm in its simplest form.

a $\log 10 + \log 2.4$ **b** $\frac{1}{2}\log 9 + \frac{1}{3}\log 27$

c $4\log 18 - 3\log 9 - 4\log 2$ **d** $3\log 20 - 2\log 5 - 4\log 2$

3 Solve the following equations, giving x to three significant figures.

a $6^x = 18$ **b** $(3.4)^x = 12$ **c** $8^x = 32$ **d** $\frac{1}{4^x} = 0.84$

4 In a geometric series the first term is 4 and the common ratio is $\frac{1}{5}$. Find the sum to infinity.

Calculate the least value of n for which the sum of n terms differs from the sum to infinity by less than 10^{-14}.

5 The population of a village was 3750 on 1 January 1980. The population grew in such a way that after n years the population P was $3750(1.08)^n$. Show that by 1 January 1985 the population had increased by approximately 50%.

Find the year during which the population could be expected to reach 7500.

6 The functions f and g are defined for $x > 0$ by $f(x) = \log_{10}x$, $g(x) = \frac{1}{x}$.

a Find $fg(x)$ and state the domain and range of fg.

b Find $(fg)^{-1}(x)$.

c Find $gf(x)$.

d Find $(gf)^{-1}(x)$ and state the domain and range of $(gf)^{-1}$.

Miscellaneous Exercise 7

1 Simplify the following to an integer or fraction.

a $49^{\frac{3}{2}}$ **b** $32^{-\frac{3}{5}}$ **c** $\left(\frac{27}{8}\right)^{-\frac{2}{3}}$ **d** $\left(\frac{121}{16}\right)^{-\frac{1}{2}}$

2 Sketch the graph of $y = 2^{-x}$ for $|x| \leqslant 3$.

3 Solve the equation $2^{x+4} = 3^{x-1}$, giving x correct to four significant figures. Check by calculator.

4 By writing $3^x = t$, solve the equation $9^x - 6(3^x) + 8 = 0$, giving x correct to four significant figures. Check by calculator.

5 Solve the equation $8^x - 13(2^x) + 12 = 0$ by writing $2^x = t$ and using the factor theorem. Give x correct to three significant figures, unless the value is exact.

6 Find $\sum_{n=1}^{50} \log_{10} 9^n$, giving the answer correct to four significant figures.

7 Express as a single logarithm in its simplest form.

a $\log(x^2 - 3x + 2) - \log(x - 1) + \log(x - 2)$

b $2 \log(x - 4) - \log(x^2 - 6x + 8)$

c $\log(x^3 - 8) - 3 \log(x - 2)$

d $\log(x^3 + 27) - \log(x^2 - 3x + 9) + \log(x + 3)$

e $\log(x^2 - 1) - 2 \log(x + 1) + 3 \log(x - 1)$

f $2 \log(x + 1) + 3 \log(x - 1) - 4 \log x$

8 a Given that $c = \log_a b$,

(i) express b in terms of a and c (ii) express a in terms of b and c.

Given also that $c = 2$, find the values of

(iii) $\log_a b^3$ (iv) $\log_a (ab)^3$ (v) $\log_a \left(\frac{b^5}{a^4}\right)$.

b Without using tables or calculators, find the value of

$$2 \log\left(\frac{3}{4}\right) + \log\left(13\frac{1}{3}\right) - \log\left(7\frac{1}{2}\right).$$

c Solve the equation $\frac{10^{x+1}}{9^{x-1}} = 8^x$, giving your answer correct to two places of decimals.

(*JMB*)

9 A pan of soup is heated to a temperature of 85°C above that of the kitchen. It is then left to cool. After n minutes the temperature of the soup above that of the kitchen is θ°C, where $\theta = 85(0.92)^n$. Find to the nearest degree the temperature of the soup above that of the kitchen after ten minutes.

Find also after how many minutes, to the nearest minute, the temperature of the soup is 25°C above that of the kitchen.

10 A man suffering from insomnia is given a sleeping pill. This causes an initial level of 4 mg of a drug per litre of his blood. After t hours the number of mg per litre in the blood is N, where $N = 4(0.76)^t$.

a Calculate N for $t = 4$, correct to one decimal place.

b Calculate the number of hours, to the nearest half hour, after which the amount of the drug per litre of blood will have fallen to half its initial level.

11 Given that $\mathrm{f}(x) = \log_{10} x$ and $\mathrm{g}(x) = \sqrt{x}$, find

a $\mathrm{fg}(x)$ **b** $(\mathrm{fg})^{-1}(x)$ **c** $\mathrm{gf}(x)$ **d** $(\mathrm{gf})^{-1}(x)$.

12 The functions f and g are defined for $x > 0$ by $\mathrm{f}(x) = \log_2 x$, $\mathrm{g}(x) = x + 2$.

Find $\mathrm{gf}(x)$ and state the domain and range of gf. Find $(\mathrm{gf})^{-1}(x)$ and state the domain and range of $(\mathrm{gf})^{-1}$.

Sketch on the same axes the graph of $\mathrm{gf}(x)$ and the graph of $(\mathrm{gf})^{-1}(x)$. Mark on the diagram the solution of the equation $x = \mathrm{gf}(x)$.

Chapter 8

Vectors 1

8.1 Introduction

This chapter starts with a reminder of some properties of vectors in two dimensions. Vectors in three dimensions are then introduced, and the scalar product of two vectors is defined.

Given two points A and B, the line segment from A to B represents the vector $\overrightarrow{AB}$.

When we are considering vectors in two dimensions only, all the line segments lie in one plane, which is often the Cartesian x–y plane.

The characteristic of a vector is that it has both a *magnitude*, which is the length of the line joining the starting and finishing points, and a *direction*, that of the line from the starting point to the finishing point. It follows that, in a diagram showing vectors, each vector *must* be clearly marked with an arrow, as above.

Vectors may be used to represent a variety of physical quantities; the simplest of these is a *displacement*, the vector $\overrightarrow{AB}$ representing the displacement from the point A to the point B; other examples are velocity, acceleration, force, momentum.

Notation

The vector $\overrightarrow{AB}$ may be represented by a single letter, for example, **p**. Single letters used in this way are usually *printed* in bold type, but when handwritten it is essential that the letter is underlined. This is to distinguish the letter from the same letter used without underlining to mean the magnitude or length of the vector. It must always be clear whether the vector, or its length, is intended. The length of the vector **p** may be written either p or $|\mathbf{p}|$.

The vector $\overrightarrow{AB}$ is sometimes printed **AB**.

Two vectors with the same magnitude and direction are equal in all respects; if the line segments AB and CD are equal in length and have the same direction, then $\overrightarrow{AB} = \overrightarrow{CD}$ and the same letter **p** can be used for both vectors.

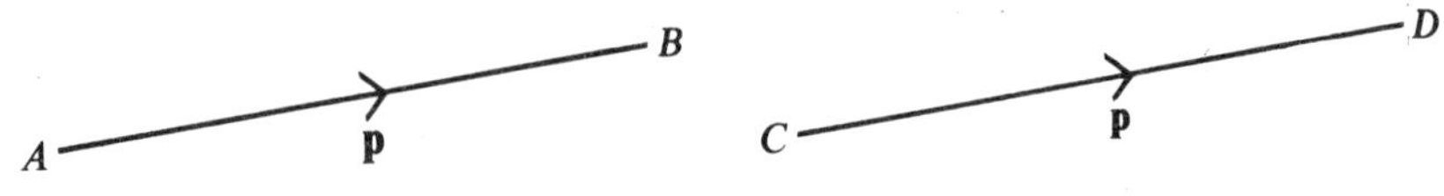

Vectors in a Cartesian plane with origin O: components

The vector $\overrightarrow{OP}$ from the origin O to the point $P(x, y)$ can be written as a column vector $\begin{pmatrix} x \\ y \end{pmatrix}$. The length and direction of $\overrightarrow{OP}$ are both fixed by the directed numbers x and y, and conversely the length and direction of a given vector $\overrightarrow{OP}$ fix a unique ordered pair of numbers x, y.

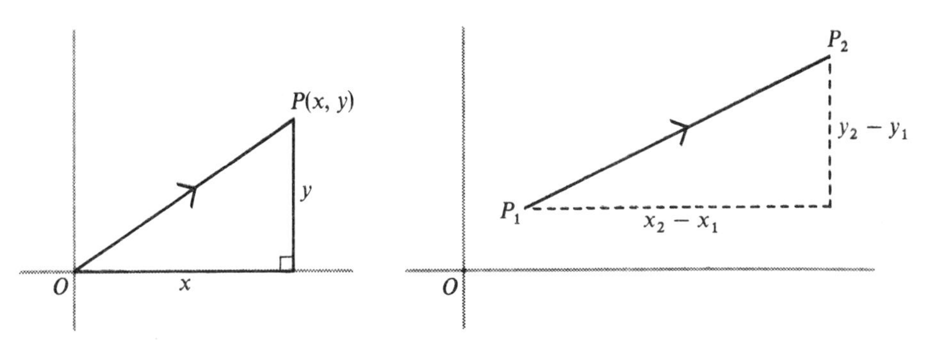

More generally, given the points $P_1(x_1, y_1)$ and $P_2(x_2, y_2)$, then

$$\overrightarrow{P_1P_2} = \begin{pmatrix} x_2 - x_1 \\ y_2 - y_1 \end{pmatrix}$$

The numbers $x_2 - x_1$ and $y_2 - y_1$ are called the *components* of the vector; the names 'x-step' and 'y-step' are also useful. Note that in the special case when a vector starts at O, the *components* are the same ordered pair of numbers as the *coordinates* of the end point. The important difference is that coordinates are always measured from O, but components can be measured from any starting point.

Examples 8.1

1 Given the points P_1 (3, 2), P_2 (5, 7), write in component form $\overrightarrow{OP_1}$, $\overrightarrow{OP_2}$, $\overrightarrow{P_1P_2}$ and $\overrightarrow{P_2P_1}$.

$$\overrightarrow{OP_1} = \begin{pmatrix} 3 \\ 2 \end{pmatrix}, \overrightarrow{OP_2} = \begin{pmatrix} 5 \\ 7 \end{pmatrix}, \overrightarrow{P_1P_2} = \begin{pmatrix} 5-3 \\ 7-2 \end{pmatrix} = \begin{pmatrix} 2 \\ 5 \end{pmatrix}, \overrightarrow{P_2P_1} = \begin{pmatrix} -2 \\ -5 \end{pmatrix}$$

2 Given the points $A(-2, 4)$, $B(3, -5)$, write in component form $\overrightarrow{AB}$ and $\overrightarrow{BA}$.

$$\overrightarrow{AB} = \begin{pmatrix} 3 & +2 \\ -5 & -4 \end{pmatrix} = \begin{pmatrix} 5 \\ -9 \end{pmatrix}; \overrightarrow{BA} = \begin{pmatrix} -5 \\ 9 \end{pmatrix}$$

3 Given the points $A(1, 3)$, $B(3, 7)$, $C(4, 9)$, write in component form $\overrightarrow{AB}$ and $\overrightarrow{BC}$. Deduce that A, B and C are collinear (i.e. lie on one straight line) and state the ratio $AB : BC$.

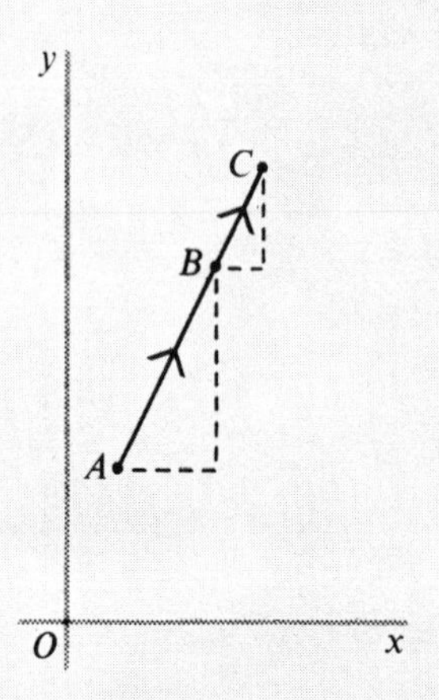

$$\overrightarrow{AB} = \begin{pmatrix} 2 \\ 4 \end{pmatrix}, \overrightarrow{BC} = \begin{pmatrix} 1 \\ 2 \end{pmatrix}$$

Since the components of $\overrightarrow{AB}$ are each twice those of $\overrightarrow{BC}$, it follows that $\overrightarrow{AB}$ is parallel to $\overrightarrow{BC}$.

$\therefore$ the points A, B, C lie on one straight line

The Cartesian equation of this line may be seen to be $y = 2x + 1$.

The ratio $AB : BC$ is the same as the ratio of the components of $\overrightarrow{AB}$ to those of $\overrightarrow{BC}$, i.e. $2 : 1$.

4 Given the points $P(4, 7)$, $Q(2, 1)$, $R(5, 10)$, write in component form $\overrightarrow{PQ}$ and $\overrightarrow{QR}$. Deduce that P, Q, R are collinear and state the ratio $PQ : QR$.

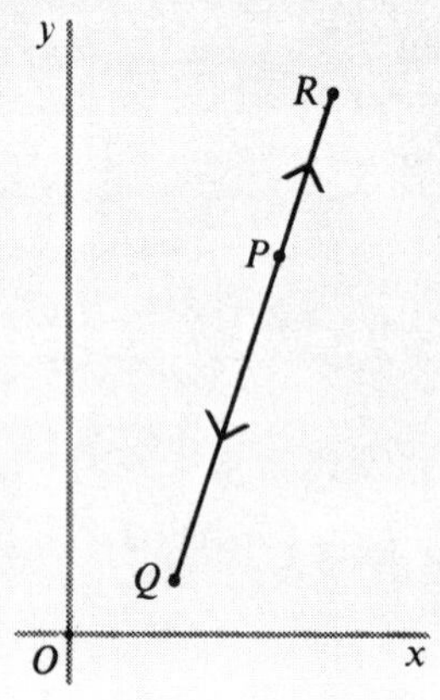

$$\overrightarrow{PQ} = \begin{pmatrix} -2 \\ -6 \end{pmatrix}, \overrightarrow{QR} = \begin{pmatrix} 3 \\ 9 \end{pmatrix}$$

The components of $\overrightarrow{PQ}$ are each $-\frac{2}{3}$ times those of $\overrightarrow{QR}$, showing that $\overrightarrow{PQ}$ and $\overrightarrow{QR}$ are parallel, though in opposite directions. So the points P, Q, R are collinear.

Also $PQ : QR = 2 : 3$; the negative sign is not relevant to the ratio of the *lengths*.

Exercise 8.1A

1 In each of the following cases, write in component form $\overrightarrow{OP_1}$, $\overrightarrow{OP_2}$, $\overrightarrow{P_1P_2}$, $\overrightarrow{P_2P_1}$.

a $P_1(4, 3)$, $P_2(7, 8)$ **b** $P_1(-2, 1)$, $P_2(3, 4)$

c $P_1(1, -3)$, $P_2(-4, 5)$ **d** $P_1(1, 2)$, $P_2(-2, -4)$

2 Given that A is (2, 5), B is (4, 11), C is (5, 14), write in component form $\overrightarrow{AB}$ and $\overrightarrow{AC}$. Deduce that A, B, C are collinear and write down the ratio $AB : AC$.

3 The vector $\overrightarrow{AB}$ is $\begin{pmatrix}2\\3\end{pmatrix}$ and A is $(-1, 4)$. Write down the coordinates of B.

The vector $\overrightarrow{BC}$ is in the same direction as $\overrightarrow{AB}$ and is twice as long. Write down $\overrightarrow{BC}$ and calculate the coordinates of C.

The vector $\overrightarrow{CD}$ is in the opposite direction to $\overrightarrow{AB}$ and three times as long. Write down $\overrightarrow{CD}$ and the coordinates of D.

4 Given that $\overrightarrow{AB} = \begin{pmatrix}4\\-3\end{pmatrix}$ and that B is (6, 5), write down the coordinates of A. Find also the coordinates of the point C such that $\overrightarrow{BC} = \overrightarrow{AB}$.

5 Three vertices of the parallelogram $ABCD$ are $A(3, 4)$, $B(7, 6)$ and $D(5, 9)$. Calculate $\overrightarrow{AB}$ and hence write down the coordinates of the vertex C, which is opposite A. Check by calculating $\overrightarrow{AD}$ and $\overrightarrow{BC}$.

Exercise 8.1B

1 In each of the following cases write in component form $\overrightarrow{OA}$, $\overrightarrow{OB}$, $\overrightarrow{AB}$, $\overrightarrow{BA}$.

a $A(5, 2)$, $B(3, 6)$ **b** $A(4, -3)$, $B(6, 1)$

c $A(-2, -1)$, $B(-3, 4)$ **d** $A(-4, 2)$, $B(1, -1)$

2 Given that A is (3, 1), B is $(5, -2)$, C is $(11, -11)$, write in component form $\overrightarrow{AB}$ and $\overrightarrow{BC}$. Hence show that A, B and C are collinear and write down the ratio $AB : BC$.

3 Given that $\overrightarrow{AB} = \begin{pmatrix}4\\-3\end{pmatrix}$ and that A is $(-1, 5)$, write down the coordinates of B. Given also that $BC = 3AB$ and that $\overrightarrow{BC}$ is in the opposite direction to $\overrightarrow{AB}$, write down $\overrightarrow{BC}$ and calculate the coordinates of C.

4 Given that $\overrightarrow{AB} = \begin{pmatrix}-2\\5\end{pmatrix}$ and that B is $(-1, 3)$, write down the coordinates of A. Find the coordinates of C so that $BC = AB$.

5 The diagonals of a rhombus $ABCD$ meet at M; A is (3, 1), B is $(13, -4)$, and $\overrightarrow{AM} = \begin{pmatrix}4\\3\end{pmatrix}$. Calculate the coordinates of M, C and D.

8.2 Addition of vectors

Given two vectors **a** and **b**, their sum is defined by the triangle law. In Fig. 1 $\overrightarrow{PQ}$ represents **a**, and $\overrightarrow{QR}$ represents **b**. The displacement **a** followed by the displacement **b** is a displacement from P to Q followed by a displacement from Q to R, i.e. the displacement from P to R. This leads to the definition

$$\mathbf{a} + \mathbf{b} = \overrightarrow{PQ} + \overrightarrow{QR} = \overrightarrow{PR}.$$

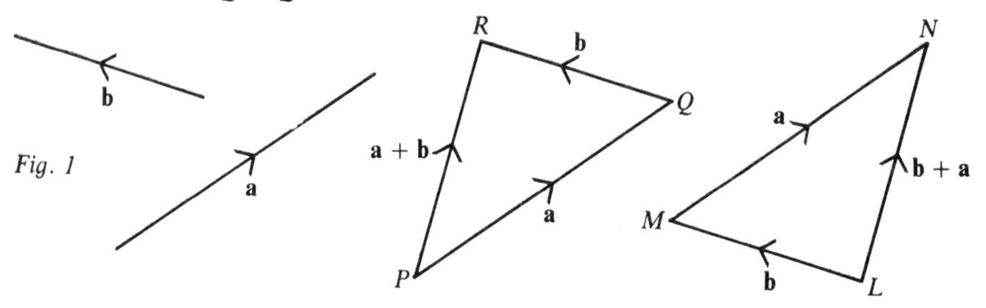

Fig. 1

Using the triangle LMN shows that $\mathbf{b} + \mathbf{a} = \mathbf{a} + \mathbf{b}$, i.e. vector addition is commutative.

In component form, given that $\mathbf{a} = \begin{pmatrix} a_1 \\ a_2 \end{pmatrix}$, $\mathbf{b} = \begin{pmatrix} b_1 \\ b_2 \end{pmatrix}$, then

$$\mathbf{a} + \mathbf{b} = \begin{pmatrix} a_1 + b_1 \\ a_2 + b_2 \end{pmatrix}.$$

Since addition of numbers is associative, it follows that addition of vectors is associative; this is also shown by Fig. 2:

$$(\mathbf{a} + \mathbf{b}) + \mathbf{c} = \mathbf{a} + (\mathbf{b} + \mathbf{c}).$$

Fig. 2

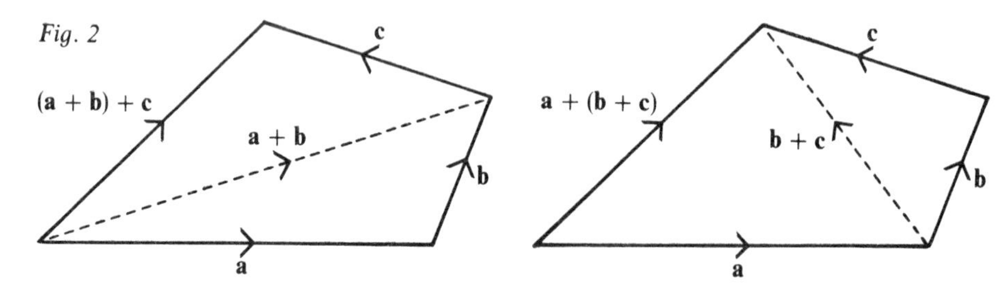

Subtraction of vectors

The vector $-\mathbf{a}$ is defined as the vector with the same length as **a** and in the opposite direction to **a**.

Definition $\mathbf{a} - \mathbf{b} = \mathbf{a} + (-\mathbf{b})$

In component form $\mathbf{a} - \mathbf{b} = \begin{pmatrix} a_1 - b_1 \\ a_2 - b_2 \end{pmatrix}$

It follows that $\mathbf{a} - \mathbf{a} = \mathbf{0}$, where $\mathbf{0}$ represents the zero vector; this has zero length and its direction is undefined.

Exercise 8.2A

1 Given that $\mathbf{p} = \begin{pmatrix} 3 \\ -2 \end{pmatrix}$, $\mathbf{q} = \begin{pmatrix} -4 \\ 5 \end{pmatrix}$, $\mathbf{r} = \begin{pmatrix} -6 \\ -3 \end{pmatrix}$, calculate

a $\mathbf{p} + \mathbf{q}$ **b** $\mathbf{q} + \mathbf{r}$ **c** $\mathbf{r} + \mathbf{p}$
d $\mathbf{p} + (\mathbf{q} + \mathbf{r})$ **e** $(\mathbf{p} + \mathbf{q}) + \mathbf{r}$ **f** $\mathbf{p} - \mathbf{q}$
g $\mathbf{q} - \mathbf{r}$ **h** $(\mathbf{p} - \mathbf{q}) - \mathbf{r}$ **i** $\mathbf{p} - (\mathbf{q} - \mathbf{r})$.

2 Use the diagram to express
a **f** in terms of **a** and **b**
b **g** in terms of **f** and **c**
c **g** in terms of **d** and **e**
d **g** in terms of **a**, **b** and **c**
e **e** in terms of **f**, **c** and **d**.

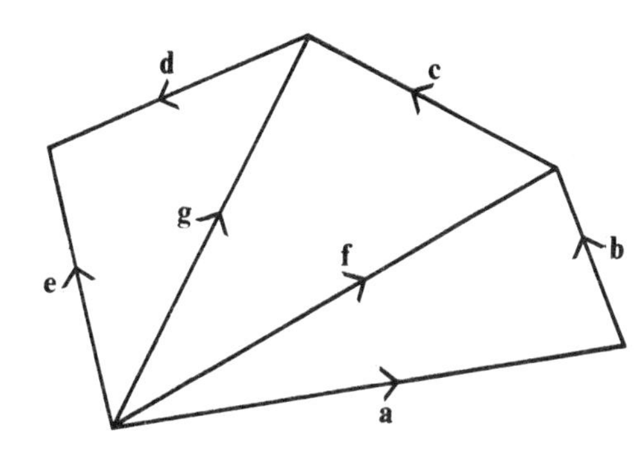

3

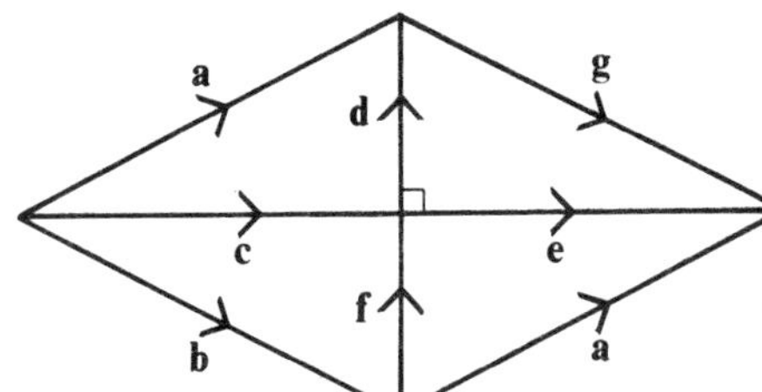

Name the quadrilateral shown in the diagram. Express
a **g** in terms of **b**
b **c** in terms of **a** and **d**
c **c** in terms of **e**.

4 In the diagram, *OABCDE* is a regular hexagon with centre *M*. Express in terms of **a** and **b** each of $\overrightarrow{CD}$, $\overrightarrow{AB}$, $\overrightarrow{MC}$.

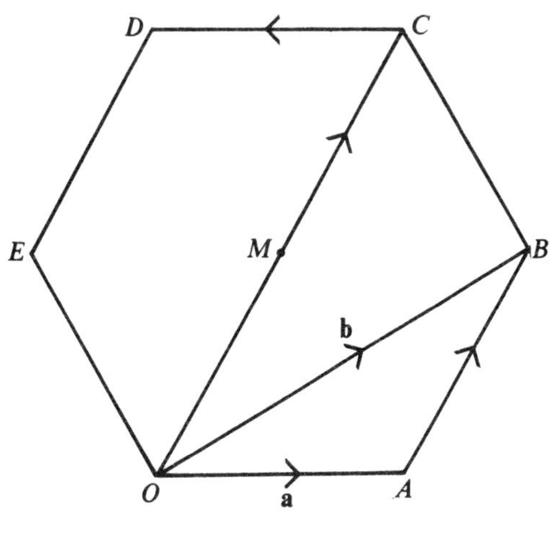

Exercise 8.2B

1 Given that $\mathbf{a} = \begin{pmatrix} -4 \\ 3 \end{pmatrix}$, $\mathbf{b} = \begin{pmatrix} 2 \\ -1 \end{pmatrix}$, $\mathbf{c} = \begin{pmatrix} 4 \\ -5 \end{pmatrix}$, calculate

a $\mathbf{a} + \mathbf{b}$ **b** $(\mathbf{a} + \mathbf{b}) + \mathbf{c}$ **c** $\mathbf{b} - \mathbf{c}$
d $\mathbf{a} - (\mathbf{b} - \mathbf{c})$ **e** $\mathbf{a} - \mathbf{b} - \mathbf{c}$.

2 Use the diagram to express
a **t** in terms of **p** and **q**
b **u** in terms of **q** and **r**
c **s** in terms of **p**, **q** and **r**
d **r** in terms of **t** and **s**.

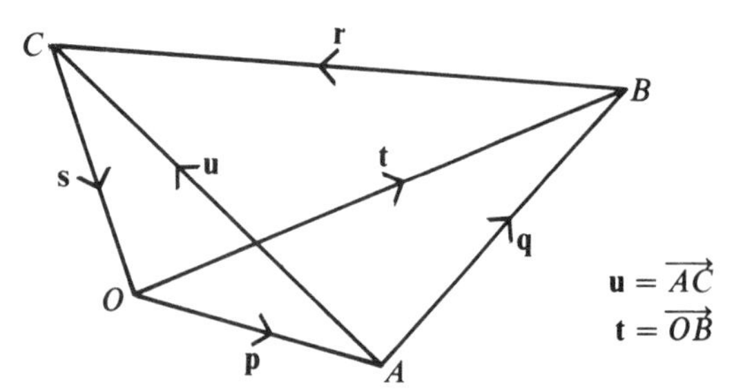

8.3 Multiplication of a vector by a number

For $t > 0$, $t\mathbf{p}$ is in the same direction as $\mathbf{p}$ and has length $t\mathbf{p}$.
For $t < 0$, $t\mathbf{p}$ is in the *opposite* direction to $\mathbf{p}$ and has length $|t|\mathbf{p}$.
Two immediate results are the distributive laws:

$$t\mathbf{p} + u\mathbf{p} \equiv (t + u)\mathbf{p}$$
$$t(\mathbf{p} + \mathbf{q}) = t\mathbf{p} + t\mathbf{q}.$$

The latter may be seen as the result of an enlargement of scale factor t, applied to the triangle showing the vector sum $\mathbf{p} + \mathbf{q}$.

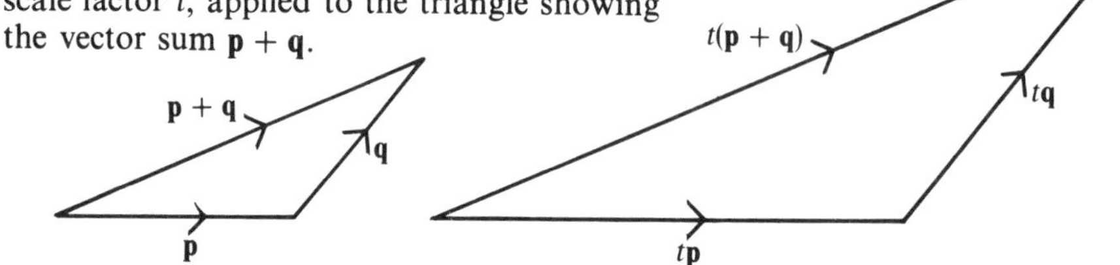

Parallel vectors

The statement that two non-zero vectors are parallel is equivalent to the statement that $\mathbf{a} = t\mathbf{b}$ for some number t. If $t > 0$ then $\mathbf{a}$ and $\mathbf{b}$ are in the same direction; if $t < 0$ then $\mathbf{a}$ and $\mathbf{b}$ are in opposite directions. In the case $t > 0$ the notation $\mathbf{a} \uparrow\uparrow \mathbf{b}$ may conveniently be used; in the case $t < 0$ the notation $\mathbf{a} \uparrow\downarrow \mathbf{b}$ may be used.

The unit base vectors i and j

An alternative to column vector notation is to use the symbol **i** for the column vector $\begin{pmatrix}1\\0\end{pmatrix}$ and to use the symbol **j** for the column vector $\begin{pmatrix}0\\1\end{pmatrix}$.

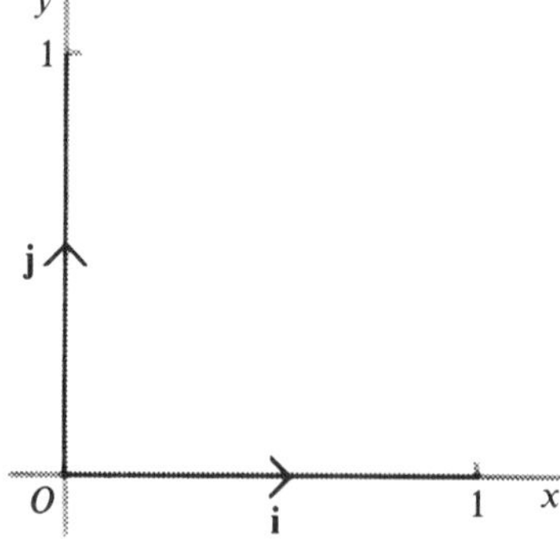

Then **i** and **j** are each of unit length, and are in the directions of the x-axis and the y-axis respectively.

Since the vector $\begin{pmatrix}x\\y\end{pmatrix}$ may be written as $x\begin{pmatrix}1\\0\end{pmatrix} + y\begin{pmatrix}0\\1\end{pmatrix}$, it may also be written as $x\mathbf{i} + y\mathbf{j}$. The vectors **i** and **j** are called unit base vectors.

Position vectors

Definition Given a point O, the position of any other point P is defined by the vector $\overrightarrow{OP}$, which is called the *position vector* of P relative to O.

A convenient notation is to use $\mathbf{a}$ for the position vector of A, $\mathbf{b}$ for the position vector of B, etc. This notation will be used from now on without comment. The one exception to this convention is that $\mathbf{r}$ is used for the position vector of P; this exception is dictated by long tradition; but occasionally $\mathbf{p}$ will be used.

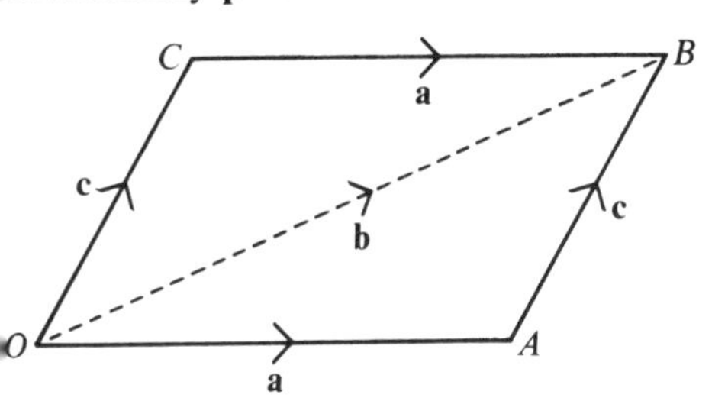

The use of $\mathbf{a}$ for the position vector of A does not prevent $\mathbf{a}$ being used also for any vector equal to $\overrightarrow{OA}$. For example, in the parallelogram $OABC$ shown in the diagram, the points A, B and C have position vectors $\mathbf{a}$, $\mathbf{b}$ and $\mathbf{c}$ relative to O. Then $\overrightarrow{CB} = \mathbf{a}$ and $\overrightarrow{AB} = \mathbf{c}$.

Two important results

1 In the diagram, $\overrightarrow{AB} = \overrightarrow{AO} + \overrightarrow{OB} = -\mathbf{a} + \mathbf{b}$

$$\therefore \overrightarrow{AB} = \mathbf{b} - \mathbf{a}$$

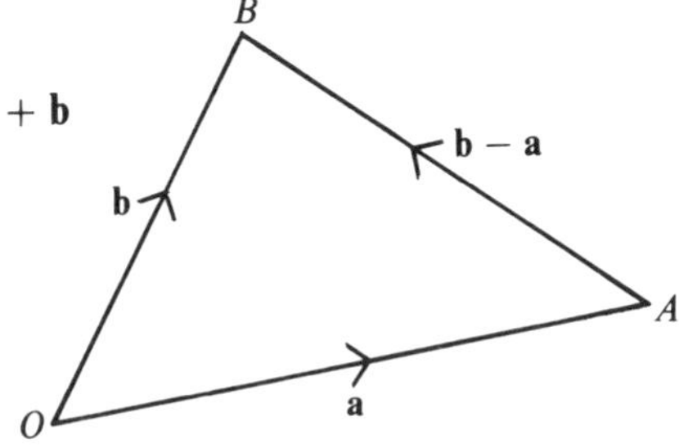

This result is independent of the particular point used as origin for the position vectors of A and B.

This result will be used frequently and should be remembered.

2 In the triangle OAB, M is the mid-point of AB. Then $\mathbf{m} = \dfrac{\mathbf{a} + \mathbf{b}}{2}$.

First proof

$\overrightarrow{AM} = \mathbf{m} - \mathbf{a}$, $\overrightarrow{MB} = \mathbf{b} - \mathbf{m}$.

Since $\overrightarrow{AM} = \overrightarrow{MB}$,

$$\mathbf{m} - \mathbf{a} = \mathbf{b} - \mathbf{m}$$
$$\therefore 2\mathbf{m} = \mathbf{a} + \mathbf{b}$$
$$\therefore \mathbf{m} = \frac{\mathbf{a} + \mathbf{b}}{2}.$$

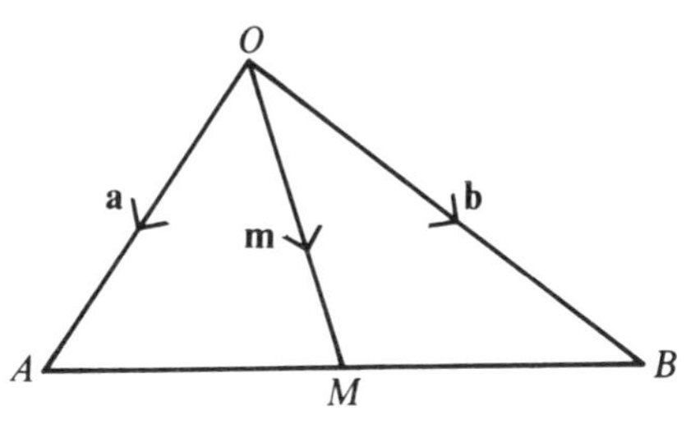

Second proof

$$\overrightarrow{AB} = \mathbf{b} - \mathbf{a} \qquad \therefore \overrightarrow{AM} = \frac{\mathbf{b} - \mathbf{a}}{2}$$
$$\therefore \overrightarrow{OM} = \overrightarrow{OA} + \overrightarrow{AM} = \mathbf{a} + \frac{\mathbf{b} - \mathbf{a}}{2}$$
$$\therefore \mathbf{m} = \frac{\mathbf{a} + \mathbf{b}}{2}$$

This result should be remembered.

Exercise 8.3A

1 Given the points $P(4, -2)$ and $Q(-5, 3)$, express the following in terms of $\mathbf{i}$ and $\mathbf{j}$.

a $\mathbf{p}$ **b** $\mathbf{q}$ **c** $2\mathbf{p} + 3\mathbf{q}$ **d** $\frac{\mathbf{p}}{2} - 3\mathbf{q}$

2 Given the points $P(2, 5)$, $Q(-3, 4)$, $R(2, -1)$, express in terms of $\mathbf{i}$ and $\mathbf{j}$ each of

a $\overrightarrow{PQ}$ **b** $\overrightarrow{QR}$ **c** $\overrightarrow{PR}$.

3 Given the points $P(3, 5)$, $Q(1, 8)$, $R(-3, 14)$, express $\overrightarrow{PQ}$ and $\overrightarrow{QR}$ in terms of $\mathbf{i}$ and $\mathbf{j}$. State what conclusion can be drawn about the points P, Q, R, and state the ratio of PQ to QR.

4 Given the points $A(5, 7)$, $B(3, -5)$, $C(1, -3)$, express in terms of $\mathbf{i}$ and $\mathbf{j}$ the position vector of

a the mid-point D of BC **b** the mid-point E of CA.

Calculate $\overrightarrow{DE}$ and $\overrightarrow{BA}$, and hence verify that DE is parallel to BA and half the length of BA.

Exercise 8.3B

1 Given the points $A(-3, 4)$, $B(7, -6)$, express the following in terms of $\mathbf{i}$ and $\mathbf{j}$

a $\mathbf{a}$ **b** $\mathbf{b}$ **c** $3\mathbf{a} + \mathbf{b}$ **d** $\frac{\mathbf{a} + \mathbf{b}}{2}$

2 Given the points $A(-1, 4)$, $B(3, 6)$, $C(-3, 8)$, express in terms of $\mathbf{i}$ and $\mathbf{j}$

a $\overrightarrow{AB}$ **b** $\overrightarrow{BC}$ **c** $\overrightarrow{CA}$. Verify that the sum of your answers is $\mathbf{0}$.

3 Given the points $A(-2, 5)$, $B(4, 3)$, $C(10, 1)$, express $\overrightarrow{AB}$ and $\overrightarrow{AC}$ in terms of $\mathbf{i}$ and $\mathbf{j}$. State what can be deduced about the points A, B, C. State the ratio $AB : AC$.

4 Given the points $P(6, 3)$, $Q(2, 7)$, express in terms of $\mathbf{i}$ and $\mathbf{j}$ the position vector of the mid-point M of PQ. Given also the point $S(1, 2)$ and that $PSQT$ is a rhombus, find the position vector of T.

8.4 The length and direction of a vector

The vector $\overrightarrow{OP}$ in two dimensions may be given by its components x and y, or it may be given by its length r and the angle θ it makes with the x-axis, this angle being a directed angle measured from the x-axis to the vector in the usual way; r and θ are the polar coordinates of the point P.

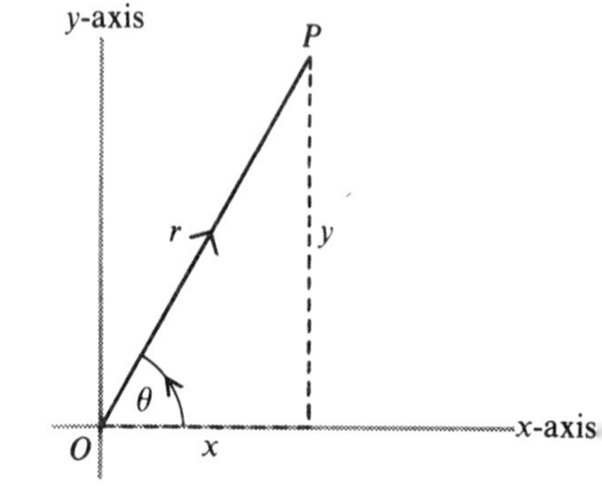

In the diagram, $OP = r = \sqrt{(x^2 + y^2)}$

$\cos\theta = \frac{x}{r}$, $\sin\theta = \frac{y}{r}$, $\tan\theta = \frac{y}{x}$.

The length (or magnitude) of a given vector has only one possible value, which may be zero or positive.

The angle θ has an unlimited number of possible values, but only one value in each complete revolution; all the possible values differ by multiples of 360°. In this book the angle θ will be used for which $-180° < \theta \leqslant 180°$.

The angle θ for a given vector may be found using either the cosine or the sine or the tangent, *together with* a rough diagram. The use of the cosine or sine or tangent *alone* gives two possible values for θ in the given interval; a rough diagram will show which of these is correct. The blind use of inverse trigonometric functions on a calculator has a probability of $\frac{1}{2}$ of giving the correct angle.

Examples 8.4

1 Given that P is the point (3, 5), write $\overrightarrow{OP}$ as a column vector. Find its length r and angle θ.

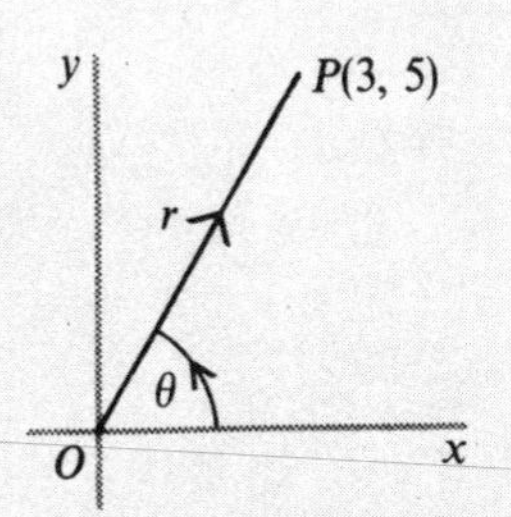

$$\overrightarrow{OP} = \begin{pmatrix} 3 \\ 5 \end{pmatrix}; \; r^2 = 3^2 + 5^2 = 34, \; r = \sqrt{34}$$

$$\tan\theta = \frac{5}{3}; \text{ using the diagram, } \theta = 59.0°.$$

2 Given that $\overrightarrow{OP}$ has length 3.4 and angle 156°, determine $\overrightarrow{OP}$ in component form, giving 3 s.f.

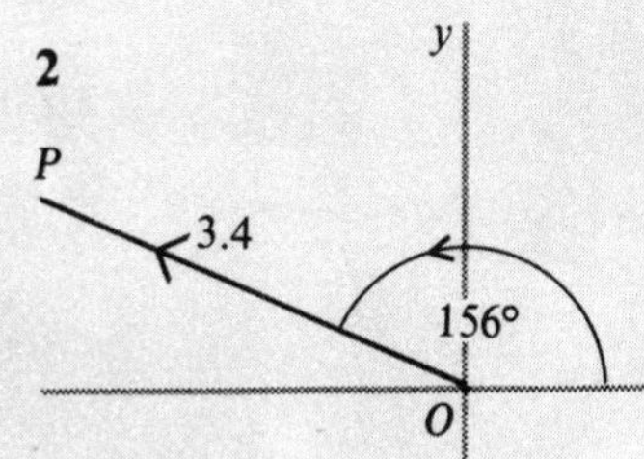

$$x = 3.4\cos 156° = -3.11, \qquad y = 3.4 \sin 156° = 1.38$$

$$\therefore \overrightarrow{OP} = \begin{pmatrix} -3.11 \\ 1.38 \end{pmatrix}$$

3 Given that $\mathbf{r} = \overrightarrow{OP} = \begin{pmatrix} -4 \\ 7 \end{pmatrix}$, calculate r and θ.

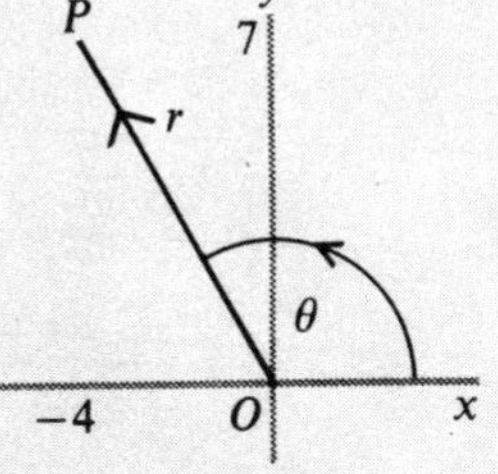

$$r^2 = 65, \qquad r = \sqrt{65}$$

$$\tan\theta = -\frac{7}{4}; \text{ using the diagram, } \theta = 119.7°.$$

4 Given the points $A(-5, 2)$ and $B(2, -7)$, write $\overrightarrow{AB}$ as a column vector and find its length r and angle θ.

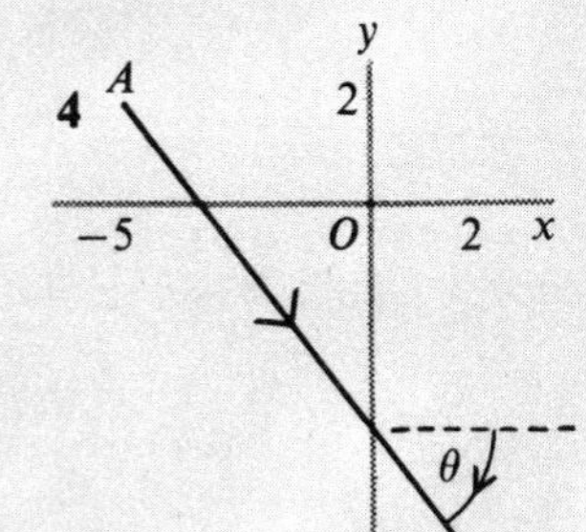

$$\overrightarrow{AB} = \begin{pmatrix} 7 \\ -9 \end{pmatrix}; \qquad r = \sqrt{130},$$

$$\tan\theta = -\frac{9}{7}; \text{ using the diagram, } \theta = -52.1°.$$

5

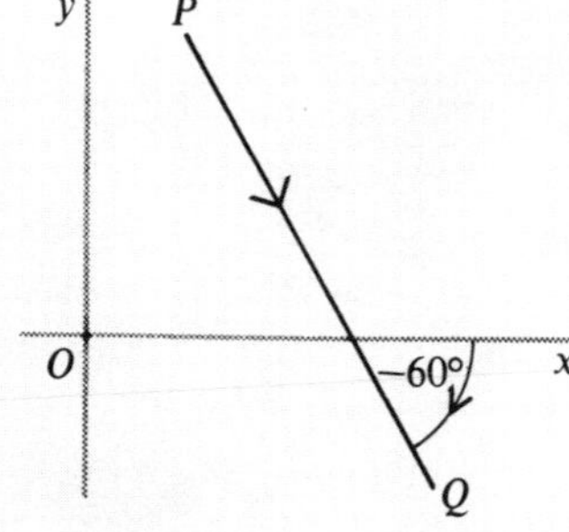

Given the point $P(2, 6)$, and that $\overrightarrow{PQ}$ has length 10 units and is at $-60°$ to the x-axis, find the coordinates of Q in surd form.

$$\overrightarrow{PQ} = \begin{pmatrix} 10\cos(-60°) \\ 10\sin(-60°) \end{pmatrix} = \begin{pmatrix} 5 \\ -5\sqrt{3} \end{pmatrix}$$

$$\therefore Q = (7, 6 - 5\sqrt{3})$$

6 Given the diagram, in which $\mathbf{r} = \mathbf{p} + \mathbf{q}$, $p = 3$ and $q = 4$, calculate the components, and the magnitude and direction, of $\mathbf{r}$,

(i) by using components

(ii) by using the cosine and sine rules.

Give approximate answers to 3 s.f.

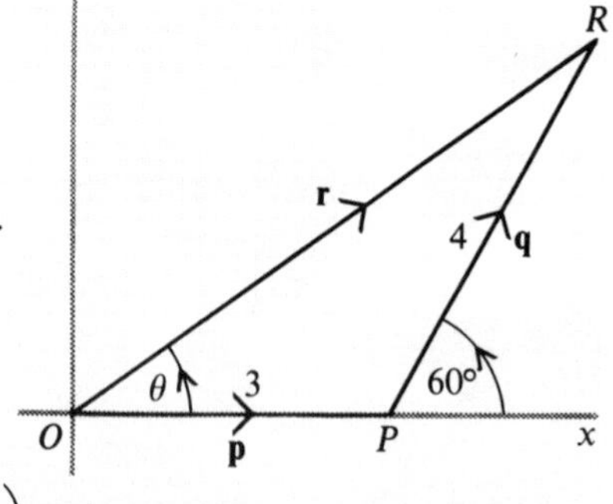

(i) $$\mathbf{p} = \begin{pmatrix} 3 \\ 0 \end{pmatrix},$$

$$\mathbf{q} = \begin{pmatrix} 4\cos 60° \\ 4\sin 60° \end{pmatrix} = \begin{pmatrix} 2 \\ 2\sqrt{3} \end{pmatrix}$$

$$\therefore \mathbf{r} = \begin{pmatrix} 5 \\ 2\sqrt{3} \end{pmatrix} = \begin{pmatrix} 5 \\ 3.46 \end{pmatrix}$$

$$\mathbf{r}^2 = 25 + 12 = 37, \qquad r = 6.08$$

$$\tan\theta = \frac{2}{5}\sqrt{3}$$

Using the diagram, $\theta = 34.7°$.

(ii) By the cosine rule, $r^2 = 9 + 16 - 2.3.4.\cos 120° = 37$

$$r = 6.08$$

By the sine rule, $\dfrac{\sin\theta}{4} = \dfrac{\sin 120°}{\sqrt{37}}$

$\theta = 34.7°$ ($\theta < 90°$ since angle OPR is obtuse)

In component form, $\mathbf{r} = \begin{pmatrix} \sqrt{37}\cos 34.7° \\ \sqrt{37}\sin 34.7° \end{pmatrix} = \begin{pmatrix} 5.00 \\ 3.46 \end{pmatrix}$

(Note that method (i) is the quicker.)

7 Given the diagram, in which $p = 4.6$, $q = 3.2$, find $\mathbf{p} + \mathbf{q}$ and $\mathbf{p} - \mathbf{q}$ in component form, giving the components correct to 1 d.p.

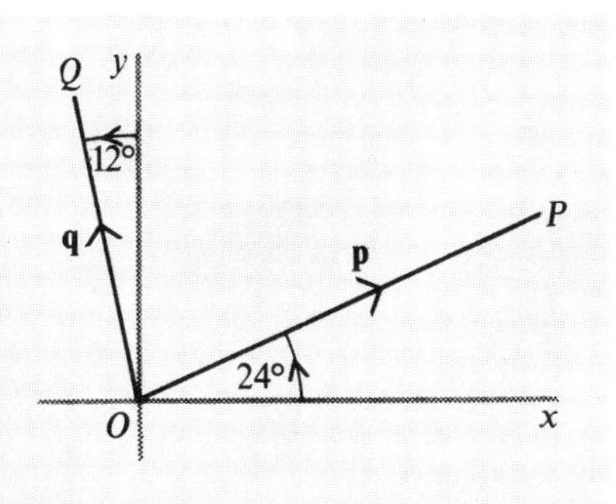

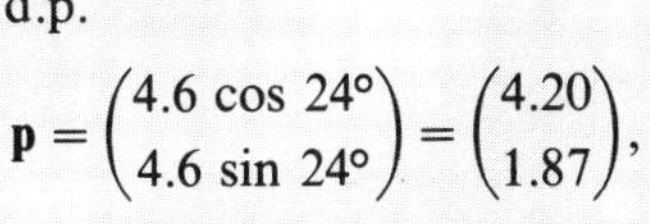

$$\mathbf{p} = \begin{pmatrix} 4.6\cos 24^\circ \\ 4.6\sin 24^\circ \end{pmatrix} = \begin{pmatrix} 4.20 \\ 1.87 \end{pmatrix},$$

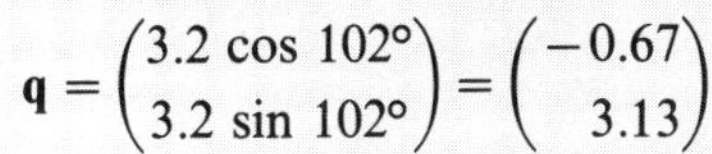

$$\mathbf{q} = \begin{pmatrix} 3.2\cos 102^\circ \\ 3.2\sin 102^\circ \end{pmatrix} = \begin{pmatrix} -0.67 \\ 3.13 \end{pmatrix}$$

$$\therefore \mathbf{p} + \mathbf{q} = \begin{pmatrix} 3.5 \\ 5.0 \end{pmatrix}, \quad \mathbf{p} - \mathbf{q} = \begin{pmatrix} 4.9 \\ -1.3 \end{pmatrix}$$

Exercise 8.4A

Give angles in degrees correct to one d.p. In questions **1** to **6** give exact values for lengths, coordinates and components.

1 For each of the following vectors find the length r and the angle θ.

a $\overrightarrow{OA} = \begin{pmatrix} 3 \\ 4 \end{pmatrix}$ **b** $\overrightarrow{OB} = \begin{pmatrix} -3 \\ 4 \end{pmatrix}$ **c** $\overrightarrow{OC} = \begin{pmatrix} -5 \\ -7 \end{pmatrix}$ **d** $\overrightarrow{OD} = \begin{pmatrix} 2 \\ -3 \end{pmatrix}$

2 In each of the following cases, write $\overrightarrow{AB}$ as a column vector and find its length r and angle θ.

a $A(3, 7)$, $B(5, 10)$ **b** $A(4, -3)$, $B(1, 2)$ **c** $A(-1, -4)$, $B(4, 6)$

3 Given the point $P(3, 5)$, and that $\overrightarrow{PQ}$ has length 6 units and is at 30° to the x-axis, find Q.

4 Given the point $P(4, -2)$, and that $\overrightarrow{PQ}$ has length 8 units and is at 135° to the x-axis, find Q.

5 Given the point $Q(3, 6)$, and that $\overrightarrow{PQ}$ has length 10 units and is at 60° to the x-axis, find P.

6 In the diagram $p = 5$, $q = 8$, $\mathbf{r} = \mathbf{p} + \mathbf{q}$.
Find $\mathbf{r}$ in component form.

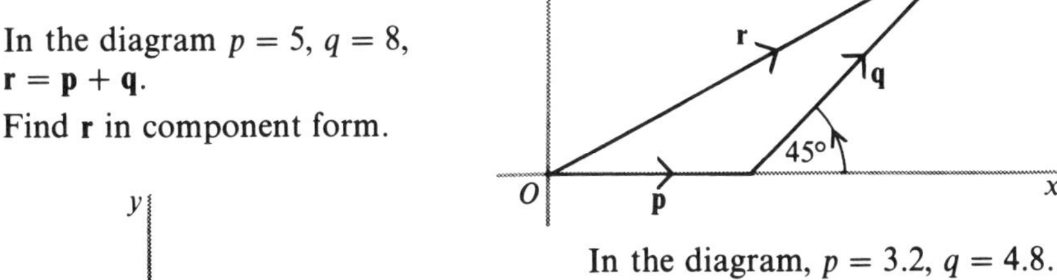

7

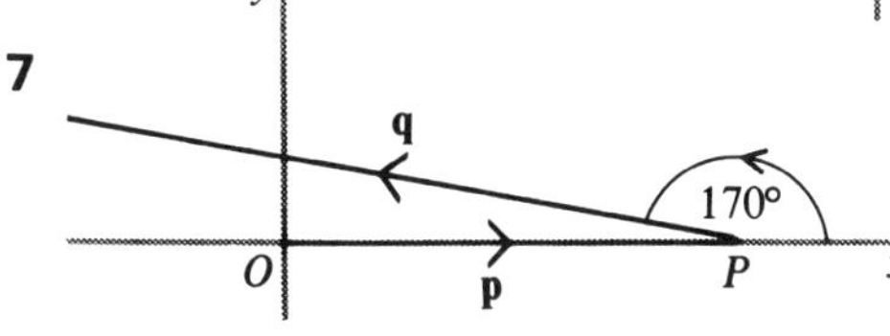

In the diagram, $p = 3.2$, $q = 4.8$.
Calculate the magnitude, correct to 2 s.f., and the direction of $\mathbf{p} + \mathbf{q}$.

8 In the diagram, $p = 4.6$, $q = 2.8$. Calculate $\mathbf{p} + \mathbf{q}$ and $\mathbf{p} - \mathbf{q}$ in component form, giving the components correct to two s.f.

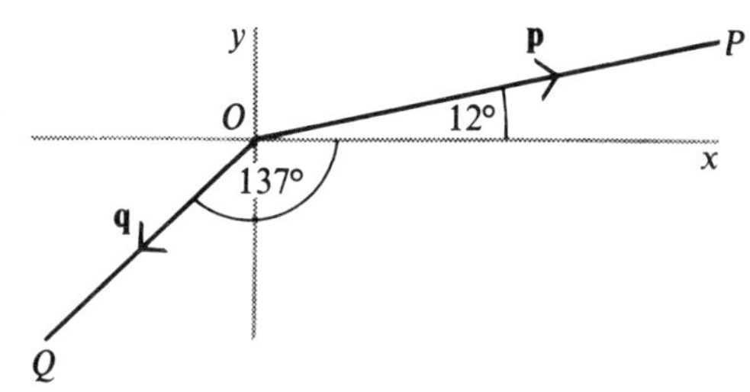

Exercise 8.4B

In each of the following give exact values for lengths and coordinates unless otherwise stated, and give angles in degrees correct to one decimal place, when not exact.

1 For each of the following vectors find the length r and the angle θ.

a $\overrightarrow{OP} = \begin{pmatrix} 1 \\ 1 \end{pmatrix}$ **b** $\overrightarrow{OQ} = \begin{pmatrix} 2 \\ -1 \end{pmatrix}$ **c** $\overrightarrow{OR} = \begin{pmatrix} -5 \\ 12 \end{pmatrix}$ **d** $\overrightarrow{OS} = \begin{pmatrix} -3 \\ -2 \end{pmatrix}$

2 In each of the following cases write $\overrightarrow{PQ}$ as a column vector and find its length r and angle θ.

a $P(2, 5)$, $Q(7, 9)$ **b** $P(-1, 2)$, $Q(4, -10)$ **c** $P(3, -4)$, $Q(2, -3)$

3 Given that P is $(-2, 4)$, and that $\overrightarrow{PQ}$ is of length 10 units and is at 120° to the x-axis, find the coordinates of Q.

4 Given that Q is $(5, -3)$, and that $\overrightarrow{PQ}$ has length 4 units and is at 45° to the x-axis, find P.

5 In the diagram, $a = 3$, $b = 4$.
Express $\mathbf{c}$ as a column vector.

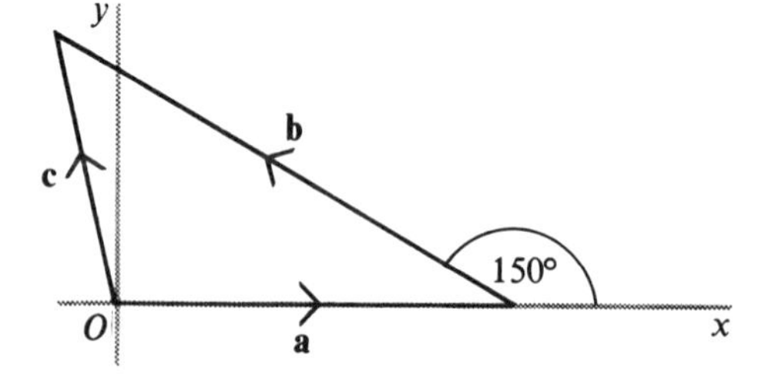

6

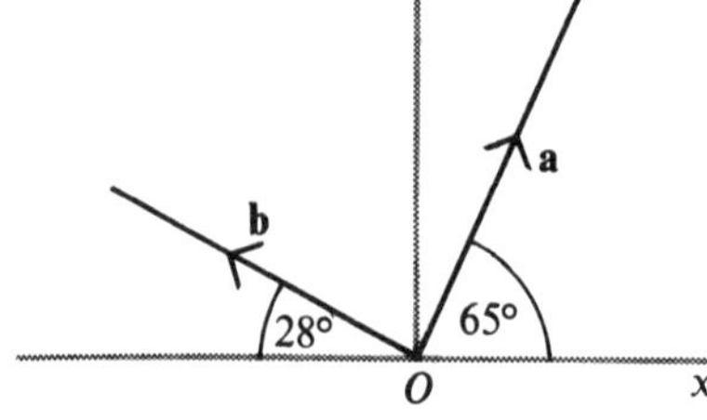

In the diagram, $a = 4.2$, $b = 3.6$.
Calculate the components of $\mathbf{a} + \mathbf{b}$ and $\mathbf{a} - \mathbf{b}$, correct to two s.f.

7 In the diagram, $a = 2.4$, $b = 3.2$.
Calculate the components, and the magnitude and direction, of $\mathbf{a} + \mathbf{b}$, giving numbers to two s.f.

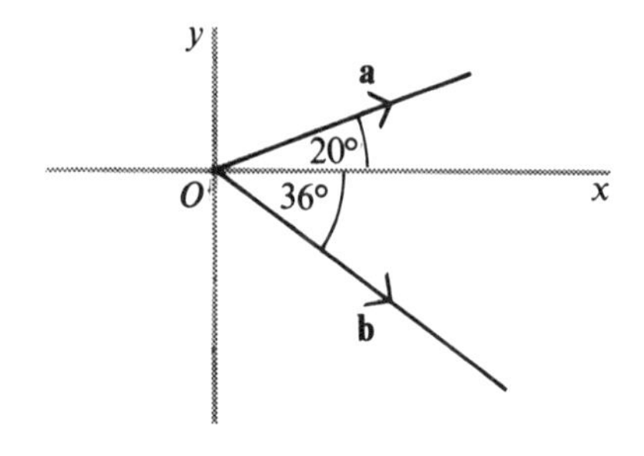

8.5 Vectors in three dimensions

The main difference in using vectors in three dimensions is that a Cartesian system in three dimensions is of course needed. Three axes are taken through an origin O. The two axes for x and y are as usual; the third axis, Oz, is at right angles to each of the axes Ox and Oy, and so is at right angles to the x–y plane. The positive direction of the z-axis is chosen so that looking at the x–y plane from a point with a positive z-coordinate, such as A in Fig. 3, the rotation from Ox to Oy is anticlockwise.

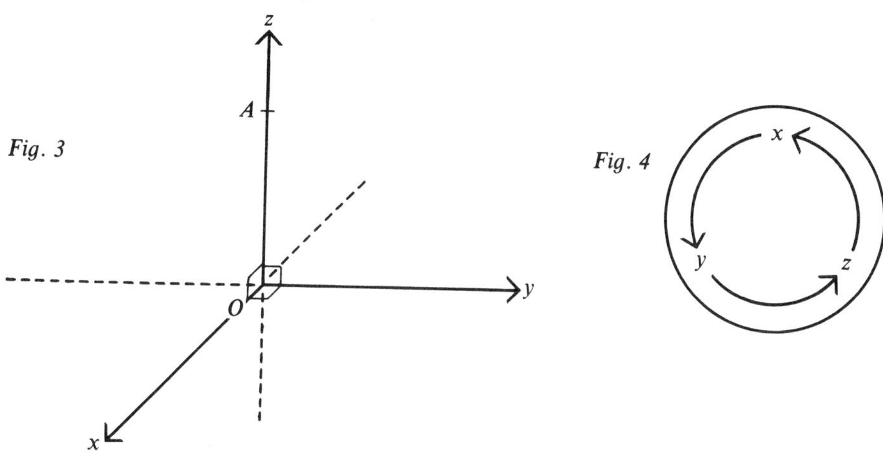

Fig. 3 *Fig. 4*

It may be seen that, with the z-axis as shown, looking at the y–z plane from a point on the positive x-axis the rotation from Oy to Oz is also anticlockwise; and that looking at the z–x plane from a point on the positive y-axis the rotation from Oz to Ox is anticlockwise. The anticlockwise rotations are illustrated in Fig. 4. A set of axes as described is called a right-handed set.

An ordered trio of numbers (x, y, z) defines the position of a unique point in space, and conversely any point in space determines a unique ordered trio of numbers (a, b, c).

Given a point $P(x, y, z)$, the vector $\overrightarrow{OP}$ may be written as a column vector $\begin{pmatrix} x \\ y \\ z \end{pmatrix}$; the vector $\overrightarrow{P_1P_2}$, with an obvious notation, may be written $\begin{pmatrix} x_2 - x_1 \\ y_2 - y_1 \\ z_2 - z_1 \end{pmatrix}$.

An alternative notation is an extension of the use of the unit vectors **i** and **j** as a basis for vectors in two dimensions. The vector **i** is now $\begin{pmatrix} 1 \\ 0 \\ 0 \end{pmatrix}$, **j** is $\begin{pmatrix} 0 \\ 1 \\ 0 \end{pmatrix}$, and **k** is $\begin{pmatrix} 0 \\ 0 \\ 1 \end{pmatrix}$, the unit vector in the direction of the positive z-axis. The vector $\overrightarrow{OP}$ may be written as $x\mathbf{i} + y\mathbf{j} + z\mathbf{k}$. The unit vectors **i**, **j**, **k** form a *basis* for vectors in three dimensions.

The addition of vectors in three dimensions is defined, as in two dimensions, by the triangle law. In component form, given that

$$\mathbf{a} = \begin{pmatrix} a_1 \\ a_2 \\ a_3 \end{pmatrix}, \qquad \mathbf{b} = \begin{pmatrix} b_1 \\ b_2 \\ b_3 \end{pmatrix}, \qquad \text{then} \qquad \mathbf{a} + \mathbf{b} = \begin{pmatrix} a_1 + b_1 \\ a_2 + b_2 \\ a_3 + b_3 \end{pmatrix}.$$

As in two dimensions the associative law holds for addition; Fig. 2 in **8.2** need not be in one plane.

Subtraction of vectors is defined as in two dimensions.

The distance formula in three dimensions

In Fig. 5, $OP^2 = ON^2 + NP^2 = ON^2 + z^2$ (Pythagoras' theorem ΔONP)

and $ON^2 = x^2 + y^2$ (" " ΔONA)

$\therefore OP^2 = x^2 + y^2 + z^2$

and more generally, in Fig. 6,

$P_1P_2^{\ 2} = (x_2 - x_1)^2 + (y_2 - y_1)^2 + (z_2 - z_1)^2$.

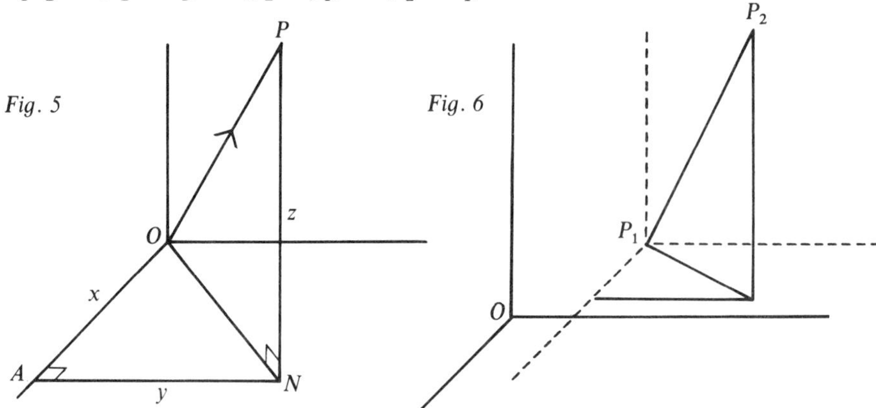

A notation for unit vectors

Given a non-zero vector **a** of length a, a vector in the same direction as **a** and of unit length may be written $\dfrac{1}{a}\mathbf{a}$.

A special symbol for this vector is sometimes useful; it is written $\hat{\mathbf{a}}$ and read as '**a** hat'. For example, if $\mathbf{a} = 3\mathbf{i} + 4\mathbf{j} + 5\mathbf{k}$, then $a^2 = 3^2 + 4^2 + 5^2 = 50$,

$a = 5\sqrt{2}$, and $\hat{\mathbf{a}} = \dfrac{1}{5\sqrt{2}}\mathbf{a}$.

Direction cosines of a vector

In two dimensions, the direction of a vector is known if the directed angle θ from the x-axis to the vector is known. The directed angle from the y-axis to the vector is then also known and is $\theta - 90°$. The components of a unit vector in this direction are $\cos\theta$ and $\sin\theta$, or $\cos\theta$ and $\cos(\theta - 90°)$.

In three dimensions the situation is more complicated. The set of vectors $\overrightarrow{OP}$ of length r which make an angle α with the x-axis are the generators of a cone with vertex O and axis of symmetry the x-axis. The slant height of this cone is r and the semi-vertical angle is α. There is no way to define a direction for the angle α. Each of the vectors in this set makes some angle with the y-axis. All the vectors making an angle β with the y-axis are the generators of another cone, symmetrical about the y-axis. A vector making an angle α with the x-axis and β with the y-axis is still not fixed in direction; it will make one of two angles, which are supplementary, with the z-axis. In the special case when $\alpha + \beta = 90°$, the two supplementary angles are each 90°.

It is clearly impossible for a vector to make an angle α with the x-axis and an angle β with the y-axis unless $\alpha + \beta$ is at least 90°, since the two cones, one symmetrical about Ox and the other about Oy, could otherwise have no common generator. If $\alpha + \beta = 90°$ the vector lies in the x–y plane.

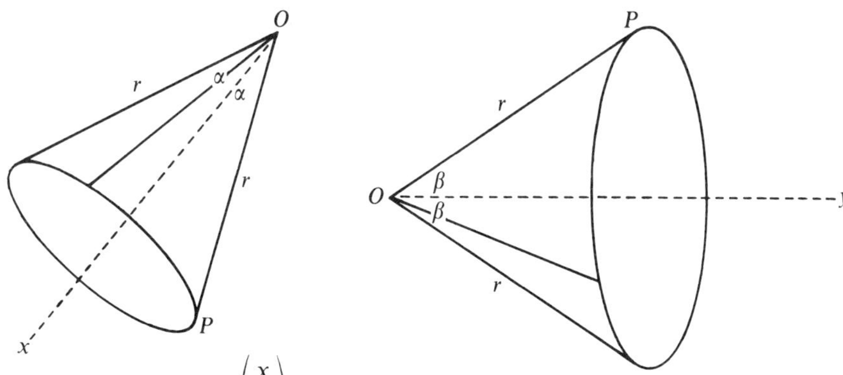

Given that the vector $\begin{pmatrix} x \\ y \\ z \end{pmatrix}$ makes angles α, β, γ with the axes Ox, Oy and Oz respectively, the angles α, β, γ are related by the important identity

$$\cos^2 \alpha + \cos^2 \beta + \cos^2 \gamma = 1.$$

The proof is simple. From Figs. 7, 8, 9 we have

$$x = r \cos \alpha, \qquad y = r \cos \beta, \qquad z = r \cos \gamma.$$

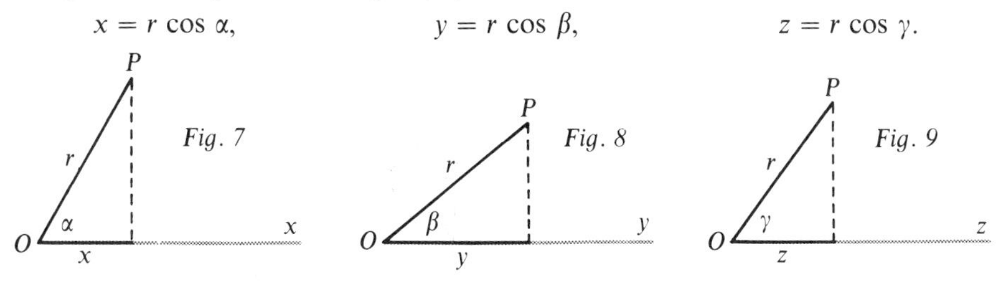

Fig. 7

Fig. 8

Fig. 9

By the distance formula, $x^2 + y^2 + z^2 = r^2$

$$\therefore\ r^2(\cos^2 \alpha + \cos^2 \beta + \cos^2 \gamma) = r^2$$

$$\therefore\quad \cos^2 \alpha + \cos^2 \beta + \cos^2 \gamma = 1.$$

This identity is the three-dimensional analogue of the important identity $\cos^2 \theta + \sin^2 \theta = 1$.

For a unit vector, $x = \cos\alpha$, $y = \cos\beta$, $z = \cos\gamma$. The numbers $\cos\alpha$, $\cos\beta$, $\cos\gamma$ are called the *direction cosines* of any vector in the direction of the unit vector with these components. The direction cosines of a given vector are clearly unique.

Examples 8.5

1 Write each of the following vectors in terms of **i**, **j**, **k**. Calculate the length of each vector.

(i) $\mathbf{a} = \begin{pmatrix} 2 \\ 3 \\ 4 \end{pmatrix}$ (ii) $\mathbf{b} = \begin{pmatrix} -3 \\ 5 \\ 1 \end{pmatrix}$

(i) $\mathbf{a} = 2\mathbf{i} + 3\mathbf{j} + 4\mathbf{k}$
$a^2 = 2^2 + 3^2 + 4^2$
$a = \sqrt{29}$

(ii) $\mathbf{b} = -3\mathbf{i} + 5\mathbf{j} + \mathbf{k}$
$b^2 = 9 + 25 + 1$
$b = \sqrt{35}$

2 In each of the following, write the vector $\overrightarrow{AB}$ in terms of **i**, **j**, **k** and calculate its length.

(i) $A(2, 5, 1)$, $B(6, 3, -2)$ (ii) $A(-4, 3, 2)$, $B(5, -1, -3)$

(i) $\overrightarrow{AB} = 4\mathbf{i} - 2\mathbf{j} - 3\mathbf{k}$, $AB^2 = 16 + 4 + 9$, $AB = \sqrt{29}$
(ii) $\overrightarrow{AB} = 9\mathbf{i} - 4\mathbf{j} - 5\mathbf{k}$, $AB^2 = 81 + 16 + 25$, $AB = \sqrt{122}$.

3 The vector $\overrightarrow{OP}$ makes an angle of 60° with the x-axis and an angle of 45° with the y-axis; find the possible angles between $\overrightarrow{OP}$ and the z-axis.

$$\cos 60° = \frac{1}{2}, \quad \cos 45° = \frac{\sqrt{2}}{2}, \quad \text{and} \quad \cos^2\alpha + \cos^2\beta + \cos^2\gamma = 1$$

$$\therefore \cos^2\gamma = \frac{1}{4}, \quad \cos\gamma = \pm\frac{1}{2}, \quad \gamma = 60° \text{ or } 120°$$

4 Find the direction cosines of the vector $\mathbf{i} + 2\mathbf{j} - 3\mathbf{k}$.

The unit vector in the same direction is $\frac{1}{\sqrt{14}}(\mathbf{i} + 2\mathbf{j} - 3\mathbf{k})$

$\therefore$ the direction cosines are $\frac{1}{\sqrt{14}}, \frac{2}{\sqrt{14}}, \frac{-3}{\sqrt{14}}$.

5 Given the points $A(7, 1, -6)$, $B(4, 5, -1)$, find in terms of **i**, **j**, **k** the vector of length 10 in the direction of $\overrightarrow{AB}$.

$\mathbf{a} = 7\mathbf{i} + \mathbf{j} - 6\mathbf{k}$, $\mathbf{b} = 4\mathbf{i} + 5\mathbf{j} - \mathbf{k}$, $\overrightarrow{AB} = \mathbf{b} - \mathbf{a} = -3\mathbf{i} + 4\mathbf{j} + 5\mathbf{k}$
$\therefore AB = \sqrt{50} = 5\sqrt{2}$
$\therefore$ the vector of length 10 in the direction of $\overrightarrow{AB}$ is
$\sqrt{2}(-3\mathbf{i} + 4\mathbf{j} + 5\mathbf{k})$.

Exercise 8.5A

1 Write each of the following as column vectors.

a $4\mathbf{i} - 5\mathbf{j} + 6\mathbf{k}$ **b** $3\mathbf{j} - 8\mathbf{k}$ **c** $7\mathbf{i} - 2\mathbf{k}$

2 Write each of the following vectors in terms of **i**, **j**, **k**. Calculate the length of each vector, giving the answers to two s.f.

a $\begin{pmatrix} 2 \\ -4 \\ 3 \end{pmatrix}$ **b** $\begin{pmatrix} 5 \\ 1 \\ -2 \end{pmatrix}$ **c** $\begin{pmatrix} -3 \\ 5 \\ 7 \end{pmatrix}$ **d** $\begin{pmatrix} 4.2 \\ -3.4 \\ -2.6 \end{pmatrix}$

3 In each of the following, write the vector $\overrightarrow{PQ}$ in terms of **i**, **j**, **k**.

a $P(4, 7, 2)$, $Q(6, 3, 5)$ **b** $P(-2, 5, -3)$, $Q(3, -5, -7)$

4 Given that $\mathbf{p} = 6\mathbf{i} - 3\mathbf{j} + 4\mathbf{k}$,

a determine the unit vector in the opposite direction to **p**

b determine the vector of length 2 units in the same direction as **p**.

5 Given the points $P(1, -3, 4)$, $Q(5, -1, 6)$ and $R(7, 0, 7)$, express $\overrightarrow{PQ}$ and $\overrightarrow{QR}$ in terms of **i**, **j**, **k**. Show that P, Q, R are collinear and state the ratio $PQ : QR$.

6 Given that $\mathbf{a} = \begin{pmatrix} 6 \\ 7 \\ 6 \end{pmatrix}$, calculate a and write down $\hat{\mathbf{a}}$.

Write down the direction cosines of **a**.

7 The vector $\overrightarrow{OP}$ makes angles of 55° with each of the x and y axes. Calculate correct to the nearest degree the possible angles between $\overrightarrow{OP}$ and the z-axis.

8 The vector $\overrightarrow{OP}$ makes angles of 40° and 70° with the y and z axes respectively. Calculate the possible angles between $\overrightarrow{OP}$ and the x-axis, giving each angle correct to the nearest degree.

Exercise 8.5B

1 Write each of the following as a column vector, and calculate the length of each vector correct to two s.f.

a $3\mathbf{i} + 5\mathbf{j} - 2\mathbf{k}$ **b** $4\mathbf{i} - 2\mathbf{j} - \mathbf{k}$ **c** $-2\mathbf{j} + 3\mathbf{k}$

2 Write each of the following vectors in terms of **i**, **j**, **k**.

a $\begin{pmatrix} 5 \\ -2 \\ 4 \end{pmatrix}$ **b** $\begin{pmatrix} -3 \\ 0 \\ 7 \end{pmatrix}$ **c** $\begin{pmatrix} 0 \\ -2 \\ 5 \end{pmatrix}$

3 Write the vector $\overrightarrow{AB}$ in terms of **i**, **j**, **k** in each of the cases

a $A(-2, 5, 3)$, $B(-1, 4, 2)$ **b** $A(3, -1, 6)$, $B(5, -3, 4)$

4 In each of the following cases write down $\hat{\mathbf{a}}$, the unit vector in the same direction as $\mathbf{a}$. Write down also the vector $\mathbf{b}$ of length 4 units in the opposite direction to $\mathbf{a}$.

a $\mathbf{a} = 2\mathbf{i} + \mathbf{j} - 2\mathbf{k}$ **b** $\mathbf{a} = 3\mathbf{i} - 5\mathbf{j} + 4\mathbf{k}$ **c** $\mathbf{a} = \mathbf{i} + \mathbf{j} - \mathbf{k}$

5 Given the points $A(-2, 3, 5)$, $B(3, 1, 6)$, $C(13, -3, 8)$, express $\overrightarrow{AB}$ and $\overrightarrow{AC}$ in terms of $\mathbf{i}, \mathbf{j}, \mathbf{k}$. Show that A, B, C are collinear and state the ratio $AB : AC$.

6 A vector $\overrightarrow{OP}$ makes 20° with the y-axis and 75° with the z-axis. Find the possible angles, correct to the nearest degree, made by $\overrightarrow{OP}$ with the x-axis.

7 Given the points $A(-4, 2, 1)$ and $B(2, -4, 4)$, find in terms of $\mathbf{i}, \mathbf{j}$ and $\mathbf{k}$ a vector of length 18 in the direction of $\overrightarrow{AB}$.

8.6 The scalar product of two vectors

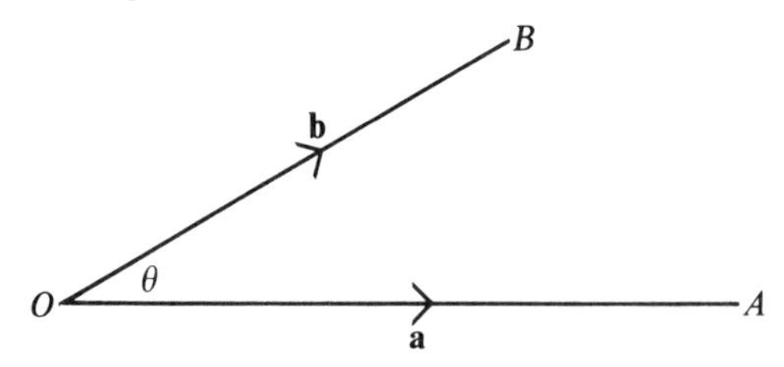

Given two non-zero vectors $\mathbf{a}$ and $\mathbf{b}$ of lengths a and b, and such that the angle between $\mathbf{a}$ and $\mathbf{b}$ is θ, their scalar product is written $\mathbf{a} \cdot \mathbf{b}$ and is defined by

$$\mathbf{a} \cdot \mathbf{b} = ab \cos\theta.$$

If either $\mathbf{a}$ or $\mathbf{b}$ is the zero vector, then θ is undefined and $\mathbf{a} \cdot \mathbf{b}$ is defined as zero.

Because of the notation used, the scalar product is also called the dot product.

The reason for the word 'scalar' in the name is that $ab \cos\theta$ is a real number, and real numbers are also called scalars.

The angle θ will be taken to be the smaller of the two angles between $\mathbf{a}$ and $\mathbf{b}$, so that $0 \leqslant \theta \leqslant 180°$.

Properties of the scalar product

1 It follows from the definition that $\mathbf{a} \cdot \mathbf{b} = \mathbf{b} \cdot \mathbf{a}$; i.e. the operation is commutative.

2 If $0 \leqslant \theta < 90°$, then $\mathbf{a} \cdot \mathbf{b} > 0$; and if $\mathbf{a} \cdot \mathbf{b} > 0$ then $0 \leqslant \theta < 90°$.
If $\theta = 90°$, then $\mathbf{a} \cdot \mathbf{b} = 0$; if $\mathbf{a} \cdot \mathbf{b} = 0$, then either $\theta = 90°$ or $a = 0$ or $b = 0$.
If $90° < \theta \leqslant 180°$, then $\mathbf{a} \cdot \mathbf{b} < 0$; and if $\mathbf{a} \cdot \mathbf{b} < 0$ then $90° < \theta \leqslant 180°$.

3 For any vector $\mathbf{a}$, $\mathbf{a} \cdot \mathbf{a} = a^2 \cos 0 = a^2 = |\mathbf{a}|^2$,
i.e. *the scalar product of any vector with itself is the square of its length.*

Exercise 8.6

1 Calculate **i . i**, **j . j**, **k . k**; **i . j**, **j . k**, **k . i**.

2 Calculate **a . b** in each case; give each answer exactly.

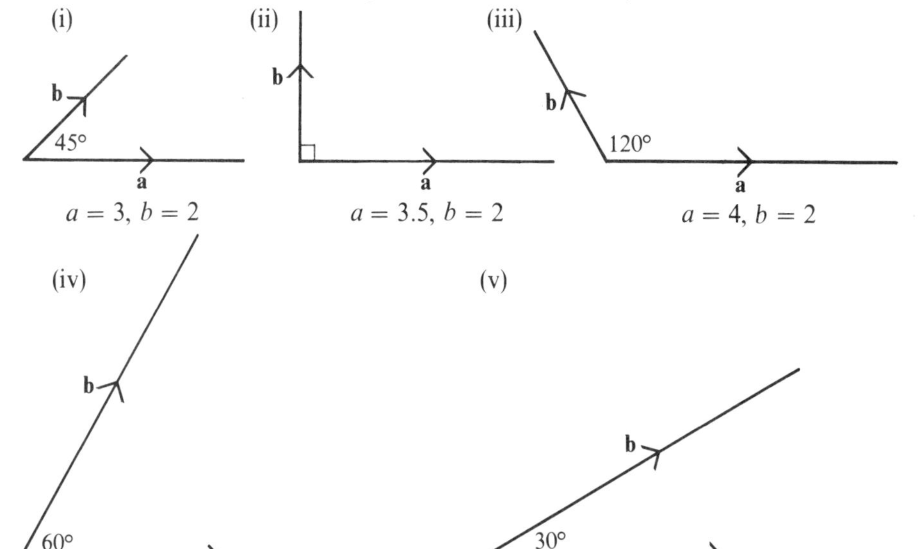

3 Calculate **a . b** in each case; give each answer to 2 s.f.

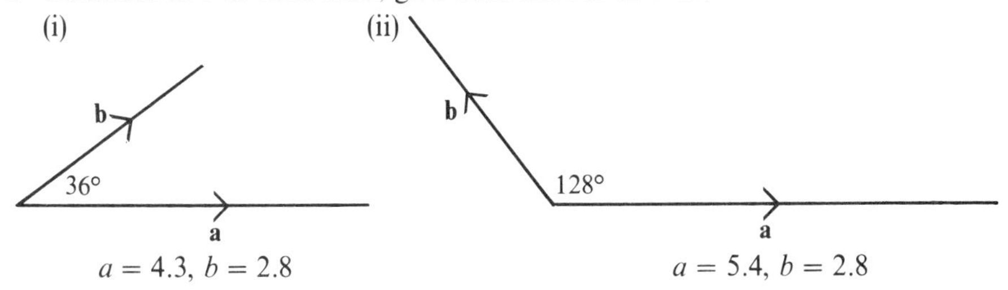

4 Given that (i) $\mathbf{a} . \mathbf{b} = 3$, (ii) $\mathbf{a} . \mathbf{b} = -2$, state in each case what can be said about the angle between **a** and **b**.

8.7 The component form of the scalar product

If the vectors **a** and **b** are given in component form, then a and b can be calculated, but we have at present no way of calculating θ. So the definition of **a . b** seems to be of little use. It is, however, a simple matter to prove that if

$$\mathbf{a} = \begin{pmatrix} a_1 \\ a_2 \\ a_3 \end{pmatrix} \quad \text{and} \quad \mathbf{b} = \begin{pmatrix} b_1 \\ b_2 \\ b_3 \end{pmatrix} \quad \text{then} \quad \mathbf{a} . \mathbf{b} = a_1 b_1 + a_2 b_2 + a_3 b_3.$$

Proof

By applying the cosine rule to the triangle OAB,

$$AB^2 = a^2 + b^2 - 2ab\cos\theta$$
$$= a_1{}^2 + a_2{}^2 + a_3{}^2 + b_1{}^2 + b_2{}^2 + b_3{}^2 - 2\mathbf{a}.\mathbf{b} \quad (1)$$

By the distance formula

$$AB^2 = (a_1 - b_1)^2 + (a_2 - b_2)^2 + (a_3 - b_3)^2$$
$$= a_1{}^2 + a_2{}^2 + a_3{}^2 + b_1{}^2 + b_2{}^2 + b_3{}^2 - 2(a_1b_1 + a_2b_2 + a_3b_3) \quad (2)$$

By comparing (1) and (2) the result follows.

With this result, the calculation of scalar products is easy. One immediate application is to the angle between two vectors, given in component form. Since $ab\cos\theta = \mathbf{a}\,.\,\mathbf{b}$,

$$\cos\theta = \frac{\mathbf{a}\,.\,\mathbf{b}}{ab} = \frac{a_1b_1 + a_2b_2 + a_3b_3}{ab}.$$

Examples 8.7

1 Given $\mathbf{a} = \begin{pmatrix} 3 \\ 4 \\ 5 \end{pmatrix}$ and $\mathbf{b} = \begin{pmatrix} 1 \\ 2 \\ 3 \end{pmatrix}$, calculate $\mathbf{a}\,.\,\mathbf{b}$ and find the angle between $\mathbf{a}$ and $\mathbf{b}$, giving it in degrees correct to 1 d.p.

$\mathbf{a}\,.\,\mathbf{b} = 3 + 8 + 15 = 26, \qquad a^2 = 50, \qquad b^2 = 14$

$\therefore \cos\theta = \dfrac{26}{\sqrt{50}\sqrt{14}} = \dfrac{2.6}{\sqrt{7}}, \qquad \theta = 10.7°$

2 Given that $\mathbf{a} = 2\mathbf{i} + 3\mathbf{j} - 4\mathbf{k}$, $\mathbf{b} = \mathbf{i} + 2\mathbf{j} + 2\mathbf{k}$, $\mathbf{c} = -\mathbf{i} + 2\mathbf{j} + \mathbf{k}$, prove that $\mathbf{a}$ is perpendicular to each of $\mathbf{b}$ and $\mathbf{c}$.

$\mathbf{a}\,.\,\mathbf{b} = 2 + 6 - 8 = 0 \qquad \therefore$ **a** is perpendicular to **b**

$\mathbf{a}\,.\,\mathbf{c} = -2 + 6 - 4 = 0 \qquad \therefore$ **a** " " " **c**

3 Given $\mathbf{a} = \begin{pmatrix} 3 \\ 4 \\ 5 \end{pmatrix}$, $\mathbf{b} = \begin{pmatrix} 2 \\ 1 \\ 2 \end{pmatrix}$, find the cosine of the angle θ between $\mathbf{a}$ and $\mathbf{b}$. Hence calculate $\sin\theta$ and the area of the triangle OAB, giving all answers in surd form or as fractions.

$\mathbf{a}\,.\,\mathbf{b} = 6 + 4 + 10 = 20, \qquad a^2 = 50, \qquad b^2 = 9$

$\therefore \cos\theta = \dfrac{20}{15\sqrt{2}} = \dfrac{4}{3\sqrt{2}}$

$\therefore \sin^2\theta = 1 - \dfrac{16}{18} = \dfrac{1}{9}$

$\therefore \sin\theta = \dfrac{1}{3} \qquad (0 \leqslant \theta \leqslant 180°)$

Area of triangle $OAB = \dfrac{1}{2} \times 5\sqrt{2} \times 3 \times \dfrac{1}{3} = \dfrac{5\sqrt{2}}{2}$

4 Given the points $P(-1, 2, 4)$, $Q(-5, 3, 2)$ and $R(3, 5, 3)$, calculate the angles of the triangle PQR, correct to 1 d.p.

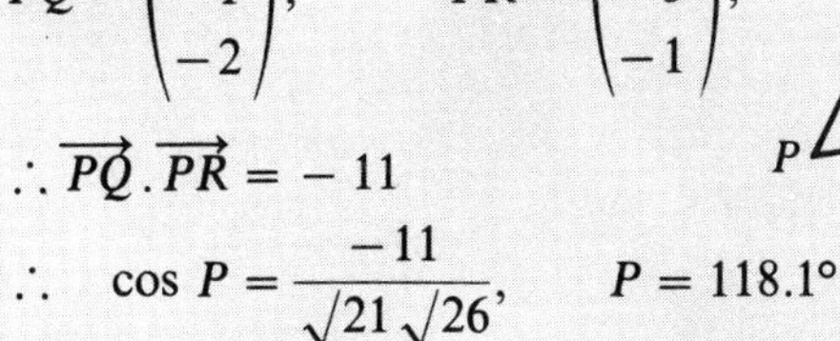

$$\overrightarrow{PQ} = \begin{pmatrix} -4 \\ 1 \\ -2 \end{pmatrix}, \qquad \overrightarrow{PR} = \begin{pmatrix} 4 \\ 3 \\ -1 \end{pmatrix},$$

$$\therefore \overrightarrow{PQ} . \overrightarrow{PR} = -11$$

$$\therefore \quad \cos P = \frac{-11}{\sqrt{21}\sqrt{26}}, \qquad P = 118.1°$$

(Note that the vectors used must start from a vertex, or an exterior angle may be found.)

$$\overrightarrow{RP} = \begin{pmatrix} -4 \\ -3 \\ 1 \end{pmatrix}, \qquad \overrightarrow{RQ} = \begin{pmatrix} -8 \\ -2 \\ -1 \end{pmatrix}, \qquad \therefore \overrightarrow{RP} . \overrightarrow{RQ} = 37$$

$$\therefore \cos R = \frac{37}{\sqrt{26}\sqrt{69}}, \qquad R = 29.1°$$

$$\overrightarrow{QR} = \begin{pmatrix} 8 \\ 2 \\ 1 \end{pmatrix}, \qquad \overrightarrow{QP} = \begin{pmatrix} 4 \\ -1 \\ 2 \end{pmatrix}, \qquad \therefore \overrightarrow{QR} . \overrightarrow{QP} = 32$$

$$\therefore \cos Q = \frac{32}{\sqrt{69}\sqrt{21}}, \qquad Q = 32.8°$$

Check: $P + Q + R = 180°$.

Note that since the vectors and their lengths are already known, it takes little time to calculate the third angle directly and use the angle sum as a check.

(An alternative method for this question is of course to calculate the sides of the triangle and use the cosine rule.)

5 Given that $\mathbf{a} = 3\mathbf{i} + 4\mathbf{k}$, $\mathbf{b} = 2\mathbf{i} + 2\mathbf{j} + \mathbf{k}$, $\mathbf{c} = 19\mathbf{i} + 10\mathbf{j} + 17\mathbf{k}$, show that $\mathbf{c}$ makes equal angles with $\mathbf{a}$ and $\mathbf{b}$.

Let the angle between $\mathbf{a}$ and $\mathbf{c}$ be α, and the angle between $\mathbf{b}$ and $\mathbf{c}$ be β.

Then $\quad \mathbf{a}.\mathbf{c} = 125 = ac \cos \alpha = 5c \cos \alpha,$

and $\quad \mathbf{b}.\mathbf{c} = 75 = bc \cos \beta = 3c \cos \beta,$

$$\therefore \cos \alpha = \frac{25}{c}, \qquad \cos \beta = \frac{25}{c}$$

(Note that it is not necessary to calculate c.)

$$\therefore \alpha = \beta$$

6 Given that $\mathbf{a} = \begin{pmatrix} 2 \\ 1 \\ 2 \end{pmatrix}$, $\mathbf{b} = \begin{pmatrix} 6 \\ 6 \\ 3 \end{pmatrix}$, find a vector which bisects the angle between **a** and **b**.

Let A and B be the points with position vectors **a** and **b** relative to an origin O. If **a** and **b** were the same length, the problem would be simpler, since the required bisector would be the vector $\overrightarrow{OM}$, where M is the mid-point of AB. But the bisector in no way depends on the lengths of **a** and **b**. So we can instead use unit vectors parallel to **a** and **b**.

Since $a = 3$ and $b = 9$,

$$\hat{\mathbf{a}} = \frac{1}{3}\begin{pmatrix} 2 \\ 1 \\ 2 \end{pmatrix}, \quad \hat{\mathbf{b}} = \frac{1}{9}\begin{pmatrix} 6 \\ 6 \\ 3 \end{pmatrix},$$

$\therefore$ the bisector is $\frac{1}{2}(\hat{\mathbf{a}} + \hat{\mathbf{b}}) = \frac{1}{6}\begin{pmatrix} 4 \\ 3 \\ 3 \end{pmatrix}$

or, more simply, a vector in the direction of the bisector is $\begin{pmatrix} 4 \\ 3 \\ 3 \end{pmatrix}$.

Exercise 8.7A

Give all angles to the nearest tenth of a degree.

1 Given that $\mathbf{a} = \begin{pmatrix} 5 \\ 2 \\ 3 \end{pmatrix}$, $\mathbf{b} = \begin{pmatrix} 3 \\ -4 \\ -2 \end{pmatrix}$, calculate $\mathbf{a} \cdot \mathbf{b}$, and deduce whether **a** and **b** contain an acute angle or an obtuse angle or neither.

2 Given that $\mathbf{a} = \begin{pmatrix} 6 \\ -2 \\ 5 \end{pmatrix}$, $\mathbf{b} = \begin{pmatrix} 2 \\ 1 \\ -2 \end{pmatrix}$, show that **a** and **b** are perpendicular.

3 Given the points $A(1, 0, 1)$, $B(3, 4, 5)$, calculate the cosine of the angle AOB as a fraction, and show that the area of the triangle AOB is 6 square units.

4 In each of the following cases, calculate $\mathbf{a} \cdot \mathbf{b}$ and the angle between **a** and **b**.

(i) $\mathbf{a} = 2\mathbf{i} + \mathbf{j}$, $\mathbf{b} = 4\mathbf{i} + 2\mathbf{k}$ (ii) $\mathbf{a} = 3\mathbf{i} + 4\mathbf{k}$, $\mathbf{b} = \mathbf{i} + 3\mathbf{j}$

(iii) $\mathbf{a} = 5\mathbf{i} + 4\mathbf{j} + 3\mathbf{k}$, $\mathbf{b} = 2\mathbf{i} + 2\mathbf{j}$

5 Given that $\mathbf{a} = \begin{pmatrix} 3 \\ 1 \\ 0 \end{pmatrix}$, $\mathbf{b} = \begin{pmatrix} t \\ 0 \\ 1 \end{pmatrix}$, and that the angle between **a** and **b** is 45°, find the value of t, in surd form.

6 The points A, B, C are (5, 3, 2), (6, 5, 4), (7, −1, 3) respectively. Find the angle between AB and AC.

7 Calculate the angles of the triangle ABC for each case.

a $A(2, -1, 5)$, $B(3, 5, 4)$, $C(2, 3, 4)$ **b** $A(3, 2, 6)$, $B(6, 3, 2)$, $C(3, -1, 5)$

8 The points A, B, C, D are (3, 2, −1), (4, 5, 4), (2, 6, 1), (1, 3, −4) respectively. Show that $ABCD$ is a parallelogram. Calculate the lengths of the sides, correct to two s.f., and the angles.

9 Given that $\mathbf{a} = \mathbf{i} + 4\mathbf{j} + \mathbf{k}$, $\mathbf{b} = 3\mathbf{i} + 4\mathbf{j} + 5\mathbf{k}$, $\mathbf{c} = 7\mathbf{i} + 16\mathbf{j} + 10\mathbf{k}$, show that **c** makes equal angles with **a** and **b**.

Exercise 8.7B

1 Given that $\mathbf{a} = 2\mathbf{i} + 4\mathbf{j} - 3\mathbf{k}$ and $\mathbf{b} = t\mathbf{i} + 2\mathbf{j} + \mathbf{k}$, and that **a** is perpendicular to **b**, calculate t.

2 In each of the following cases, calculate $\mathbf{a}\,.\,\mathbf{b}$ and the angle between **a** and **b**.

(i) $\mathbf{a} = 3\mathbf{i} + \mathbf{k}$, $\mathbf{b} = 4\mathbf{j}$ (ii) $\mathbf{a} = 6\mathbf{i} + 6\mathbf{j} + 7\mathbf{k}$, $\mathbf{b} = 2\mathbf{i} + 2\mathbf{j} + \mathbf{k}$

(iii) $\mathbf{a} = 2\mathbf{i} + 3\mathbf{j} + \mathbf{k}$, $\mathbf{b} = 2\mathbf{j} + 5\mathbf{k}$

3 The points P, Q, R are (0, 3, 5), (1, 2, 7), (4, −1, 1) respectively. Show that PQ is perpendicular to PR and find, in its simplest surd form, the area of the triangle PQR.

4 Calculate the angles of the triangle ABC for each case.

a $A(-4, 2, 4)$, $B(-3, -5, 4)$, $C(-2, 2, 3)$

b $A(2, -3, 1)$, $B(5, 0, -2)$, $C(6, -1, 4)$

5 Given the points $A(2, 5, 3)$, $B(3, 4, -1)$, $C(-2, 6, 4)$, show that $AB = AC$ and determine the angle A. Find the area of the triangle ABC in surd form.

6 Given the points $A(4, 2, 3)$, $B(3, 1, 6)$, $C(6, 0, 5)$ and $D(7, 1, 2)$, show that $ABCD$ is a rhombus. Calculate

a the lengths of the sides, correct to two s.f. **b** the angles

c the area, giving it in its simplest surd form.

7 Given that $\mathbf{a} = \begin{pmatrix} 4 \\ 1 \\ 1 \end{pmatrix}$, $\mathbf{b} = \begin{pmatrix} 2 \\ 2 \\ 0 \end{pmatrix}$, find a vector which bisects the angle between **a** and **b**.

8.8 The distributive law for scalar products

In the set of real numbers, multiplication is distributive over addition, i.e. $a(b + c) = ab + ac$. This law also holds in the set of matrices, for matrix multiplication over matrix addition.

The same law will now be shown to hold in the set of vectors for scalar multiplication over vector addition, i.e.

$$\mathbf{a}\,.\,(\mathbf{b} + \mathbf{c}) = \mathbf{a}\,.\,\mathbf{b} + \mathbf{a}\,.\,\mathbf{c}$$

Proof With the usual notation

$$\mathbf{a}\,.\,(\mathbf{b} + \mathbf{c}) = \begin{pmatrix} a_1 \\ a_2 \\ a_3 \end{pmatrix} . \begin{pmatrix} b_1 + c_1 \\ b_2 + c_2 \\ b_3 + c_3 \end{pmatrix}$$

$$= a_1(b_1 + c_1) + a_2(b_2 + c_2) + a_3(b_3 + c_3)$$

$$= a_1b_1 + a_1c_1 + a_2b_2 + a_2c_2 + a_3b_3 + a_3c_3$$

(distributive law for real numbers)

$$= a_1b_1 + a_2b_2 + a_3b_3 + a_1c_1 + a_2c_2 + a_3c_3$$

(commutative law for addition of real numbers)

$$= \mathbf{a}\,.\,\mathbf{b} + \mathbf{a}\,.\,\mathbf{c}$$

Note (i) By the commutative law for scalar products

$(\mathbf{a} + \mathbf{b})\,.\,\mathbf{c} = \mathbf{a}\,.\,\mathbf{c} + \mathbf{b}\,.\,\mathbf{c}$.

(ii) The distributive law enables brackets to be removed from expressions involving scalar products, exactly as in the algebra of real numbers:

e.g. $(\mathbf{a} + \mathbf{b})\,.\,(\mathbf{c} + \mathbf{d}) = \mathbf{a}\,.\,(\mathbf{c} + \mathbf{d}) + \mathbf{b}\,.\,(\mathbf{c} + \mathbf{d})$

$= \mathbf{a}\,.\,\mathbf{c} + \mathbf{a}\,.\,\mathbf{d} + \mathbf{b}\,.\,\mathbf{c} + \mathbf{b}\,.\,\mathbf{d}$

In particular

$$|\mathbf{a} + \mathbf{b}|^2 = (\mathbf{a} + \mathbf{b})\,.\,(\mathbf{a} + \mathbf{b})$$

$$= \mathbf{a}\,.\,\mathbf{a} + \mathbf{a}\,.\,\mathbf{b} + \mathbf{b}\,.\,\mathbf{a} + \mathbf{b}\,.\,\mathbf{b}$$

$$= a^2 + 2\mathbf{a}\,.\,\mathbf{b} + b^2$$

$$= a^2 + b^2 + 2ab\cos\theta$$

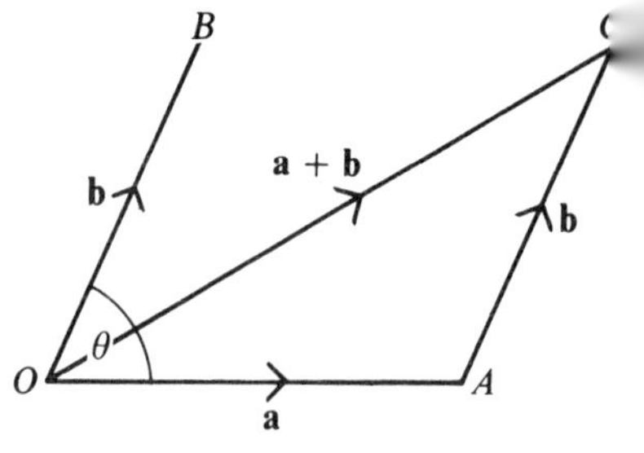

or $OC^2 = a^2 + b^2 - 2ab\cos OAC$ which is the cosine rule for the triangle OAC.

However, this is *not* a proof of the cosine rule in this case, since the cosine rule was used to prove the component form of the scalar product, which was in turn used to prove the distributive law.

(iii) The length of the vector **a** can be written either a or $|\mathbf{a}|$, but the length of the vector $\mathbf{a} + \mathbf{b}$ can be written only as $|\mathbf{a} + \mathbf{b}|$. It is only in the special case when **a** and **b** are in the same direction that $|\mathbf{a}| + |\mathbf{b}|$ is equal to $|\mathbf{a} + \mathbf{b}|$.

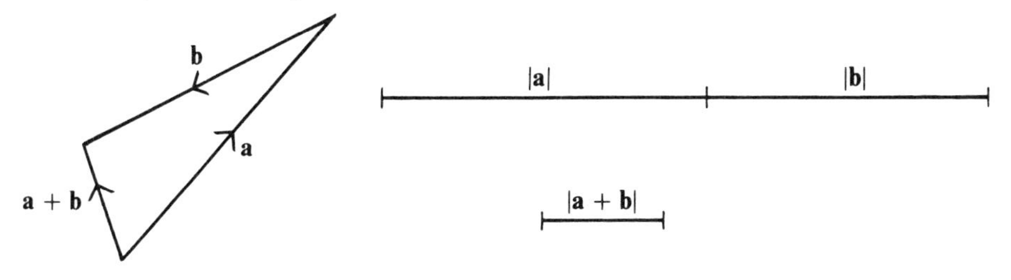

Examples 8.8

1 Given the diagram, in which **a** and **b** contain an angle of 45°, and given that $a = 3$, $b = 4$, calculate the exact values of

$\mathbf{a}.\mathbf{a}$, $\mathbf{b}.\mathbf{b}$, $\mathbf{a}.\mathbf{b}$, $\mathbf{a}.(\mathbf{a}+\mathbf{b})$, $\mathbf{b}.(\mathbf{a}+\mathbf{b})$, $(\mathbf{a}+\mathbf{b}).(\mathbf{a}+\mathbf{b})$ and $(\mathbf{a}-\mathbf{b}).(\mathbf{a}-\mathbf{b})$.

Check the last two answers by using the cosine rule.

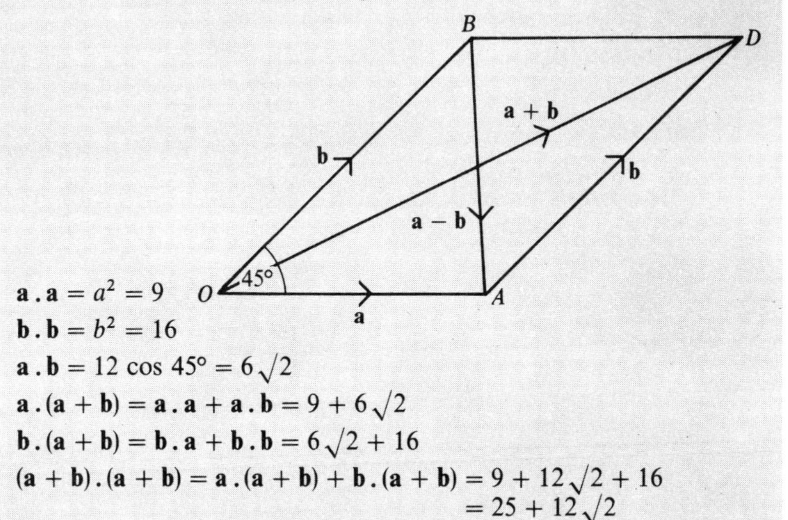

$\mathbf{a}.\mathbf{a} = a^2 = 9$

$\mathbf{b}.\mathbf{b} = b^2 = 16$

$\mathbf{a}.\mathbf{b} = 12 \cos 45° = 6\sqrt{2}$

$\mathbf{a}.(\mathbf{a}+\mathbf{b}) = \mathbf{a}.\mathbf{a} + \mathbf{a}.\mathbf{b} = 9 + 6\sqrt{2}$

$\mathbf{b}.(\mathbf{a}+\mathbf{b}) = \mathbf{b}.\mathbf{a} + \mathbf{b}.\mathbf{b} = 6\sqrt{2} + 16$

$$(\mathbf{a}+\mathbf{b}).(\mathbf{a}+\mathbf{b}) = \mathbf{a}.(\mathbf{a}+\mathbf{b}) + \mathbf{b}.(\mathbf{a}+\mathbf{b}) = 9 + 12\sqrt{2} + 16 = 25 + 12\sqrt{2}$$

$$(\mathbf{a}-\mathbf{b}).(\mathbf{a}-\mathbf{b}) = \mathbf{a}.\mathbf{a} - 2\mathbf{a}.\mathbf{b} + \mathbf{b}.\mathbf{b} = 9 - 12\sqrt{2} + 16 = 25 - 12\sqrt{2}$$

By the cosine rule

$$(\mathbf{a}+\mathbf{b}).(\mathbf{a}+\mathbf{b}) = OD^2 = 9 + 16 - 2 \times 3 \times 4 \cos 135° = 25 + 12\sqrt{2}$$

$$(\mathbf{a}-\mathbf{b}).(\mathbf{a}-\mathbf{b}) = AB^2 = 9 + 16 - 24 \cos 45° = 25 - 12\sqrt{2}$$

2 Given that **a** and **b** contain an angle of 60° and that $a = 2$, $b = 5$, calculate $(3\mathbf{a} + 4\mathbf{b}).(2\mathbf{a} - \mathbf{b})$.

$$\begin{aligned}(3\mathbf{a} + 4\mathbf{b}).(2\mathbf{a} - \mathbf{b}) &= 6\mathbf{a}.\mathbf{a} - 3\mathbf{a}.\mathbf{b} + 8\mathbf{b}.\mathbf{a} - 4\mathbf{b}.\mathbf{b}\\ &= 24 + 5.10.\cos 60° - 100\\ &= -51\end{aligned}$$

3 Given that $a = b$, simplify $(\mathbf{a} + \mathbf{b}).(\mathbf{a} - \mathbf{b})$. State what follows from your answer about $\mathbf{a} + \mathbf{b}$ and $\mathbf{a} - \mathbf{b}$.

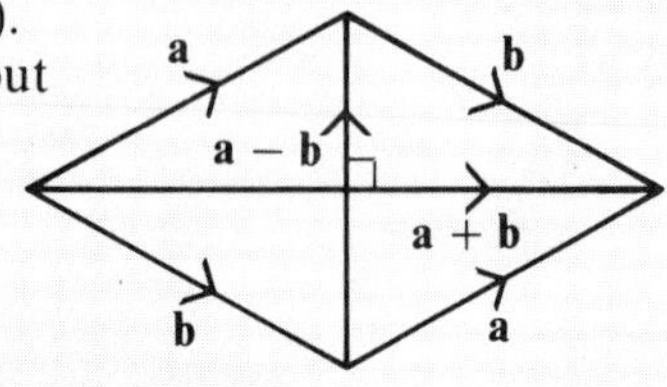

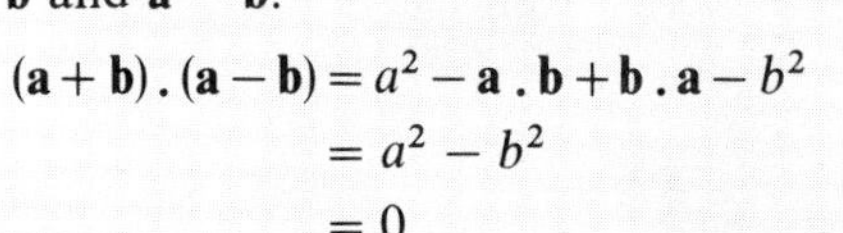

$$\begin{aligned}(\mathbf{a}+\mathbf{b}).(\mathbf{a}-\mathbf{b}) &= a^2 - \mathbf{a}.\mathbf{b} + \mathbf{b}.\mathbf{a} - b^2\\ &= a^2 - b^2\\ &= 0\end{aligned}$$

$\therefore$ $\mathbf{a} + \mathbf{b} = 0$ or $\mathbf{a} - \mathbf{b} = 0$ or $\mathbf{a} + \mathbf{b}$ is perpendicular to $\mathbf{a} - \mathbf{b}$, in the latter case giving a vector proof that the diagonals of a rhombus meet at right angles.

4 Given that $\mathbf{a} = \begin{pmatrix} 2 \\ 3 \\ 1 \end{pmatrix}$, $\mathbf{b} = \begin{pmatrix} -1 \\ 4 \\ 2 \end{pmatrix}$, calculate $\mathbf{a}.\mathbf{a}$, $\mathbf{b}.\mathbf{b}$ and $\mathbf{a}.\mathbf{b}$.

Hence by using the distributive law calculate $(\mathbf{a} + \mathbf{b}).(\mathbf{a} + \mathbf{b})$, $(\mathbf{a} - \mathbf{b}).(\mathbf{a} - \mathbf{b})$ and $(\mathbf{a} + \mathbf{b}).(\mathbf{a} - \mathbf{b})$.
Check the answers by using $\mathbf{a} + \mathbf{b}$ and $\mathbf{a} - \mathbf{b}$ as column vectors.

$\mathbf{a}.\mathbf{a} = 4 + 9 + 1 = 14$, $\quad \mathbf{b}.\mathbf{b} = 1 + 16 + 4 = 21$,

$\mathbf{a}.\mathbf{b} = -2 + 12 + 2 = 12$

$$\begin{aligned}(\mathbf{a} + \mathbf{b}).(\mathbf{a} + \mathbf{b}) &= \mathbf{a}.\mathbf{a} + 2\mathbf{a}.\mathbf{b} + \mathbf{b}.\mathbf{b} = 59\\ (\mathbf{a} - \mathbf{b}).(\mathbf{a} - \mathbf{b}) &= \mathbf{a}.\mathbf{a} - 2\mathbf{a}.\mathbf{b} + \mathbf{b}.\mathbf{b} = 11\\ (\mathbf{a} + \mathbf{b}).(\mathbf{a} - \mathbf{b}) &= \mathbf{a}.\mathbf{a} - \mathbf{b}.\mathbf{b} \qquad\quad = -7\end{aligned}$$

Check: $\mathbf{a} + \mathbf{b} = \begin{pmatrix} 1 \\ 7 \\ 3 \end{pmatrix}$, $\quad \mathbf{a} - \mathbf{b} = \begin{pmatrix} 3 \\ -1 \\ -1 \end{pmatrix}$

giving the same answers as above.

5 Given that $a = 8$, $b = 5$ and $\mathbf{a}.\mathbf{b} = 16$, calculate by using the distributive law $(\mathbf{a} + \mathbf{b}).(\mathbf{a} + \mathbf{b})$, $(\mathbf{a} - \mathbf{b}).(\mathbf{a} - \mathbf{b})$ and $(\mathbf{a} + \mathbf{b}).(\mathbf{a} - \mathbf{b})$.
Hence find the angle θ between $\mathbf{a} + \mathbf{b}$ and $\mathbf{a} - \mathbf{b}$ correct to the nearest degree.

$$\begin{aligned}(\mathbf{a} + \mathbf{b}).(\mathbf{a} + \mathbf{b}) &= a^2 + 2\mathbf{a}.\mathbf{b} + b^2 = 64 + 32 + 25 = 121\\ (\mathbf{a} - \mathbf{b}).(\mathbf{a} - \mathbf{b}) &= a^2 - 2\mathbf{a}.\mathbf{b} + b^2 = 64 - 32 + 25 = \ \ 57\\ (\mathbf{a} + \mathbf{b}).(\mathbf{a} - \mathbf{b}) &= a^2 - b^2 \qquad\qquad\ = 64 - 25 \qquad = \ \ 39\end{aligned}$$

$\therefore 11\sqrt{57}\cos\theta = 39$

$\theta = 62°$ to nearest degree.

Exercise 8.8A

1 Given that $\mathbf{a} = \begin{pmatrix} 2 \\ 3 \\ -4 \end{pmatrix}$, $\mathbf{b} = \begin{pmatrix} 5 \\ 2 \\ 3 \end{pmatrix}$, $\mathbf{c} = \begin{pmatrix} 1 \\ -2 \\ 4 \end{pmatrix}$, calculate $\mathbf{a}\,.\,\mathbf{b}$ and $\mathbf{a}\,.\,\mathbf{c}$.

Hence by using the distributive law calculate $\mathbf{a}\,.(\mathbf{b}+\mathbf{c})$ and $(\mathbf{b}-\mathbf{c})\,.\,\mathbf{a}$.
Check by using $\mathbf{b}+\mathbf{c}$ and $\mathbf{b}-\mathbf{c}$ as column vectors.

2 Given that $\mathbf{a}$ and $\mathbf{b}$ contain an angle of 28° and that $a = 2$, $b = 5$, calculate to three s.f. $\mathbf{a}\,.\,\mathbf{b}$, $\mathbf{a}\,.(\mathbf{a}+\mathbf{b})$, $(\mathbf{a}+\mathbf{b})\,.(\mathbf{a}+\mathbf{b})$, and the length of $\mathbf{a}+\mathbf{b}$.
Hence find the angle between $\mathbf{a}$ and $\mathbf{a}+\mathbf{b}$ to the nearest degree.

3 Given that $a = 3$, $b = 2$, and that the length of $\mathbf{a}+2\mathbf{b}$ is 5, use the distributive law to show that $\mathbf{a}$ is perpendicular to $\mathbf{b}$.

4 Given that $|\mathbf{a}+\mathbf{b}| = 3$, $|\mathbf{a}-2\mathbf{b}| = 1$ and that $\mathbf{a}\,.\,\mathbf{b} = 2$, calculate a and b in surd form.

5 In the diagram O is the centre of the circle and CA is a diameter; B is any point on the circle. Use the distributive law to prove that $\overrightarrow{CB}$ is perpendicular to $\overrightarrow{BA}$, so proving that 'the angle in a semicircle is a right angle'.

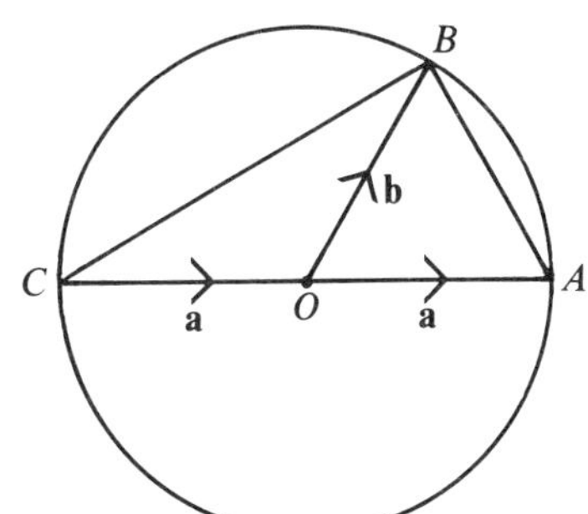

Exercise 8.8B

1 Given that $\mathbf{a}$ and $\mathbf{b}$ contain an angle of 60° and that $a = 4$, $b = 5$, $\mathbf{p} = s\mathbf{a} + t\mathbf{b}$, $\mathbf{q} = \mathbf{a} - \mathbf{b}$, determine $\mathbf{p}\,.\,\mathbf{q}$ in terms of s and t.
Deduce the ratio of s to t for which $\mathbf{p}$ and $\mathbf{q}$ are at right angles.

2 Given that $a = 4$, $b = 5$, and that the length of $2\mathbf{a}+\mathbf{b}$ is 7, calculate the exact angle between $\mathbf{a}$ and $\mathbf{b}$.

3 Given that $a = 6$, $b = 2$ and $\mathbf{a}\,.\,\mathbf{b} = 9$, calculate $|\mathbf{a}+2\mathbf{b}|$, $|\mathbf{a}-3\mathbf{b}|$ and $(\mathbf{a}+2\mathbf{b})\,.(\mathbf{a}-3\mathbf{b})$.
Hence find the angle between $\mathbf{a}+2\mathbf{b}$ and $\mathbf{a}-3\mathbf{b}$, correct to the nearest degree.

4 In the diagram, $\overrightarrow{AD}$ is perpendicular to $\overrightarrow{BC}$ and $\overrightarrow{BE}$ is perpendicular to $\overrightarrow{CA}$; AD and BE meet at H. Use the distributive law to prove that $\overrightarrow{CH}$ is perpendicular to $\overrightarrow{AB}$, so proving that the three altitudes of a triangle are concurrent.

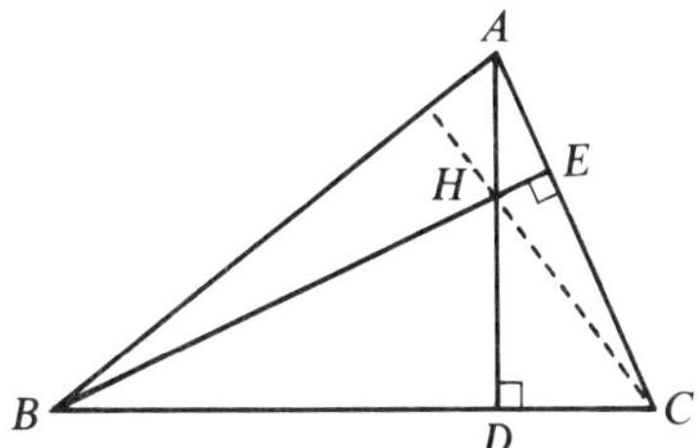

Miscellaneous Exercise 8

1 In the quadrilateral $OABC$, $\overrightarrow{OA} = \mathbf{a}$, $\overrightarrow{OB} = \mathbf{b}$ and $\overrightarrow{OC} = \mathbf{b} - \frac{3}{4}\mathbf{a}$.

Prove that OA is parallel to CB.

Express $\overrightarrow{AC}$ in terms of $\mathbf{a}$ and $\mathbf{b}$.

The diagonals OB and AC of the quadrilateral $OABC$ meet at the point P. Given that $\overrightarrow{AP} = k\,\overrightarrow{AC}$, where k is a scalar constant, show that

$$\overrightarrow{OP} = \left(1 - \frac{7}{4}k\right)\mathbf{a} + k\mathbf{b}.$$

Use this result to write down

a the value of k **b** the vector $\overrightarrow{OP}$ in terms of $\mathbf{b}$ only.

Find the ratio of the area of $\triangle OAC$ to the area of $\triangle ABC$. (*L*)

2 The vertices A, B, C of a triangle have position vectors $\mathbf{a}$, $\mathbf{b}$, $\mathbf{c}$ respectively. Write down expressions in terms of $\mathbf{a}$, $\mathbf{b}$ and $\mathbf{c}$ for the position vectors $\mathbf{d}$, $\mathbf{e}$, $\mathbf{f}$ of the points D, E, F, the mid-points of BC, CA, AB respectively. H has position vector $\mathbf{h} = \frac{1}{3}(\mathbf{a} + \mathbf{b} + \mathbf{c})$.

Give expressions in terms of $\mathbf{a}$, $\mathbf{b}$, $\mathbf{c}$ for $\mathbf{FH}$ and $\mathbf{HC}$, and show that $\mathbf{HC} = 2\mathbf{FH}$. State what this tells you about the positions of points F, H and C.

It may similarly be shown that $\mathbf{HA} = 2\mathbf{DH}$ and that $\mathbf{HB} = 2\mathbf{EH}$. State what this tells you about the position of H. (*SMP*)

3 $ABCD$ is a quadrilateral. P, Q, R, S are the mid-points of AB, BC, CD, DA respectively. The position vector of the point A is denoted by $\mathbf{a}$, and the position vectors of other points are denoted similarly.

Express in terms of $\mathbf{a}$, $\mathbf{b}$, $\mathbf{c}$, $\mathbf{d}$:

(i) $\mathbf{p}$;
(ii) $\mathbf{s}$;
(iii) $\mathbf{PS}$;
(iv) $\mathbf{QR}$;
(v) the position vector of X, the mid-point of BD;
(vi) the position vector of Y, the mid-point of PR.

Show that if X and Y coincide then $ABCD$ is a parallelogram. (*SMP*)

4 The three points $A(5, 2, 5)$, $B(3, 7, 2)$ and $C(7, 11, 6)$ form a triangle. Write down $\mathbf{AB}$ and $\mathbf{AC}$ as column vectors.

Show that $\mathbf{AB}\,.\,\mathbf{AC} = 38$, and calculate the lengths of AB and AC. Hence calculate $\cos A$.

Verify that $AC \cos A = AB$. Deduce the size of the angle B and write down the value of $\mathbf{AB}\,.\,\mathbf{BC}$. (*SMP*)

5 $OPQR$ is a rhombus of side 2 units; K, L, M and N are the mid-points of the sides OP, PQ, QR and RO respectively.

$\overrightarrow{OK}$ is a representative of the vector $\mathbf{a}$ and $\overrightarrow{ON}$ of the vector $\mathbf{b}$.

a Express $\overrightarrow{OL}$ and $\overrightarrow{OM}$ in terms of $\mathbf{a}$ and $\mathbf{b}$.

b Prove that $\overrightarrow{OL} \,.\, \overrightarrow{OM} = 5\mathbf{a}\,.\,\mathbf{b} + 4$.

c Hence deduce the size of the angle POR, given that angle LOM is a right angle. *(S)*

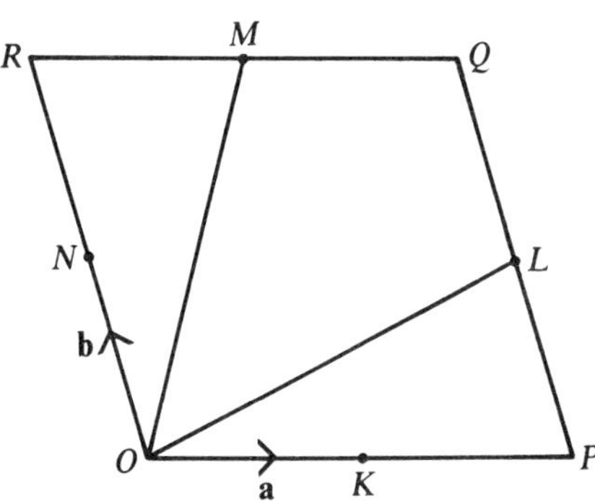

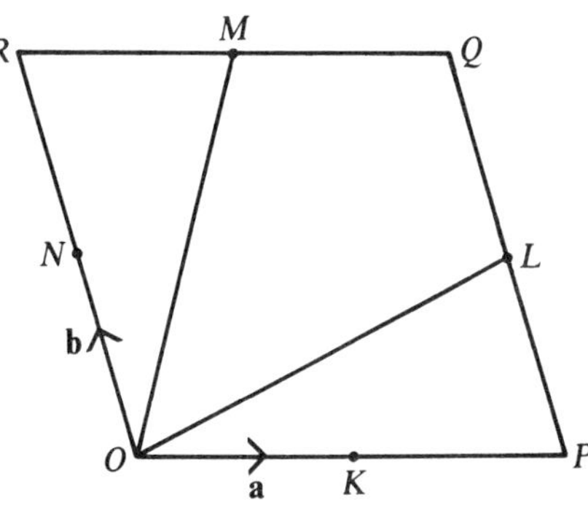

6

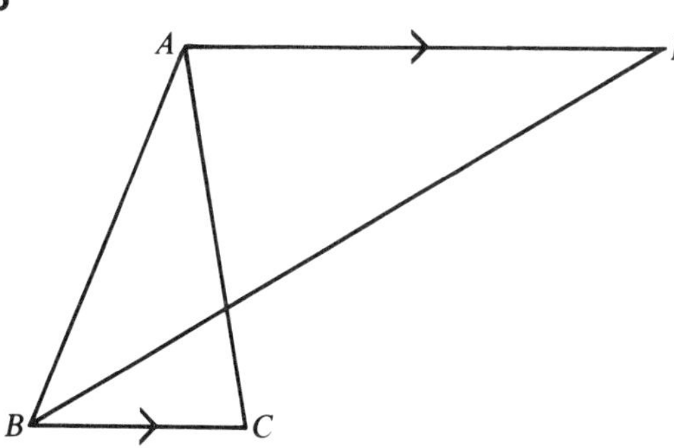

In the diagram, $\cos ABC = \frac{1}{3}$, $BC = 1\,\text{cm}$ and $BA = 2\,\text{cm}$. AD is parallel to BC and $AD = k\,\text{cm}$.

If $\mathbf{p}$ and $\mathbf{q}$ are unit vectors in the directions $\overrightarrow{BC}$ and $\overrightarrow{BA}$ respectively, express $\overrightarrow{BD}$ and $\overrightarrow{AC}$ in terms of $\mathbf{p}$, $\mathbf{q}$ and k.

Hence, or otherwise, find the length of AD such that AC is perpendicular to BD. *(S)*

7 In the tetrahedron $OABC$, $\overrightarrow{OA}$, $\overrightarrow{OB}$, and $\overrightarrow{OC}$ represent the unit vectors $\mathbf{a}$, $\mathbf{b}$ and $\mathbf{c}$ respectively. M is the mid-point of BC.

a Express $\overrightarrow{MO}$ and $\overrightarrow{MA}$ in terms of $\mathbf{a}$, $\mathbf{b}$ and $\mathbf{c}$.

b Simplify the expression for $\overrightarrow{MO} \,.\, \overrightarrow{MA}$ if $\mathbf{a}$, $\mathbf{b}$ and $\mathbf{c}$ are mutually perpendicular. *(S)*

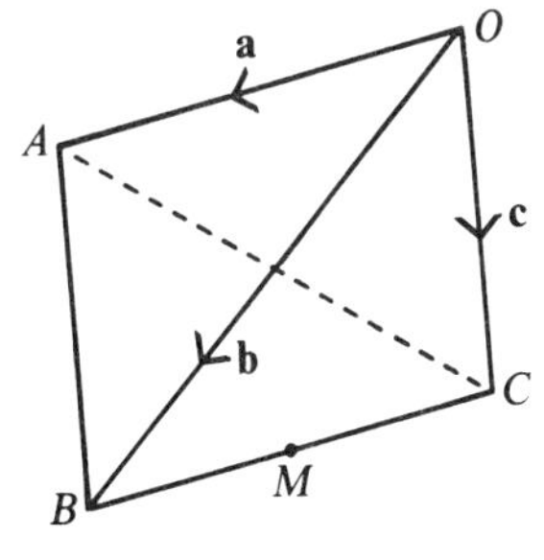

8 A is the point $(6, -8, 0)$, B is $(12, -11, 6)$ and O is the origin.

(i) Calculate the lengths of OA and AB.

(ii) Calculate the value of $\cos OAB$ and show that $\sin OAB = \sqrt{5}/3$. Hence calculate the area of the triangle OAB.

(iii) C is the point $(8, y, z)$ and OC is perpendicular both to OA and to OB. Write down two equations involving y and z and hence find the values of y and z.

(iv) Verify that OC is perpendicular to AB.

(v) Calculate the length of OC and deduce that the volume of the pyramid $OABC$ is 125. *(SMP)*

Chapter 9

Transformations of graphs: the quadratic and bilinear functions

9.1 Transformations of graphs

Given the graph of $y = f(x)$, several other graphs may be sketched by applying simple transformations to this graph. The transformations which are used in this chapter are translations, stretches and reflections.

Translations

The graph of $y = f(x - d)$ is the result of the translation $\begin{pmatrix} d \\ 0 \end{pmatrix}$ applied to the graph of $y = f(x)$. For example, the graph of $y = (x - 2)^3$ is the result of the translation $\begin{pmatrix} 2 \\ 0 \end{pmatrix}$ applied to the graph of $y = x^3$; the graph of $y = (x + 3)^3$ is the result of the translation $\begin{pmatrix} -3 \\ 0 \end{pmatrix}$.

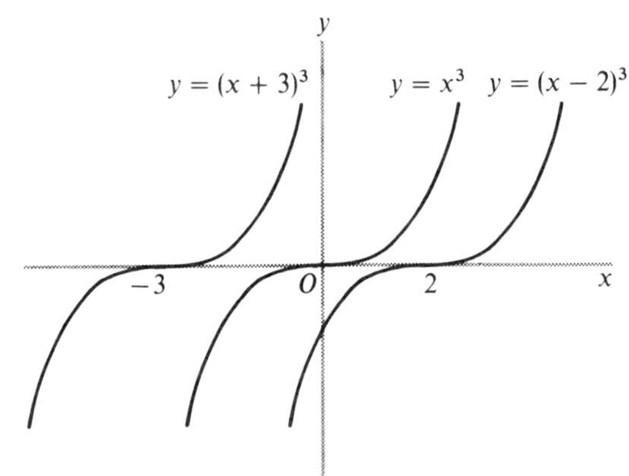

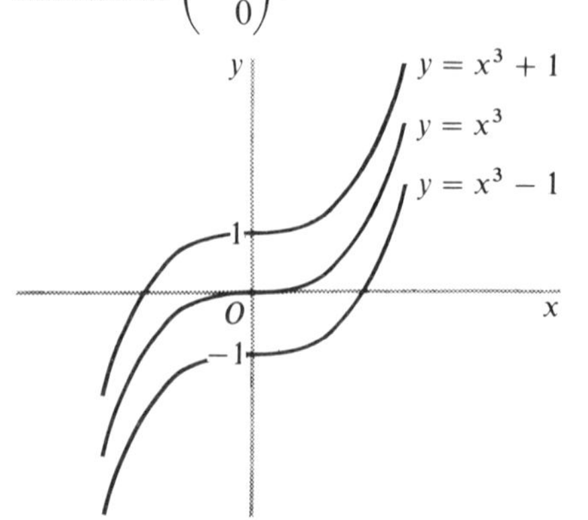

The graph of $y = f(x) + e$ is the result of the translation $\begin{pmatrix} 0 \\ e \end{pmatrix}$ applied to the graph of $y = f(x)$. For example, the graph of $y = x^3 + 1$ is the result of the translation $\begin{pmatrix} 0 \\ 1 \end{pmatrix}$ applied to the graph of $y = x^3$ and the graph of $y = x^3 - 1$ is the result of the translation $\begin{pmatrix} 0 \\ -1 \end{pmatrix}$.

In general the graph of $y = f(x - d) + e$ is the result of the translation $\begin{pmatrix} d \\ e \end{pmatrix}$ applied to the graph of $y = f(x)$.

Stretches parallel to the y-axis

The graph of $y = af(x)$ is the result of multiplying the y-coordinate of each point on the graph of $y = f(x)$ by a. This transformation is called a stretch parallel to the y-axis of scale factor a. For example, $y = 2x$ is the result of a stretch parallel to the y-axis of scale factor 2 applied to the graph of $y = x$.

If $a < 0$ the stretch has the same effect as a reflection in the x-axis and a stretch of scale factor $|a|$; for example, $y = -2x$ is the result of a stretch parallel to the y-axis of scale factor -2 applied to $y = x$, or a reflection of $y = x$ in the x-axis followed by a stretch parallel to the y-axis of scale factor 2. The reflection and the stretch may be applied in either order.

Stretches parallel to the x-axis

The graph of $y = f(ax)$ is the result of multiplying the x-coordinate of each point on the graph of $y = f(x)$ by $\frac{1}{a}$. This transformation is called a stretch parallel to the x-axis of scale factor $\frac{1}{a}$. For example, if the x-coordinate of each point on the line $y = x$ is halved, the points (2, 2), (4, 4), (6, 6) become the points (1, 2), (2, 4), (3, 6), which lie on the line $y = 2x$. Thus the line $y = 2x$ may be obtained from the line $y = x$ by a stretch parallel to the x-axis of scale factor $\frac{1}{2}$, or by a stretch parallel to the y-axis of scale factor 2.

The graph of $y = 9x^2$ may be obtained from the graph of $y = x^2$ by a stretch parallel to the y-axis of scale factor 9, or by a stretch parallel to the x-axis of scale factor $\frac{1}{3}$, since $9x^2 = (3x)^2$. The use of the scale factor 9 is simpler, and only stretches parallel to the y-axis will be used in the remainder of this chapter. Stretches parallel to the x-axis are used in Chapter 10.

Graphs of quadratic functions

A function f is a quadratic if

$$f(x) = ax^2 + bx + c, \text{ where } a \neq 0.$$

The domain of f may be $\mathbb{R}$ or any subset of $\mathbb{R}$. In this chapter it will be $\mathbb{R}$ unless otherwise stated, as in **9.5**.

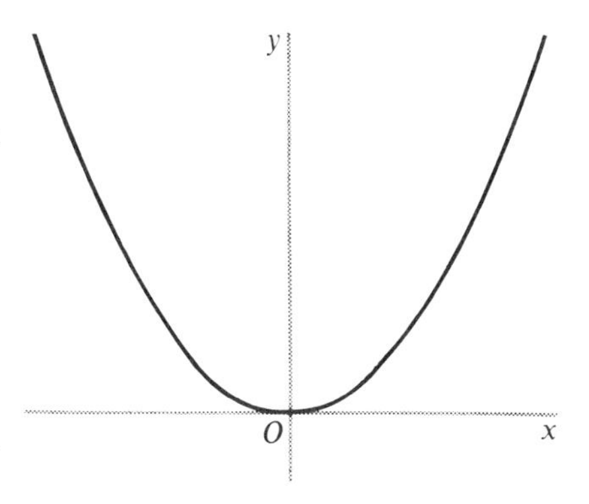

The simplest quadratic function is given by $a = 1$, $b = c = 0$, so that $f(x) = x^2$. The graph of $y = x^2$ is shown in the diagram. It has the important property that the least value of y is 0, which is given by $x = 0$; since the square of every non-zero number is positive, the range of f is all non-negative numbers. The point (0, 0) is a minimum point on the graph. The curve is called a parabola.

An important feature of the parabola is that it is a symmetrical curve; for the parabola given by the equation $y = x^2$, the axis of symmetry is the y-axis.

The graph of $y = (x - d)^2 + e$

This may be obtained from the graph of $y = x^2$ by applying the translation $\begin{pmatrix} d \\ e \end{pmatrix}$. The minimum point at (0, 0) is translated to a minimum point at (d, e). The axis of symmetry becomes the line $x = d$.

The graph of $y = a[(x - d)^2 + e]$

This may be obtained from the graph of $y = x^2$ by the translation $\begin{pmatrix} d \\ e \end{pmatrix}$ followed by a stretch parallel to the y-axis of scale factor a. For $a > 0$ the minimum point at (0, 0) on $y = x^2$ is mapped to a minimum point at (d, ae). For $a < 0$, $y = x^2$ has been reflected in the x-axis, so the minimum point at (0, 0) is mapped to a *maximum* point at (d, ae).

Examples 9.1

Sketch the graph of each of the following, and state the coordinates of the minimum or maximum point.

1 $y = (x - 3)^2 + 1$

2 $y = 2[(x - 2)^2 + 3]$

3 $y = \frac{1}{2}[(x - 3)^2 - 4]$

4 $y = -3[(x + 1)^2 - 4]$

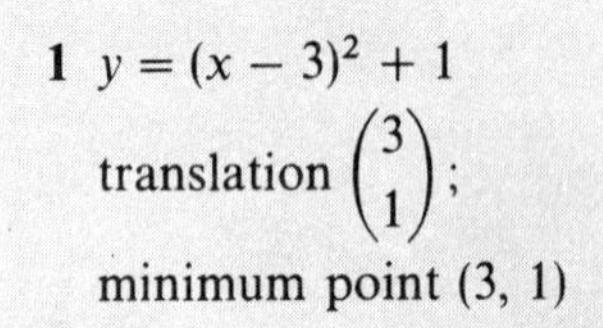

1 $y = (x - 3)^2 + 1$

translation $\begin{pmatrix} 3 \\ 1 \end{pmatrix}$;

minimum point (3, 1)

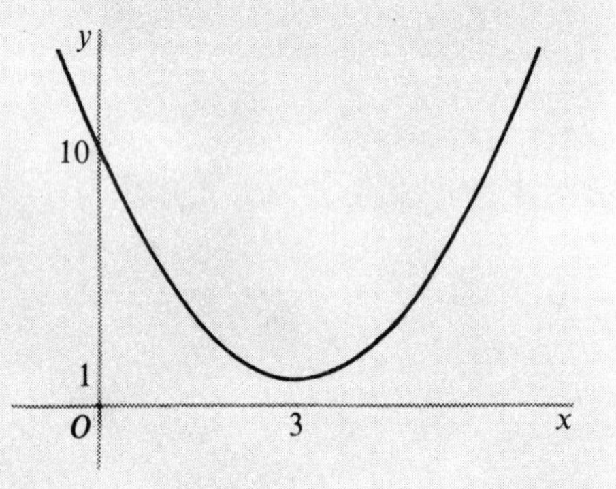

2

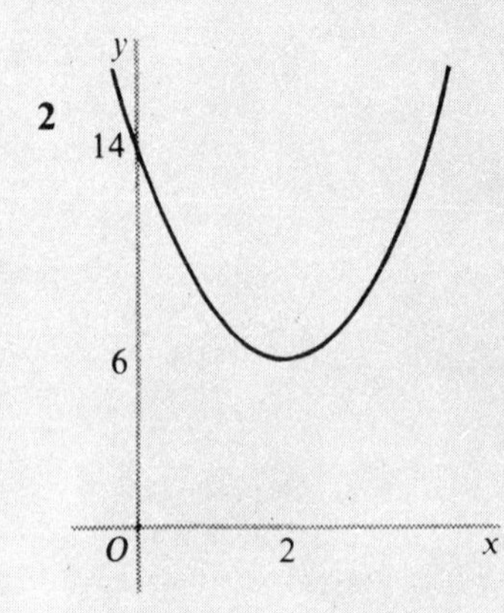

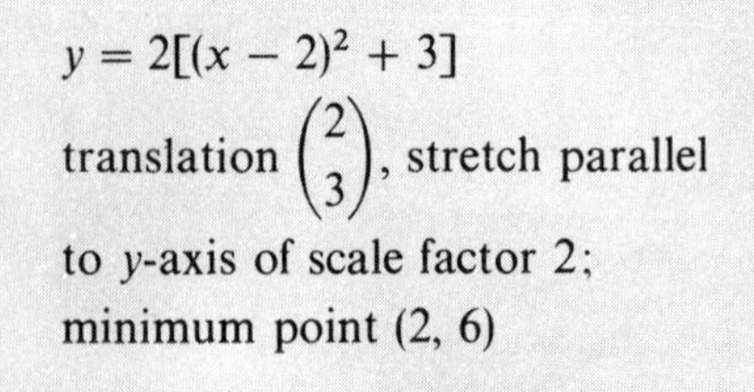

$y = 2[(x - 2)^2 + 3]$

translation $\begin{pmatrix} 2 \\ 3 \end{pmatrix}$, stretch parallel to y-axis of scale factor 2;

minimum point (2, 6)

3 $y = \frac{1}{2}[(x - 3)^2 - 4]$

translation $\begin{pmatrix} 3 \\ -4 \end{pmatrix}$,
stretch parallel to
y-axis of scale factor $\frac{1}{2}$;
minimum point $(3, -2)$

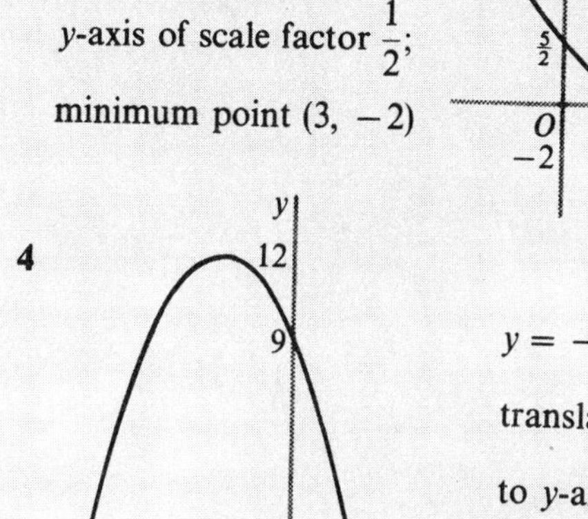

4

$y = -3[(x + 1)^2 - 4]$

translation $\begin{pmatrix} -1 \\ -4 \end{pmatrix}$, stretch parallel to y-axis of scale factor -3;
maximum point $(-1, 12)$

Exercise 9.1

Sketch the graph of each of the following, and state the coordinates of the maximum or minimum point.

1 $y = 2[(x + 1)^2 + 5]$

2 $y = 4[(x - 2)^2 - 1]$

3 $y = \frac{1}{3}[(x + 2)^2 - 4]$

4 $y = -3[(x - 4)^2 + 2]$

5 $y = \frac{3}{4}[(x - 1)^2 - 3]$

9.2 Completing the square

The methods of **9.1** may be applied to any graph; the graph of $y = a[f(x - d) + e]$ may be obtained from the graph of $y = f(x)$ by applying first the translation $\begin{pmatrix} d \\ e \end{pmatrix}$ and then a stretch parallel to the y-axis of scale factor a. The method is particularly useful for quadratics since *every* quadratic can be expressed in the form $a[(x - d)^2 + e]$. The process of changing a quadratic to this form uses the method of 'completing the square'. This method was used in simple cases in **5.2**.

Examples 9.2

Use the method of completing the square to express each of the following in the form $a[(x - d)^2 + e]$.

1 $y = x^2 - 8x + 4$

$y = (x - 4)^2 - 16 + 4 = (x - 4)^2 - 12$

2 $y = x^2 + 10x + 28$

$y = (x + 5)^2 - 25 + 28 = (x + 5)^2 + 3$

3 $y = 2x^2 - 12x + 5$

$$y = 2\left[x^2 - 6x + \frac{5}{2}\right] = 2\left[(x - 3)^2 - 9 + \frac{5}{2}\right] = 2\left[(x - 3)^2 - \frac{13}{2}\right]$$

4 $y = -3x^2 + 24x - 54$

$y = -3(x^2 - 8x + 18) = -3[(x - 4)^2 - 16 + 18] = -3[(x - 4)^2 + 2]$

5 $y = 2x^2 + 5x - 4$

$$y = 2\left(x^2 + \frac{5}{2}x - 2\right) = 2\left[\left(x + \frac{5}{4}\right)^2 - \frac{25}{16} - 2\right] = 2\left[\left(x + \frac{5}{4}\right)^2 - \frac{57}{16}\right]$$

Exercise 9.2

Use the method of completing the square to express each of the following in the form $a[(x - d)^2 + e]$, and hence sketch the graph of y in each case.

1 $y = x^2 + 4x + 5$

2 $y = x^2 - 6x + 14$

3 $y = x^2 - 4x + 2$

4 $y = x^2 - 6x + 4$

5 $y = 2x^2 + 12x + 3$

6 $y = 3x^2 - 6x + 4$

7 $y = -3x^2 + 6x - 4$

8 $y = 4x^2 - 5x + 2$

9.3 The general quadratic function

This is the function f defined for all real x by

$$f(x) = ax^2 + bx + c, \qquad a \neq 0.$$

Let $y = f(x)$; then by the method of completing the square,

$$y = a\left[x^2 + \frac{b}{a}x + \frac{c}{a}\right] = a\left[\left(x + \frac{b}{2a}\right)^2 - \frac{b^2 - 4ac}{4a^2}\right] \qquad (1$$

which is of the form $a[(x - d)^2 + e]$, so the graph of $y = f(x)$ may be obtained from the graph of $y = x^2$ by a translation followed by a stretch parallel to the y-axis.

The number $b^2 - 4ac$ is called the discriminant of f; this is because it discriminates between cases where y can, and cannot, be zero for real x. The discriminant is usually denoted by Δ.

Using the form (1) for f(x) gives $ax^2 + bx + c = 0$ for

$$x = \frac{\pm\sqrt{(b^2 - 4ac)} - b}{2a} = \frac{\pm\sqrt{\Delta} - b}{2a}$$

which is the formula for the roots of the quadratic equation, as obtained in **5.3**. The roots are real if and only if $\Delta \geqslant 0$.

Examples 9.3

Calculate the discriminant, Δ, of each of the following. State with reasons whether the graph of y crosses the x-axis, touches the x-axis, lies wholly above the x-axis or lies wholly below the x-axis.

1 $y = 3x^2 - 2x + 4$

2 $y = 2x^2 - 5x - 3$

3 $y = -5x^2 + 2x - 1$

4 $y = 9x^2 - 12x + 4$

1 $y = 3x^2 - 2x + 4$
$\Delta = 4 - 48 < 0$, so $y = 0$ for no real x
stretch factor $= 3 > 0$, so graph is wholly above x-axis

2 $y = 2x^2 - 5x - 3$
$\Delta = 25 + 24 > 0$, so $y = 0$ for two values of x
$\therefore$ graph crosses x-axis

3 $y = -5x^2 + 2x - 1$
$\Delta = 4 - 20 < 0$, so $y = 0$ for no real x
stretch factor $= -5 < 0$, so graph is wholly below x-axis

4 $y = 9x^2 - 12x + 4$
$\Delta = 144 - 144 = 0$, so $y = 0$ for one real value of x
$\therefore$ graph touches x-axis

Exercise 9.3

Calculate the discriminant, Δ, of each of the following. Indicate in a sketch the relative positions of the graph of y and the x-axis. No other detail need be shown.

1 $y = 2x^2 - 3x - 4$

2 $y = 2x^2 - 3x + 4$

3 $y = -3x^2 + 5x - 4$

4 $y = 4x^2 - 20x + 25$

9.4 Graphs of quadratics which can easily be factorised

The graph of any quadratic may be sketched by using the method of completing the square. Once the general shape of the quadratic graph is known, a simpler method is available in some cases, namely, those in which the quadratic can be factorised using integer coefficients in the factors.

Simple cases of irrational coefficients are also useful, for example, $x^2 - 3 = (x - \sqrt{3})(x + \sqrt{3})$.

Examples 9.4

Factorise the quadratic in each of the following, and hence sketch the graph of y. Find the coordinates of the maximum or minimum point.

1 $y = x^2 - 5x + 6$ **2** $y = 6x - x^2 - 8$ **3** $y = x^2 - 4x$

1 $y = x^2 - 5x + 6 = (x - 2)(x - 3)$

$\therefore$ the points of intersection of the graph with the axes are $(2, 0)$, $(3, 0)$ and $(0, 6)$. These three points and the known shape of the graph give the sketch shown.

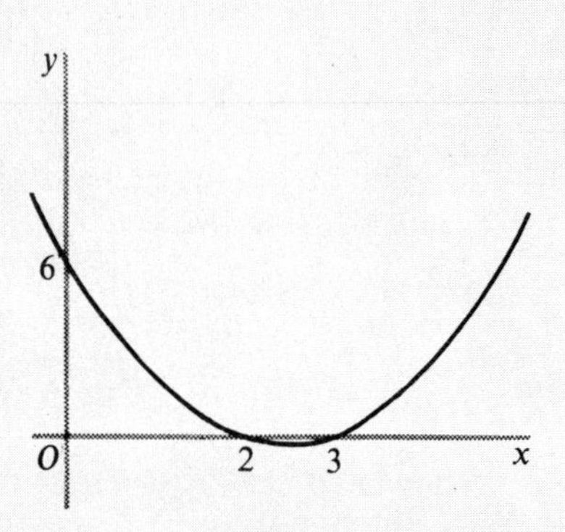

By symmetry the minimum point is at $x = \frac{2+3}{2} = \frac{5}{2}$;

$\therefore$ the point is $\left(\frac{5}{2}, -\frac{1}{4}\right)$

2

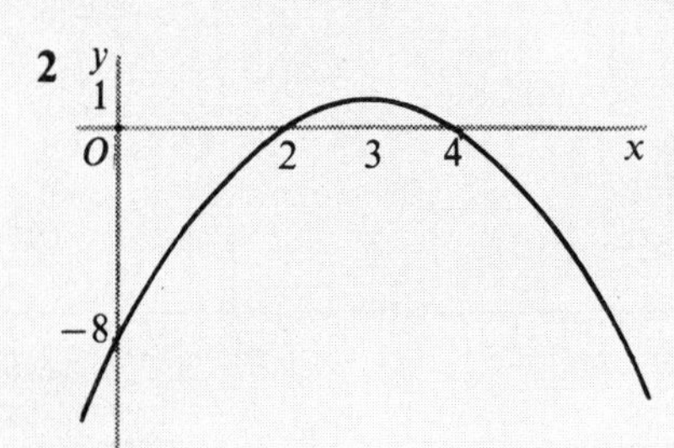

$y = 6x - x^2 - 8 = -(x^2 - 6x + 8)$
$= -(x-2)(x-4)$

$\therefore$ the points of intersection with the axes are $(2, 0)$, $(4, 0)$ and $(0, -8)$. The maximum point is $(3, 1)$.

3 $y = x^2 - 4x = x(x - 4)$

The points of intersection with the axes are $(0, 0)$ and $(4, 0)$, so that there are only two points of intersection with the axes. Since the scale factor is 1, two points suffice; or a third point could be used. The point $(2, -4)$ is the most useful, and is the minimum point.

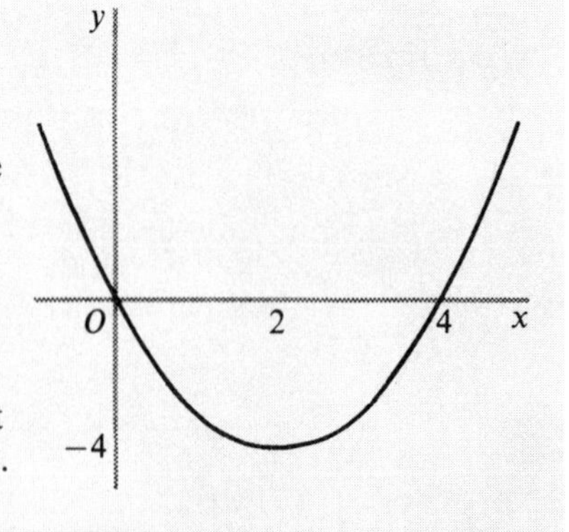

Exercise 9.4A

Factorise the quadratic in each of the following and hence sketch the graph of y. Find the coordinates of the maximum or minimum point.

1 $y = x^2 - 8x + 15$ **4** $y = 3 - x^2 + 2x$ **7** $y = 9 - x^2$

2 $y = x^2 - 4x - 12$ **5** $y = x^2 + 2x$ **8** $y = 3 - x^2$

3 $y = x^2 + 4x + 3$ **6** $y = 3x - x^2$

Exercise 9.4B

Factorise the quadratic in each of the following and hence sketch the graph of f(x). Given that the domain of f in each case is ℝ, find the range of f.

1 $f(x) = x^2 - 5x + 4$

2 $f(x) = x^2 + 3x - 10$

3 $f(x) = x^2 - 2x$

4 $f(x) = x^2 + 7x + 12$

5 $f(x) = 2x^2 - 9x + 4$

6 $f(x) = 3x^2 + x - 2$

7 $f(x) = 4x^2 + 9x + 2$

8 $f(x) = x^2 - 2$

9.5 Quadratics in which the domain is a subset of ℝ

In all the examples so far discussed in this chapter, the domain of the quadratic function has been ℝ. In such cases the range of the function is known when the y-coordinate of the maximum or minimum point has been found. In the examples which follow this is not the case.

Examples 9.5

Sketch the graph of each of the functions f defined on the given domains, and state the range of each function.

1 $f(x) = x^2 - 3x + 2, \quad 0 \leqslant x \leqslant 4$

2 $f(x) = 2x - x^2, \quad -2 \leqslant x \leqslant 3$

3 $f(x) = x^2 + 3, \quad 1 \leqslant x \leqslant 2$

1 $f(x) = x^2 - 3x + 2, \quad 0 \leqslant x \leqslant 4$

Let $y = f(x)$, then $y = (x - 1)(x - 2)$

The points of intersection with the axes are (1, 0), (2, 0) and (0, 2). Also $f(4) = 6$, and the graph is as shown.

The minimum point is $\left(\frac{3}{2}, -\frac{1}{4}\right)$;

the range is $\left\{y: -\frac{1}{4} \leqslant y \leqslant 6\right\}$.

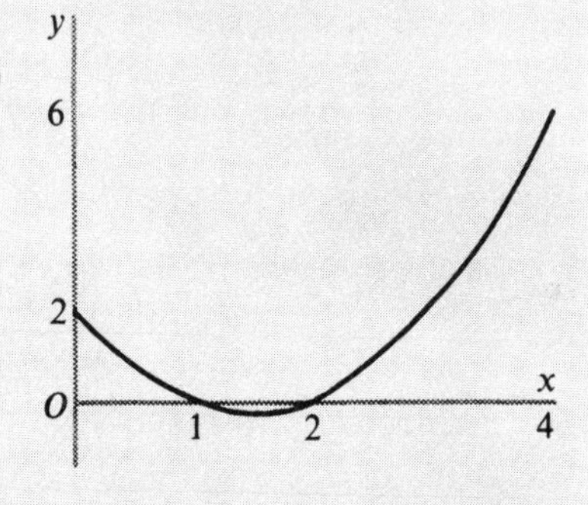

2

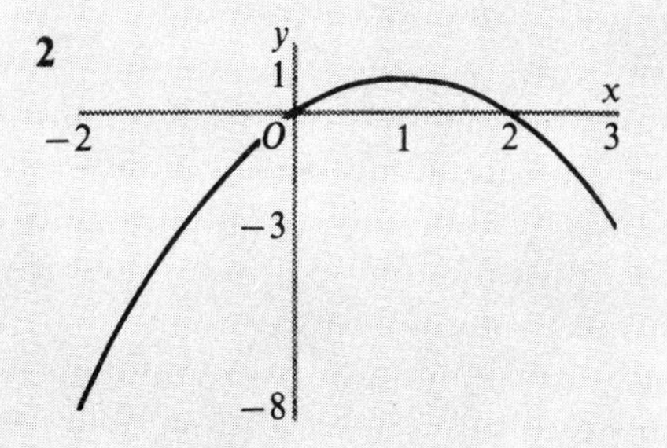

$f(x) = 2x - x^2, \quad -2 \leqslant x \leqslant 3$

Let $y = f(x)$, then $y = x(2 - x)$

The points of intersection with the axes are (0, 0) and (2, 0). Also $f(-2) = -8$, $f(3) = -3$, and the graph is as shown.

The maximum point is (1, 1); the range is $\{y: -8 \leqslant y \leqslant 1\}$.

3 $f(x) = x^2 + 3, \quad 1 \leqslant x \leqslant 2$

Let $y = x^2 + 3$; in this case y does not factorise, but the graph is easily sketched by applying the translation $\begin{pmatrix} 0 \\ 3 \end{pmatrix}$ to the graph of $y = x^2$. The graph is as shown for $-3 \leqslant x \leqslant 3$.

The graph of $y = f(x)$ is the part of this graph between the points $A(1, 4)$ and $B(2, 7)$, so the range of f is $\{y: 4 \leqslant y \leqslant 7\}$.

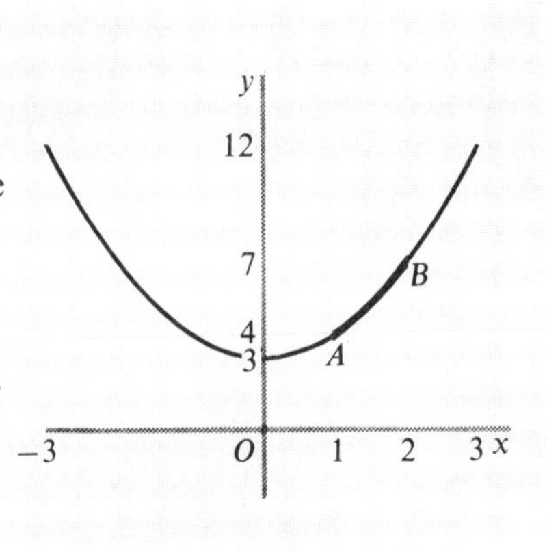

Exercise 9.5

Sketch the graph of each of the functions f defined on the given domains, and state the range of each function.

1 $f(x) = x^2 + 4x + 3, \quad -1 \leqslant x \leqslant 1$

2 $f(x) = x^2 - x - 6, \quad 1 \leqslant x \leqslant 4$

3 $f(x) = x^2 - 4, \quad -1 \leqslant x \leqslant 3$

4 $f(x) = 3x - x^2, \quad 0 \leqslant x \leqslant 4$

5 $f(x) = x^2 - 4x + 5, \quad -1 \leqslant x \leqslant 1$

9.6 Graphs of bilinear functions

A function f is bilinear if $f(x) = \dfrac{ax + b}{cx + d}$, where $c \neq 0$ and $ad \neq bc$.

The name 'bilinear' is used because two linear expressions are involved.

The domain of f can be any set of real numbers which excludes $-\dfrac{d}{c}$. In this chapter the domain of f will be all real numbers except $-\dfrac{d}{c}$ unless otherwise stated.

If $c = 0$ or $ad = bc$ then f reduces to a linear function.

The simplest bilinear function is the reciprocal function, given by $f(x) = \dfrac{1}{x}$.

This is the case $a = d = 0$, $b = c = 1$.

The graph of $y = \dfrac{1}{x}$ is shown in the diagram.

The curve has two axes of symmetry, the lines $y = x$ and $y = -x$. There are no maximum or minimum points.

As $|x|$ increases, $|y|$ decreases; the curve approaches the x-axis.

As $|x|$ decreases towards zero, $|y|$ increases; the curve approaches the y-axis. These facts may be written

$$\text{as } |x| \to \infty,\ |y| \to 0; \quad \text{as } |x| \to 0,\ |y| \to \infty.$$

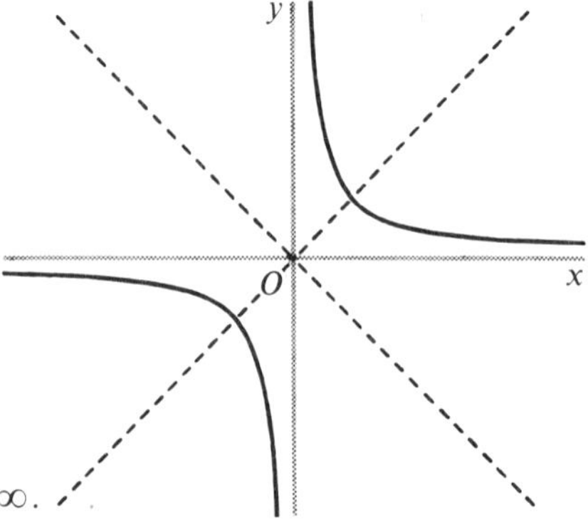

More precisely, using '0+' to mean 'zero through positive values':

as $x \to +\infty$, $y \to 0+$; as $x \to -\infty$, $y \to 0-$

as $x \to 0+$, $y \to +\infty$; as $x \to 0-$, $y \to -\infty$.

The axes are 'asymptotes' to the curve.
The name of the curve is a rectangular hyperbola.

Examples 9.6

By applying suitable transformations to the graph of $y = \frac{1}{x}$, sketch the graph of each of the following. Describe the transformations in the order in which they are used.

1 $y = \dfrac{x+1}{x-2}$ **2** $y = \dfrac{2x-3}{x+1}$

1 $y = \dfrac{x+1}{x-2} = 1 + \dfrac{3}{x-2}$ (or by long division)

A translation of $y = \frac{1}{x}$ using $\begin{pmatrix} 2 \\ 0 \end{pmatrix}$ gives $y = \dfrac{1}{x-2}$.

A stretch parallel to the y-axis of scale factor 3 gives $y = \dfrac{3}{x-2}$.

A translation of $\begin{pmatrix} 0 \\ 1 \end{pmatrix}$ gives $y = 1 + \dfrac{3}{x-2}$, as required.

Alternatively, a stretch parallel to the y-axis of scale factor 3 may be followed by a translation $\begin{pmatrix} 2 \\ 1 \end{pmatrix}$.

The transformations used map the asymptotes $y = 0$ and $x = 0$ to the lines $y = 1$ and $x = 2$ respectively; these are the asymptotes to the final graph.

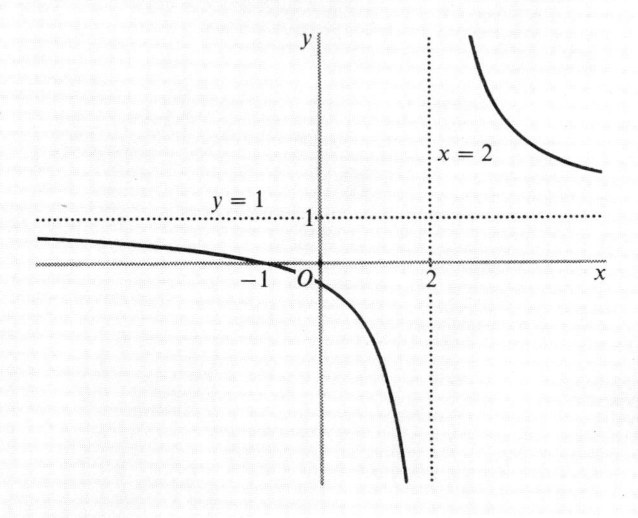

2 $y = \dfrac{2x-3}{x+1} = \dfrac{2(x+1)-5}{x+1} = 2 - \dfrac{5}{x+1}$

Apply to $y = \dfrac{1}{x}$ a translation $\begin{pmatrix}-1\\0\end{pmatrix}$, then a stretch parallel to the y-axis of scale factor -5, then a translation $\begin{pmatrix}0\\2\end{pmatrix}$.

These give in turn

$y = \dfrac{1}{x+1}$, $y = \dfrac{-5}{x+1}$, $y = 2 - \dfrac{5}{x+1}$.

Alternatively, the stretch may be used first, followed by the translation $\begin{pmatrix}-1\\2\end{pmatrix}$.

The asymptotes transform to $y = 2$, $x = -1$.

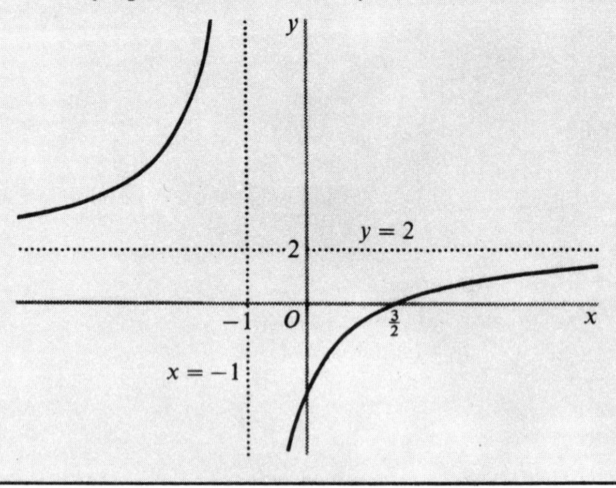

Exercise 9.6

By applying suitable transformations to the graph of $y = \dfrac{1}{x}$, sketch the graph of each of the following. Describe the transformations in the order in which they are used.

1 $y = \dfrac{x-1}{x+3}$ **2** $y = \dfrac{3x+2}{x-2}$ **3** $y = \dfrac{4-x}{x-1}$ **4** $y = \dfrac{2x-1}{x-3}$

9.7 The general bilinear function

It may be verified that for $c \neq 0$, $\dfrac{ax+b}{cx+d} = \dfrac{a}{c} + \left(\dfrac{bc-ad}{c^2}\right)\dfrac{1}{\left(x+\dfrac{d}{c}\right)}$

which is of the form $E + F\dfrac{1}{(x+G)}$ where $F \neq 0$ unless $ad = bc$.

This identity shows that the graph of any bilinear function may be obtained from the graph of $y = \frac{1}{x}$ by a translation parallel to the x-axis, followed by a stretch parallel to the y-axis, followed by a translation parallel to the y-axis.

Neither the translations nor the stretch change the general appearance of the graph, so that every bilinear function has a graph of similar appearance to those in Examples **9.6**. Each graph is a rectangular hyperbola.

Once this fact is known it may be used to sketch each graph directly, as in the following examples.

Examples 9.7

Sketch the graph of each of the following. State the coordinates of the points of intersection with the axes, and the equations of the asymptotes.

1 $y = \dfrac{x+4}{x-2}$ **2** $y = \dfrac{3-2x}{x+1}$ **3** $y = \dfrac{x-4}{2x-3}$

1 $y = \dfrac{x+4}{x-2}$

The points of intersection with the axes are $A(-4, 0)$, $B(0, -2)$.

y is undefined when $x = 2$; as $x \to 2+$, $y \to \infty$; as $x \to 2-$, $y \to -\infty$

$\therefore$ one asymptote is $x = 2$.

For *large* x, $x + 4 \approx x$ and $x - 2 \approx x$, so $y \approx \frac{x}{x} = 1$

$\therefore$ the second asymptote is $y = 1$.

(An alternative argument is: $y = \dfrac{1 + \frac{4}{x}}{1 - \frac{2}{x}}$, $\therefore$ as $x \to \infty$, $y \to 1$)

Using the points A and B, the asymptotes and the known shape of the graph give the sketch as shown.

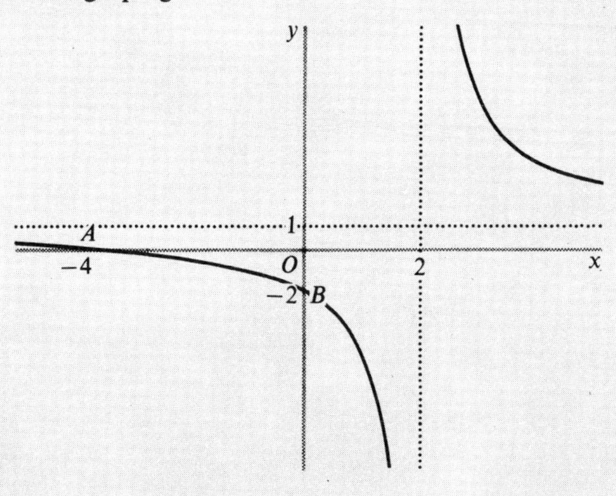

2 $y = \dfrac{3 - 2x}{x + 1}$

The points of intersection with the axes are $A\left(\dfrac{3}{2}, 0\right)$, $B(0, 3)$.

One asymptote is $x = -1$.

For large x, $y \approx \dfrac{-2x}{x} = -2$ $\therefore$ the other asymptote is $y = -2$.

The sketch is as shown.

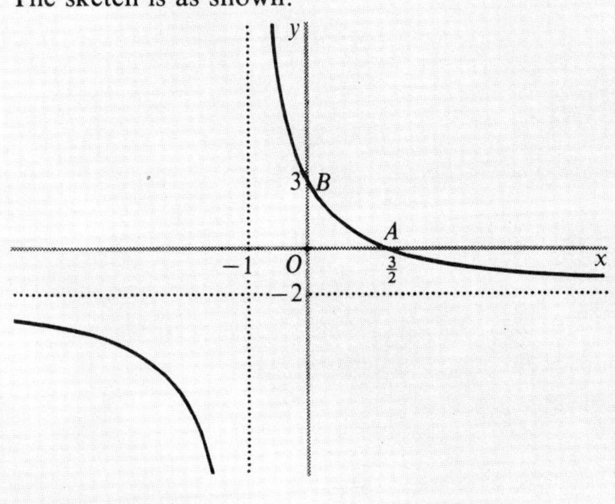

3 $y = \dfrac{x - 4}{2x - 3}$

The points of intersection with the axes are $A(4, 0)$, $B\left(0, \dfrac{4}{3}\right)$.

One asymptote is $x = \dfrac{3}{2}$; the other, by the usual method, is $y = \dfrac{1}{2}$. The sketch is as shown.

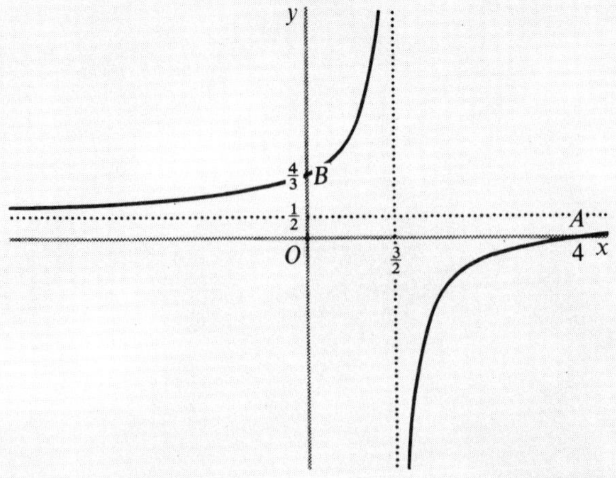

Exercise 9.7

Sketch the graph of each of the following. State the coordinates of the points of intersection with the axes and the equations of the asymptotes.

1 $y = \dfrac{x-3}{x-1}$ **3** $y = \dfrac{2x-1}{x+1}$ **5** $y = \dfrac{3x-2}{x+3}$

2 $y = \dfrac{x+2}{x-4}$ **4** $y = \dfrac{x-1}{3(x+2)}$ **6** $y = \dfrac{2-x}{x-1}$

9.8 Graphs of polynomials of degree $\geqslant 3$; some special cases

If n is an even integer, the graph of $y = x^n$ is of the form shown in Fig. 1. If n is an odd integer and $n \geqslant 3$, the graph is of the form shown in Fig. 2.

For all even values of n the graph is symmetrical about the y-axis. For all odd values of n the graph has half-turn rotational symmetry about the origin. As n increases the graphs become 'flatter' near the origin.

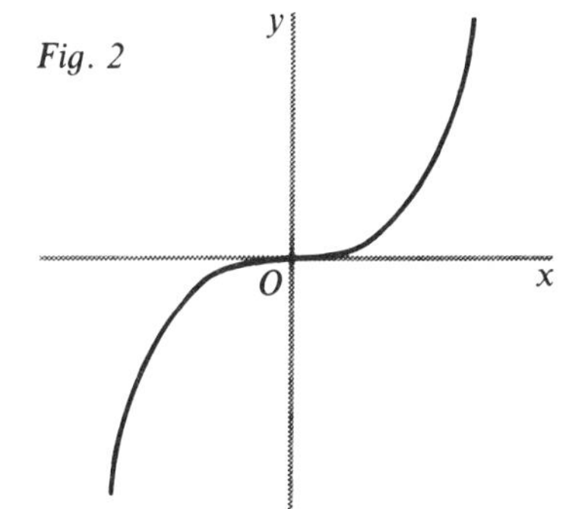

Fig. 2

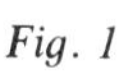
Fig. 1

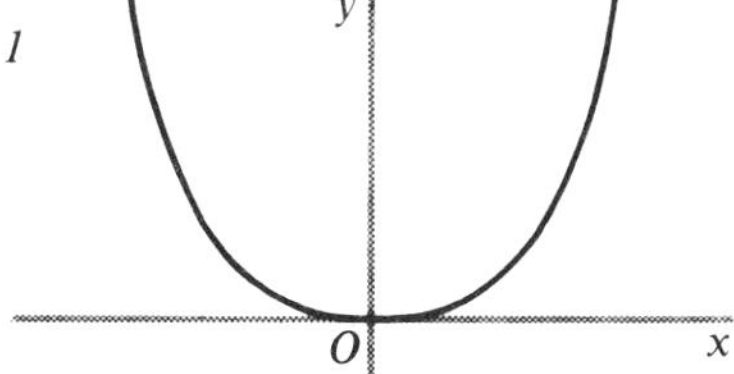

The graph of $y = a[(x-d)^n + e]$ may be sketched by applying a translation $\begin{pmatrix} d \\ e \end{pmatrix}$ to $y = x^n$, followed by a stretch parallel to the y-axis of scale factor a.

Examples 9.8

Sketch a graph of each of the following by applying suitable transformations to a simpler graph.

1 $y = 4[(x-1)^3 + 2]$

2 $y = -2[(x+1)^4 - 3]$

1 $y = 4[(x-1)^3 + 2]$

Apply the translation $\begin{pmatrix} 1 \\ 2 \end{pmatrix}$ to $y = x^3$, followed by a stretch parallel to the y-axis of scale factor 4.

The origin O is mapped to the point (1, 8).

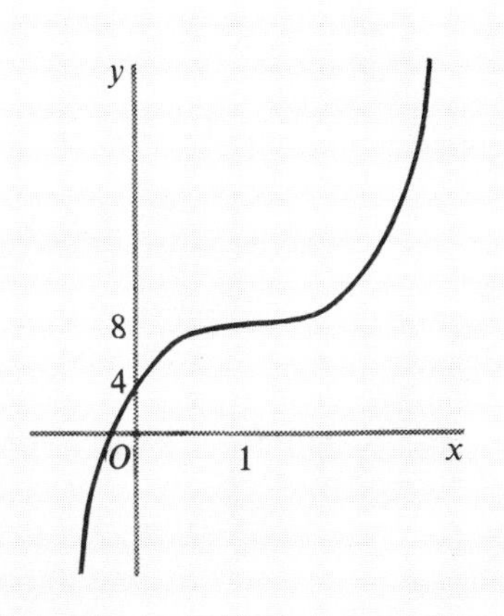

2 $y = -2[(x+1)^4 - 3]$

Apply the translation $\begin{pmatrix} -1 \\ -3 \end{pmatrix}$ to $y = x^4$, followed by *either* a stretch parallel to the y-axis of scale factor -2, *or* a reflection in the x-axis followed by a stretch parallel to the y-axis of scale factor 2.

The minimum point at O is mapped to a maximum point at $(-1, 6)$.

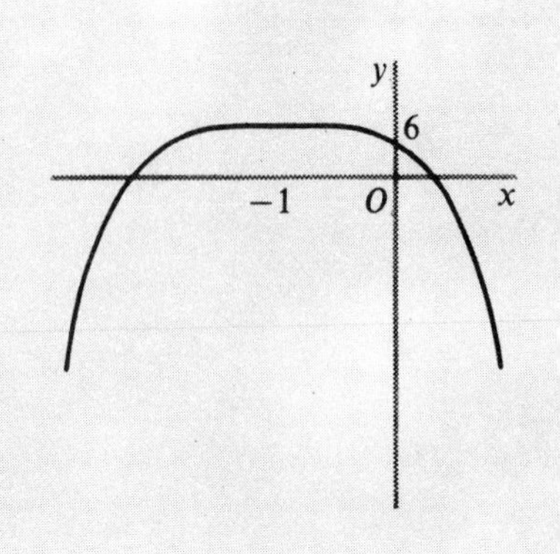

Exercise 9.8A

Sketch a graph of each of the following by applying suitable transformations to a simpler graph.

1 $y = (x+1)^4 - 2$

2 $y = (x-2)^5 + 4$

3 $y = 3[(x-2)^4 + 1]$

4 $y = -5[(x-1)^3 - 2]$

Exercise 9.8B

Apply the instruction of Exercise **9.8A** for each of the following.

1 $y = 2 - (x-1)^3$

2 $y = 3[(x+1)^4 + 2]$

3 $y = 4[3 - (x-2)^5]$

4 $y = -2[(x+1)^6 + 4]$

9.9 Some more polynomials

If a polynomial $f(x)$ of degree n has n distinct linear factors, then the graph of the corresponding polynomial function may be sketched by using the points of intersection with the axes and an approximation for large x. The coordinates of maximum and minimum points can be found only by using calculus; this method will be discussed in Chapter 12. The graphs of other types of polynomials will also be discussed in Chapter 12.

The graph of $f(|x|)$ and of $|f(x)|$

Given the graph of $f(x)$, the graph of $f(|x|)$ is easily sketched. For $x \geqslant 0$, the graph is identical with that of $f(x)$, since $|x| = x$ for $x \geqslant 0$. Also $|x|$ is not changed by changing the sign of x, and so $f(|x|)$ is also not changed, and the graph is symmetrical about the y-axis. So the graph of $f(|x|)$ for $x < 0$ is obtained by reflecting the graph for $x \geqslant 0$ in the y-axis.

The graph of $|f(x)|$ is identical with the graph of $f(x)$ at all points where $f(x) \geqslant 0$. At points where $f(x) < 0$, the graph of $f(x)$ must be reflected in the x-axis to give the graph of $|f(x)|$.

Examples 9.9

1 Sketch the graph of $y = (x + 2)(x - 1)(x - 3)$.

The points of intersection with the axes are $A(-2, 0)$, $B(1, 0)$, $C(3, 0)$, $D(0, 6)$. One of the factors of y changes sign at each of A, B and C, so the graph crosses the x-axis at each of these points.

For large x, $y \approx (x)(x)(x) = x^3$.

The framework shown in Fig. 3 can now be drawn, and the sketch can be completed as shown in Fig. 4.

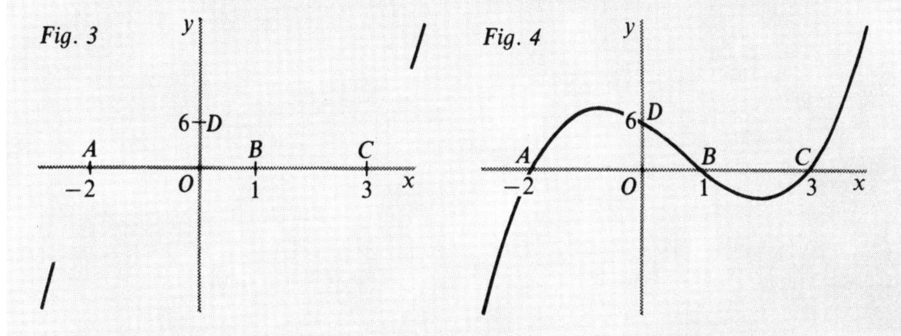

2 Given that $f(x) = (x + 2)(x - 1)(x - 3)$, sketch for $-3 \leqslant x \leqslant 3$ the graph of **a** $f(|x|)$ **b** $|f(x)|$.

a the graph of $f(x)$ is shown in Fig. 4. Reflecting this graph in the y-axis for $0 \leqslant x \leqslant 3$ gives the required graph, shown in Fig. 5.

b In Fig. 4, $y < 0$ for $-3 \leqslant x < -2$ and for $1 < x < 3$. Reflecting these parts of the graph in the x-axis gives the required graph, shown in Fig. 6.

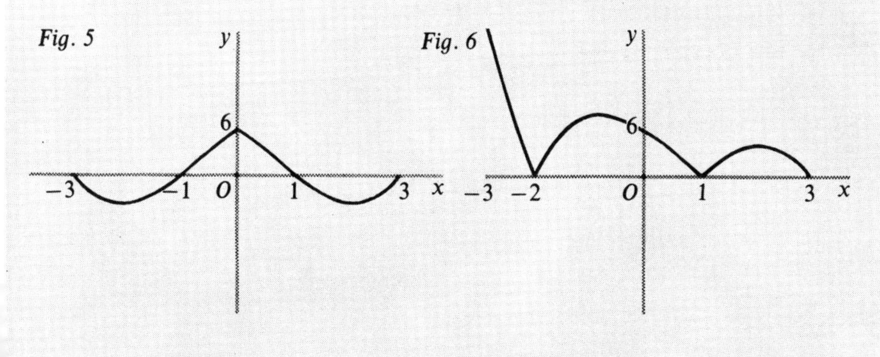

Exercise 9.9A

In questions **1–3**, sketch the graph of y. Show on the graph the coordinates of the points of intersection with the axes.

1 $y = (x + 3)(x - 2)(x - 4)$

2 $y = (x^2 - 4)(x^2 - 9)$

3 $y = x(x^2 - 9)(x^2 - 16)$

In questions **4–7**, sketch the graph of

a $f(x)$ **b** $f(|x|)$ **c** $|f(x)|$.

4 $f(x) = (x - 1)(x - 3)$

5 $f(x) = (x - 1)(x - 2)(x - 4)$

6 $f(x) = \dfrac{1}{x}$

7 $f(x) = \dfrac{1}{x - 2}$

Exercise 9.9B

In questions **1–3**, sketch the graph of y. Show on the graph the coordinates of the points of intersection with the axes.

1 $y = x(x - 2)(x + 2)$

2 $y = (x + 3)(x + 1)(2x - 1)$

3 $y = (x + 2)(x^2 - 9)(5x - 4)$

In questions **4–7**, sketch the graph of

a $f(x)$ **b** $f(|x|)$ **c** $|f(x)|$.

4 $f(x) = (x + 2)(x - 4)$

5 $f(x) = (x + 3)(x + 2)(x - 1)(x - 4)$

6 $f(x) = \dfrac{x - 2}{x - 4}$

7 $f(x) = \dfrac{1}{x^2} - 3$

Miscellaneous Exercise 9

1 In each of the following, express $f(x)$ as a product of linear factors and sketch the graph of $f(x)$.

a $3x^2 + 13x - 10$

b $5x - 2x^2$

c $9 - 4x^2$

d $x^3 - 2x^2 - x + 2$

e $9 + 9x - x^2 - x^3$

f $2x^3 - 5x^2 - 4x + 3$

2 Given that $f(x) = \dfrac{x + 2}{x - 3}$, $x \neq 3$, find $f^{-1}(x)$.

Sketch on the same diagram the graphs of $f(x)$ and $f^{-1}(x)$, labelling each graph clearly.

3 Given that $f(x) = \dfrac{2x + 5}{x - 3}$, $x \neq 3$, sketch the graph of $f(x)$. Hence sketch on the same axes the graph of $f^{-1}(x)$, labelling each graph clearly.

4 The function f is defined by $f(x) = \dfrac{x - a}{x - 1}$, $x \neq 1$.

Show that f is self-inverse for all values of the constant a except $a = 1$. Sketch the graph of $f(x)$ in the case $a = 2$.

5 The functions f and g are defined by

$f(x) = \dfrac{x + 2}{x - 1}$, $x \neq 1$; $g(x) = \dfrac{x + 1}{x - 3}$, $x \neq 3$.

Find $fg(x)$ and state its domain. Sketch in separate diagrams the graphs of $f(x)$, $g(x)$ and $fg(x)$.

6 Given that $f(x) = \dfrac{x - 1}{x - 4}$, $x \neq 4$, sketch the graph of

a $f(x)$ **b** $f(|x|)$ **c** $|f(x)|$.

7 Given that $f(x) = (x - 1)(x - 2)(x - 3)$, sketch the graph of $f(x)$. Hence sketch in separate diagrams the graphs of

a $(x - 3)(x - 4)(x - 5)$ **b** $(x - 1)(x - 2)(x - 3) + 2$

c $2(3 - x)(2 - x)(1 - x)$.

8 Sketch the graph of each of the following by applying suitable transformations to the graph of $y = 2^x$.

a $y = 2^{x-3}$ **b** $y = 2^{x-3} + 1$ **c** $y = 3(2^{x-1} - 4)$

9 Sketch the graph of each of the following by applying suitable transformations to the graph of $y = \log_2 x$.

a $y = \log_2(x - 4)$ **b** $y = \log_2\left(\dfrac{1}{x - 4}\right)$

c $y = \log_2[(x - 4)^3]$ **d** $y = \log_2[8(x - 4)^2]$

10 Given that $f(x) = \dfrac{ax + b}{cx + d}$, $g(x) = \dfrac{px + q}{rx + s}$, find $fg(x)$.

Given that $\mathbf{M} = \begin{pmatrix} a & b \\ c & d \end{pmatrix}$, $\mathbf{N} = \begin{pmatrix} p & q \\ r & s \end{pmatrix}$, find $\mathbf{MN}$.

Find also $gf(x)$ and $\mathbf{NM}$. Comment on your results.

11 Given that $f(x) = \dfrac{ax + b}{cx + d}$ find $f^{-1}(x)$.

Given that $\mathbf{M} = \begin{pmatrix} a & b \\ c & d \end{pmatrix}$ and that $ad - bc = 1$, find $\mathbf{M}^{-1}$.

Given that $\mathbf{N} = \begin{pmatrix} a & b \\ c & d \end{pmatrix}$ and that $ad - bc \neq 0$, find $\mathbf{N}^{-1}$.

Comment on your results.

Chapter 10

Trigonometry 2

10.1 The addition formulae for cosines and sines

These are formulae for the cosine and sine of the sum (and difference) of two angles. Clearly $\cos(\alpha + \beta)$ is not the sum of $\cos \alpha$ and $\cos \beta$; replacing α by 60° and β by 30° is sufficient evidence of this. The following formulae will be proved for all angles α, β:

$$\cos(\alpha + \beta) = \cos \alpha \cos \beta - \sin \alpha \sin \beta \qquad (1)$$
$$\cos(\alpha - \beta) = \cos \alpha \cos \beta + \sin \alpha \sin \beta \qquad (2)$$
$$\sin(\alpha + \beta) = \sin \alpha \cos \beta + \cos \alpha \sin \beta \qquad (3)$$
$$\sin(\alpha - \beta) = \sin \alpha \cos \beta - \cos \alpha \sin \beta. \qquad (4)$$

Formula (2) is proved first. The points A and B in the diagram have polar coordinates $(1, \alpha)$ and $(1, \beta)$ respectively.

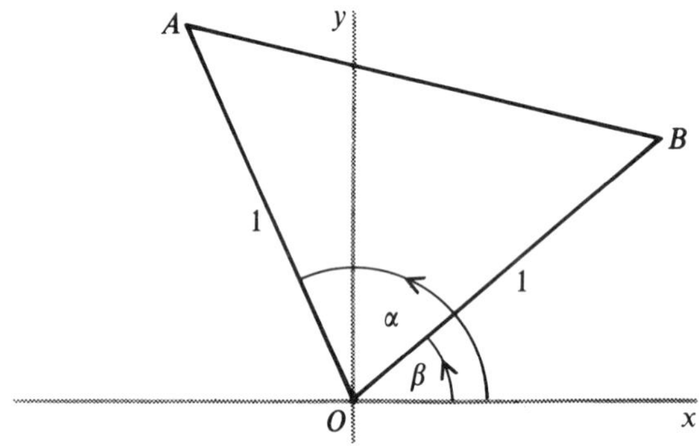

Then by the cosine rule in the triangle OAB:

$$\begin{aligned} AB^2 &= 1 + 1 - 2\cos(\alpha - \beta) \\ &= 2 - 2\cos(\alpha - \beta). \end{aligned}$$

In Cartesian coordinates A is $(\cos \alpha, \sin \alpha)$ and B is $(\cos \beta, \sin \beta)$; therefore by the distance formula

$$\begin{aligned} AB^2 &= (\cos \alpha - \cos \beta)^2 + (\sin \alpha - \sin \beta)^2 \\ &= \cos^2\alpha - 2\cos \alpha \cos \beta + \cos^2\beta + \sin^2\alpha - 2\sin \alpha \sin \beta + \sin^2\beta \\ &= 2 - 2(\cos \alpha \cos \beta + \sin \alpha \sin \beta). \end{aligned}$$

Comparing the two forms of AB^2 gives

$$\cos(\alpha - \beta) = \cos \alpha \cos \beta + \sin \alpha \sin \beta,$$

which is (2).

The proof applies for all angles α and β; if α and β are such that $180° < \alpha - \beta < 360°$, then the angle at O in the triangle OAB is $360° - (\alpha - \beta)$, and the proof is unchanged. If $\alpha < \beta$, the angle AOB is $\beta - \alpha$ and the proof is unchanged.

To prove (1), replace β by $-\beta$ in (2), giving

$$\cos(\alpha + \beta) = \cos \alpha \cos(-\beta) + \sin \alpha \sin(-\beta)$$

$$\therefore \cos(\alpha + \beta) = \cos \alpha \cos \beta - \sin \alpha \sin \beta. \qquad (1)$$

To prove (3), replace α by $90° - \alpha$ in (2), giving

$$\cos(90° - \alpha - \beta) = \cos(90° - \alpha) \cos \beta + \sin(90° - \alpha) \sin \beta$$

$$\therefore \sin(\alpha + \beta) = \sin \alpha \cos \beta + \cos \alpha \sin \beta. \qquad (3)$$

To prove (4), replace β by $-\beta$ in (3), giving

$$\sin(\alpha - \beta) = \sin \alpha \cos(-\beta) + \cos \alpha \sin(-\beta)$$

$$\therefore \sin(\alpha - \beta) = \sin \alpha \cos \beta - \cos \alpha \sin \beta. \qquad (4)$$

The addition formulae for tangents

These are

$$\tan(\alpha + \beta) = \frac{\tan \alpha + \tan \beta}{1 - \tan \alpha \tan \beta} \qquad (5)$$

$$\tan(\alpha - \beta) = \frac{\tan \alpha - \tan \beta}{1 + \tan \alpha \tan \beta}. \qquad (6)$$

Proof of (5):

$$\tan(\alpha + \beta) = \frac{\sin(\alpha + \beta)}{\cos(\alpha + \beta)}$$

$$= \frac{\sin \alpha \cos \beta + \cos \alpha \sin \beta}{\cos \alpha \cos \beta - \sin \alpha \sin \beta}. \qquad \text{by (3) and (1)}$$

Dividing each term in the numerator and in the denominator by $\cos \alpha \cos \beta$ gives

$$\tan(\alpha + \beta) = \frac{\dfrac{\sin \alpha}{\cos \alpha} + \dfrac{\sin \beta}{\cos \beta}}{1 - \dfrac{\sin \alpha \sin \beta}{\cos \alpha \cos \beta}}$$

$$= \frac{\tan \alpha + \tan \beta}{1 - \tan \alpha \tan \beta},$$

and the proof is complete.

Replacing β by $-\beta$ in (5) gives (6).

Formulae (5) and (6) are true for all angles α and β for which each side is defined; for example, (5) is true for angles α, β for which $\alpha + \beta$ is not an odd multiple of 90°. In particular, the left-hand side is not defined if $\alpha + \beta = 90°$; in this case, $\tan \alpha = \cot \beta$, $\tan \alpha \tan \beta = 1$, and the right-hand side is also not defined.

Examples 10.1

1 Express $\frac{1}{2}\cos\theta + \frac{\sqrt{3}}{2}\sin\theta$ as a single cosine.

$$\frac{1}{2} = \cos 60°, \qquad \frac{\sqrt{3}}{2} = \sin 60°$$

$$\therefore \frac{1}{2}\cos\theta + \frac{\sqrt{3}}{2}\sin\theta = \cos 60° \cos\theta + \sin 60° \sin\theta$$
$$= \cos(60° - \theta)$$

2 Find the exact value of sin 75°.

$$\sin 75° = \sin(45° + 30°)$$
$$= \sin 45° \cos 30° + \cos 45° \sin 30°$$
$$= \frac{1}{\sqrt{2}}\cdot\frac{\sqrt{3}}{2} + \frac{1}{\sqrt{2}}\cdot\frac{1}{2}$$
$$= \frac{\sqrt{3}+1}{2\sqrt{2}}$$

3 Given that $\tan(\alpha + \beta) = 3$ and that $\tan\beta = \frac{2}{3}$, find the exact value of $\tan\alpha$.

$$\tan(\alpha + \beta) = 3$$
$$\therefore \frac{\tan\alpha + \tan\beta}{1 - \tan\alpha\tan\beta} = 3$$
$$\therefore \tan\alpha + \tan\beta = 3(1 - \tan\alpha\tan\beta)$$

Also $\tan\beta = \frac{2}{3}$

$$\therefore \tan\alpha + \frac{2}{3} = 3 - 2\tan\alpha$$
$$\therefore 9\tan\alpha = 7$$
$$\tan\alpha = \frac{7}{9}$$

4 Solve the equation $\sin(\theta + 30°) = 2\cos\theta$, giving solutions between $-180°$ and $180°$.

$$\sin(\theta + 30°) = 2\cos\theta$$
$$\therefore \sin\theta\cos 30° + \cos\theta\sin 30° = 2\cos\theta$$
$$\therefore \frac{\sqrt{3}}{2}\sin\theta + \frac{1}{2}\cos\theta = 2\cos\theta$$

$\therefore \sqrt{3} \sin \theta = 3 \cos \theta$

$\therefore \tan \theta = \sqrt{3}$

$\therefore \theta = 60° \text{ or } -120°$

5 Given that $\cos \alpha = \frac{3}{5}$ and $\sin \alpha < 0$, and also that $\cos \beta = \frac{5}{13}$, find as fractions the possible values of $\cos(\alpha + \beta)$.

$\cos(\alpha + \beta) = \cos \alpha \cos \beta - \sin \alpha \sin \beta$

$\therefore$ we have to find $\sin \alpha$ and $\sin \beta$.

$\sin^2\alpha = 1 - \cos^2\alpha = \frac{16}{25}$, and $\sin \alpha < 0$

$\therefore \sin \alpha = -\frac{4}{5}$

$\sin^2\beta = 1 - \cos^2\beta = \frac{144}{169}$

$\therefore \sin \beta = \pm\frac{12}{13}$

$\therefore \cos(\alpha + \beta) = \frac{3}{5} \cdot \frac{5}{13} - \left(-\frac{4}{5} \cdot \frac{12}{13}\right) = \frac{63}{65}$

or $\cos(\alpha + \beta) = \frac{3}{5} \cdot \frac{5}{13} - \left(-\frac{4}{5}\right) \cdot \left(-\frac{12}{13}\right) = -\frac{33}{65}$

$\therefore$ the possible values are $\frac{63}{65}$ and $-\frac{33}{65}$.

6 Prove that $\dfrac{\cos(\alpha - \beta) - \cos(\alpha + \beta)}{\sin(\alpha + \beta) - \sin(\alpha - \beta)} = \tan \alpha$.

$$\text{L.H.S.} = \frac{\cos \alpha \cos \beta + \sin \alpha \sin \beta - \cos \alpha \cos \beta + \sin \alpha \sin \beta}{\sin \alpha \cos \beta + \cos \alpha \sin \beta - \sin \alpha \cos \beta + \cos \alpha \sin \beta}$$

$$= \frac{2 \sin \alpha \sin \beta}{2 \cos \alpha \sin \beta} = \tan \alpha = \text{R.H.S.}$$

Exercise 10.1A

In questions **1**–**7** find a single cosine, sine or tangent equal to the given expression.

1 $\cos 30° \cos 50° + \sin 30° \sin 50°$

2 $\sin 70° \cos 20° - \cos 70° \sin 20°$

3 $\cos 80° \cos 20° - \cos 10° \cos 70°$

4 $\dfrac{\tan 40° + \tan 15°}{1 - \tan 40° \tan 15°}$

5 $\dfrac{1 + \tan 25°}{1 - \tan 25°}$

6 $\dfrac{1 + \sqrt{3} \tan \theta}{\sqrt{3} - \tan \theta}$

7 $\dfrac{1}{\sqrt{2}} \cos \theta + \dfrac{1}{\sqrt{2}} \sin \theta$

8 Find the exact value of
a $\cos 15°$ **b** $\tan 75°$ **c** $\sin 165°$ **d** $\cos 105°$.

9 Given that $\tan(\alpha - \beta) = 4$ and that $\tan \beta = \frac{3}{4}$, find the exact value of $\tan \alpha$.

In questions **10–12** solve the equation, giving solutions between $-180°$ and $180°$ and correct to one d.p. when not exact.

10 $\cos(\theta - 60°) = \sqrt{3} \sin \theta$

11 $\sin(\theta - 45°) = \sqrt{2} \sin \theta$

12 $\tan(\theta + 45°) = 6 \tan \theta$

13 Given that $\sin \alpha = \frac{12}{13}$, $\cos \beta = \frac{4}{5}$, $\cos \alpha < 0$ and $\sin \beta > 0$, calculate $\sin(\alpha - \beta)$ as a fraction.

In questions **14–17** prove the given identity.

14 $\sin(\alpha + \beta) - \sin(\alpha - \beta) = 2 \cos \alpha \sin \beta$

15 $\cos \alpha \cos \beta(\tan \alpha - \tan \beta) = \sin(\alpha - \beta)$

16 $\cot(\alpha + \beta) = \dfrac{\cot \alpha \cot \beta - 1}{\cot \alpha + \cot \beta}$

17 $\dfrac{\sin(\alpha + \beta) + \sin(\alpha - \beta)}{\cos(\alpha + \beta) + \cos(\alpha - \beta)} = \tan \alpha$

Exercise 10.1B

1 Find the exact value of
a $\sin 75°$ **b** $\tan 15°$ **c** $\cos 165°$.

2 Given that $\tan \alpha = \frac{1}{4}$ and that $\sec \beta = \frac{5}{4}$, calculate the possible values of $\tan(\alpha + \beta)$ in fractional form.

In questions **3–5** solve the equation, giving solutions between $-180°$ and $180°$ and correct to one d.p. when not exact.

3 $2 \sin(\theta - 30°) = \cos \theta$

4 $\cos(\theta - 20°) = 2 \cos \theta$

5 $\sin(\theta + 50°) = 3 \sin(\theta - 50°)$

6 Given that $\cos \alpha = \frac{2}{3}$, $\sin \beta = \frac{1}{\sqrt{5}}$, and that $\sin \alpha > 0$, find the possible values of $\cos \beta$ and $\cos(\alpha - \beta)$ in surd form.

In questions **7–11** prove the given identity.

7 $\cos(\alpha - \beta) - \cos(\alpha + \beta) = 2 \sin \alpha \sin \beta$

8 $\sin \alpha \sin \beta(\cot \alpha + \cot \beta) = \sin(\alpha + \beta)$

9 $\sin(\alpha - \beta) + 2 \sin \alpha + \sin(\alpha + \beta) = 2 \sin \alpha(\cos \beta + 1)$

10 $\tan(\theta - 45°) + \tan(\theta + 45°) = 2 \tan 2\theta$

11 $\cos \theta + \cos(\theta + 120°) + \cos(\theta - 120°) = 0$

10.2 The double angle formulae

A 'double angle' formula is a convenient term for a formula involving the angle 2θ. Such formulae follow directly from the addition formulae by replacing each of α and β by θ. Formulae (1), (3) and (5) give

$$\cos 2\theta = \cos^2\theta - \sin^2\theta \qquad (7)$$

$$\sin 2\theta = 2 \sin \theta \cos \theta \qquad (8)$$

$$\tan 2\theta = \frac{2 \tan \theta}{1 - \tan^2\theta}. \qquad (9)$$

(Formulae (2), (4) and (6) give no new information.)

Formulae (7), (8) and (9) are the main double angle formulae. Formula (7) can be written in two alternative forms; the identity $\cos^2\theta + \sin^2\theta = 1$ gives

$$\sin^2\theta = 1 - \cos^2\theta, \qquad \cos^2\theta = 1 - \sin^2\theta,$$

$$\therefore \cos 2\theta = 2 \cos^2\theta - 1 \qquad (10)$$

$$\cos 2\theta = 1 - 2 \sin^2\theta. \qquad (11)$$

The last two formulae may be rearranged to give

$$\cos^2\theta = \frac{1}{2}(1 + \cos 2\theta) \qquad (12)$$

$$\sin^2\theta = \frac{1}{2}(1 - \cos 2\theta). \qquad (13)$$

Formulae (7) and (8) may be used to obtain expressions for $\cos 2\theta$ and $\sin 2\theta$ in terms of $\tan \theta$:

$$\begin{aligned} \cos 2\theta &= \cos^2\theta - \sin^2\theta \\ &= \cos^2\theta(1 - \tan^2\theta) \\ &= \frac{1 - \tan^2\theta}{\sec^2\theta} \\ &= \frac{1 - \tan^2\theta}{1 + \tan^2\theta} \end{aligned}$$

and similarly $\sin 2\theta = \dfrac{2 \tan \theta}{1 + \tan^2\theta}$.

These two formulae and formula (9) are often written as 'half angle' formulae, by replacing 2θ by θ; writing t for $\tan \dfrac{\theta}{2}$ gives

$$\cos \theta = \frac{1 - t^2}{1 + t^2} \qquad (14)$$

$$\sin \theta = \frac{2t}{1 + t^2} \qquad (15)$$

$$\tan \theta = \frac{2t}{1 - t^2}. \qquad (16)$$

Examples 10.2

1 Given that $\sin\theta = \frac{2}{3}$, find in surd form the possible values of $\cos\theta$ and $\sin 2\theta$.

Using $\cos^2\theta = 1 - \sin^2\theta$ gives

$$\cos^2\theta = 1 - \frac{4}{9} = \frac{5}{9}$$

$$\therefore \cos\theta = \pm\frac{\sqrt{5}}{3}$$

Using $\sin 2\theta = 2\sin\theta\cos\theta$ gives

$$\sin 2\theta = \pm\frac{4\sqrt{5}}{9}.$$

2 Solve the equation $3\sin 2\theta = 2\sin\theta$ for $-180° < \theta \leqslant 180°$; give the solutions correct to one d.p. when not exact.

Method 1 $3\sin 2\theta = 2\sin\theta$

$$\therefore 6\sin\theta\cos\theta - 2\sin\theta = 0$$

$$\therefore \sin\theta(3\cos\theta - 1) = 0$$

$$\therefore \sin\theta = 0 \text{ or } \cos\theta = \frac{1}{3}$$

$$\theta = 0°, 180°, \pm 70.5°$$

Method 2 $3\sin 2\theta = 2\sin\theta$

$$\therefore 6\sin\theta\cos\theta = 2\sin\theta$$

$\therefore \sin\theta = 0$ or $3\cos\theta = 1$ and then as above.

Note: in using method 2 it is essential not to cancel $\sin\theta$ from both sides of the equation without at the same time noting that $\sin\theta = 0$ satisfies the equation.

3 Solve the equation $3\cos 2\theta + \cos\theta + 2 = 0$ for $-180° < \theta \leqslant 180°$; give the solutions correct to one d.p. when not exact.

$$3\cos 2\theta + \cos\theta + 2 = 0$$

Since the equation contains $\cos\theta$ the method most likely to help is to replace $\cos 2\theta$ by $2\cos^2\theta - 1$, using (10).

This gives

$$3(2\cos^2\theta - 1) + \cos\theta + 2 = 0$$

$$\therefore 6\cos^2\theta + \cos\theta - 1 = 0$$

$$\therefore (3\cos\theta - 1)(2\cos\theta + 1) = 0$$

$$\cos\theta = \frac{1}{3} \text{ or } -\frac{1}{2}$$

$$\therefore \theta = \pm 70.5° \text{ or } \pm 120°.$$

4 Prove the identity $\cos 3\theta = 4\cos^3\theta - 3\cos\theta$.

$$\begin{aligned}\text{L.H.S.} &= \cos(2\theta + \theta)\\ &= \cos 2\theta \cos\theta - \sin 2\theta \sin\theta\\ &= (2\cos^2\theta - 1)\cos\theta - 2\sin\theta\cos\theta\sin\theta\\ &= 2\cos^3\theta - \cos\theta - 2(1-\cos^2\theta)\cos\theta\\ &= 4\cos^3\theta - 3\cos\theta\\ &= \text{R.H.S.}\end{aligned}$$

5 Given that $\tan\theta = \dfrac{12}{5}$ find in fractional form the possible values of $\tan\dfrac{\theta}{2}$.

Writing t for $\tan\dfrac{\theta}{2}$, $\tan\theta = \dfrac{2t}{1-t^2}$

$$\therefore \frac{2t}{1-t^2} = \frac{12}{5}$$

$$10t = 12 - 12t^2$$

$$6t^2 + 5t - 6 = 0$$

$$(3t-2)(2t+3) = 0$$

$$t = \frac{2}{3} \text{ or } -\frac{3}{2}$$

$$\therefore \tan\frac{\theta}{2} = \frac{2}{3} \text{ or } -\frac{3}{2}.$$

Exercise 10.2A

1 Write down exact values for

a $2\sin 75° \cos 75°$

b $\dfrac{2\tan 15°}{1-\tan^2 15°}$

c $1 - 2\sin^2 22\tfrac{1}{2}°$

d $\cos^2 67\tfrac{1}{2}°$

e $\tan 15° \cos^2 15°$

f $\dfrac{1-\tan^2 75°}{1+\tan^2 75°}$.

2 Given that $\cos\theta = \dfrac{3}{5}$, find in fractional form the possible values of $\sin\theta$, $\tan\theta$ and $\tan 2\theta$.

3 Given that $\tan\theta = \dfrac{2}{3}$, find the possible values of $\sin 2\theta$ in fractional form.

In questions **4**–**7** solve the given equation for $-180° < \theta \leqslant 180°$, giving the solutions correct to one d.p. when not exact.

4 $\sin 2\theta = \sqrt{3} \cos \theta$

5 $3 \cos 2\theta + 8 \sin \theta + 5 = 0$

6 $3 \tan 2\theta + 2 \tan \theta = 0$

7 $\cos 2\theta + 3 \cos \theta = 1$

8 Obtain an equation in x and y by eliminating θ.

a $x = \sin \theta,\ y = \cos 2\theta$ **b** $x = \tan \theta,\ y = \tan 2\theta$

c $x = \tan \dfrac{\theta}{2},\ y = \cos \theta$

9 Given that $t = \tan \dfrac{\theta}{2}$, express each of the following as a single fraction in terms of t.

a $1 + \cos \theta$ **b** $1 + \sin \theta$ **c** $1 - \sin \theta$

In questions **10**–**13** prove the given identities.

10 $\dfrac{\sin \alpha}{\cos \beta} + \dfrac{\cos \alpha}{\sin \beta} = \dfrac{2 \cos(\alpha - \beta)}{\sin 2\beta}$

11 $\tan \theta + \cot \theta = \dfrac{2}{\sin 2\theta}$

12 $\dfrac{\sin 2\theta}{1 + \cos 2\theta} = \tan \theta$

13 $\dfrac{\sin 4\theta}{\sin \theta} = 4 \cos \theta(\cos^2\theta - \sin^2\theta)$

Exercise 10.2B

1 Given that $\sin \theta = \dfrac{5}{13}$ and that $90° < \theta < 180°$, find the exact values of $\cos \theta$, $\sin 2\theta$ and $\cos 2\theta$.

2 Given that $\tan \theta = -\dfrac{3}{4}$ and that $-90° < \theta < 0°$, find the exact values of $\sec \theta$, $\sin \theta$ and $\sin 2\theta$.

In questions **3**–**7** solve the given equation for $-180° < \theta \leqslant 180°$, giving the solutions correct to one d.p. when not exact.

3 $4 \sin 2\theta = \sin \theta$

4 $\cos 2\theta + 2 \cos \theta + 1 = 0$

5 $\cos 2\theta = 5 \sin \theta + 3$

6 $2 \tan 2\theta = 5 \tan \theta$

7 $2 \tan 2\theta + 2 \sec 2\theta = 1$

8 Find an equation in x and y by eliminating θ.

a $x = 2 \cos \theta,\ y = \cos 2\theta$ **b** $x = \cot \theta,\ y = \tan 2\theta$

c $x = \tan \theta,\ y = \sin 2\theta$

In questions **9–13** prove the given identities.

9 $\cos^4\theta - \sin^4\theta = \cos 2\theta$

10 $\dfrac{1 - \cos 2\theta}{\sin 2\theta} = \tan\theta$

11 $\dfrac{\sin 2\theta}{\sin\theta} + \dfrac{\cos 2\theta}{\cos\theta} = \dfrac{2\sin 3\theta}{\sin 2\theta}$

12 $\sin 3\theta = 3\sin\theta - 4\sin^3\theta$

13 $\tan 3\theta = \dfrac{3\tan\theta - \tan^3\theta}{1 - 3\tan^2\theta}$

10.3 Circular measure: radians

In this course until now, and in earlier work, angles have been measured in degrees. The definition of a degree is that 360 degrees make one complete revolution; the use of the number 360 derives from the Babylonians many centuries B.C.

Another unit for measuring angles, the radian, is now introduced. The great advantage of using radians is that all results involving the calculus of trigonometric functions are much simplified.

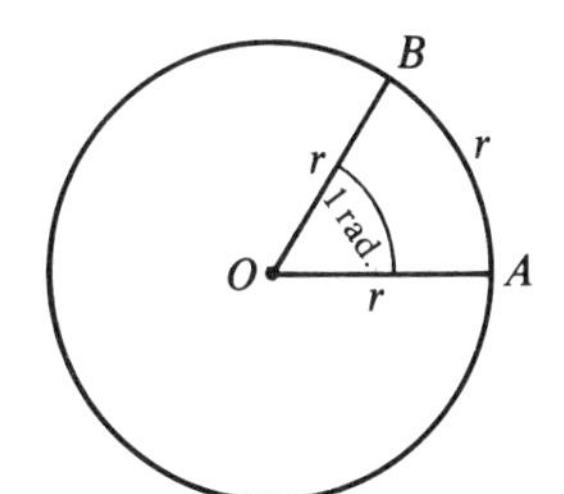

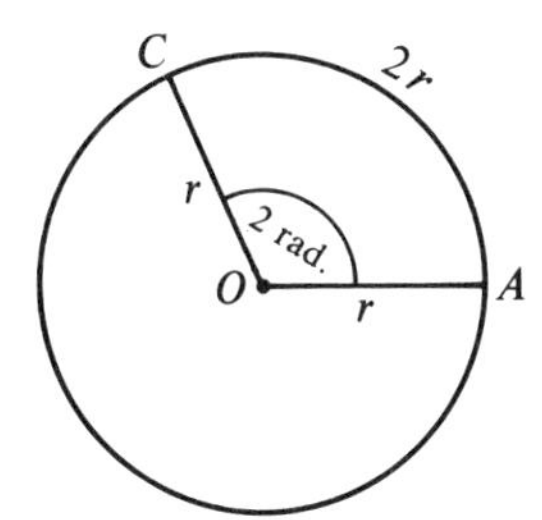

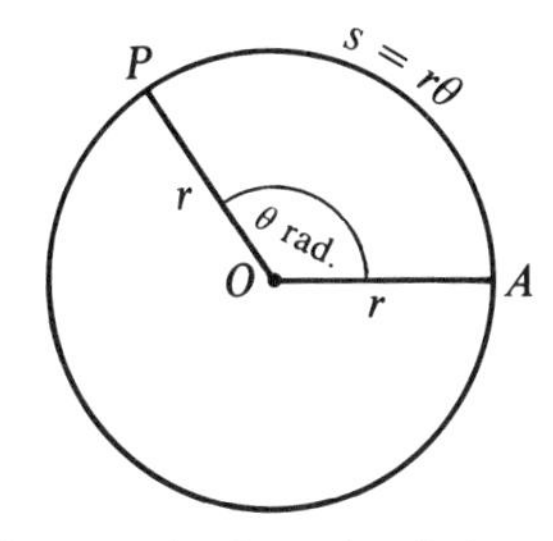

In each diagram above, the circle has centre O and radius r. The length of the *arc AB* is also r. Then the angle AOB is *one radian*. An arc AC of length $2r$ gives the angle AOC as 2 radians, and in general an arc AP of length θr gives the angle AOP as θ radians, where θ is a *number*. This number is called the 'radian measure' of the angle. For the remainder of this chapter the symbol θ denotes a number, not an angle as it has until now.

The symbol s is commonly used for the length of an arc, so that

$$s = r\theta.$$

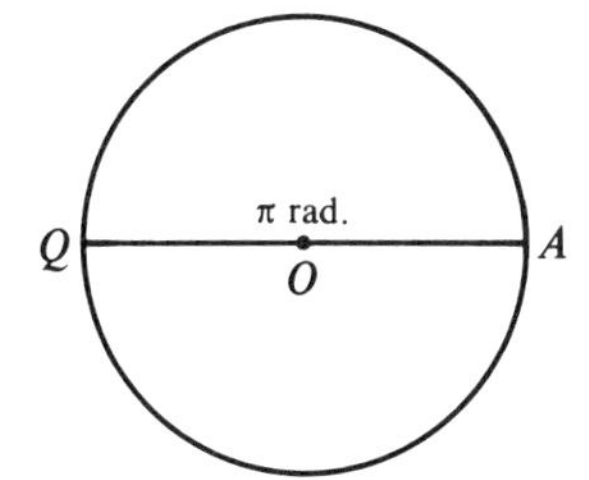

In the special case when AQ is a diameter, the arc AQ is a semicircle and its length is πr. $\therefore\ \pi r = r\theta$, and in this case $\theta = \pi$, i.e. the radian measure of an angle of 180° is π. We therefore have the important relation

$$\pi \text{ radians} = 180°. \qquad (1)$$

This relation enables us to convert the radian measure of an angle to its degree measure, and vice versa. In particular

$$1 \text{ radian} = \left(\frac{180}{\pi}\right)^\circ = 57.296° \text{ to 3 d.p.}$$

The degree measure and the corresponding radian measure of some important angles are shown in the table.

degree measure	360	180	90	60	45	30
radian measure	2π	π	$\frac{\pi}{2}$	$\frac{\pi}{3}$	$\frac{\pi}{4}$	$\frac{\pi}{6}$

Apart from these angles and simple multiples of them, the radian measure of an angle is expressed as a decimal, just as the degree measure is.

Note that since π is irrational, one radian is not an exact fraction of a complete revolution.

For obvious reasons the radian is also called the unit of circular measure.

An abbreviation for θ radians is θ^c.

The area of a sector of a circle

The area of the sector AOB shaded in the diagram is the same fraction of the area of the whole circle as the angle AOB is of a complete revolution. The area of the circle is πr^2.

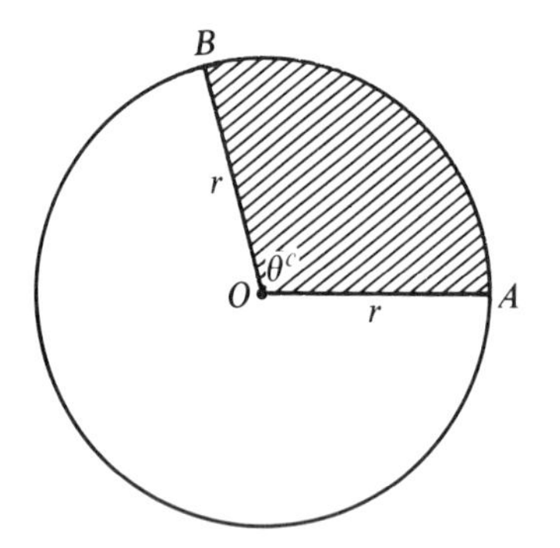

$$\therefore \quad \frac{\text{area of sector } AOB}{\pi r^2} = \frac{\theta}{2\pi}$$

$$\therefore \quad \text{area of sector } AOB = \frac{1}{2}r^2\theta$$

The area of a segment of a circle

A segment of a circle is the region bounded by a chord and an arc. Unless the chord is a diameter, there are two unequal segments corresponding to each chord, the minor segment and the major segment.

The area of the minor segment shaded in the diagram is equal to the area of the sector OPQ minus the area of the triangle OPQ.

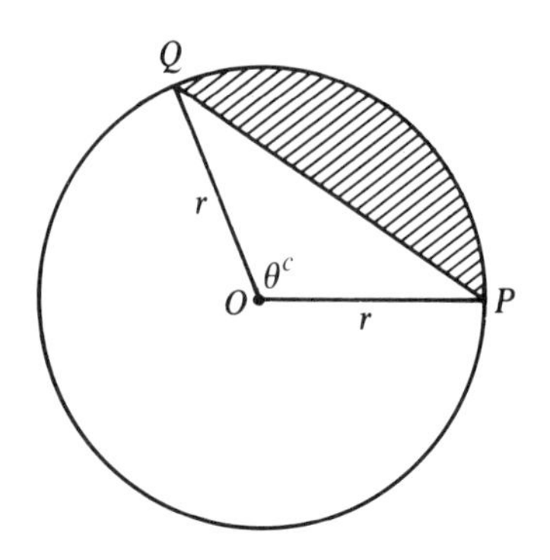

$$\therefore \quad \text{area of segment} = \frac{1}{2}r^2\theta - \frac{1}{2}r^2 \sin \theta^c$$

$$= \frac{r^2}{2}(\theta - \sin \theta^c)$$

The area of the corresponding major segment is found by subtracting the shaded area from the area of the circle.

Examples 10.3

1 A circle has centre O and radius 6 cm. An arc PQ is of length 15 cm. Calculate the angle POQ, giving it both in radians and in degrees.

The arc length s, the radius r and the radian measure θ are related by the formula

$$s = r\theta \text{ or } \theta = \frac{s}{r}$$

$$\therefore\ \theta = \frac{15}{6} = \frac{5}{2}$$

$\therefore$ the angle $POQ = 2.5$ radians

$$= 2.5 \times \frac{180}{\pi} \text{ degrees}$$

$$= 143.2° \text{ (to one d.p.)}$$

2 A circle has centre O. An arc PQ has length 12.5 cm, and the angle POQ is 2.84 radians. Calculate the radius of the circle to 2 s.f.

Using $s = r\theta$ or $r = \dfrac{s}{\theta}$ gives $r = \dfrac{12.5}{2.84}$

$\therefore$ radius = 4.4 cm (to 2 s.f.)

3 A circle has centre O and radius 8 cm. An arc PQ has length 15 cm. Calculate

a the radian measure, θ, of the angle POQ

b the area of the sector POQ

c the area, correct to 3 s.f., of the segment bounded by the given arc PQ and the chord PQ.

a $\theta = \dfrac{\text{arc length}}{\text{radius}} = \dfrac{15}{8}$

b $\dfrac{1}{2}r^2\theta = \dfrac{1}{2} . 64 . \dfrac{15}{8} = 60$

$\therefore$ area of sector $POQ = 60 \text{ cm}^2$

c $\dfrac{1}{2}r^2(\theta - \sin\theta^c) = 60 - \dfrac{1}{2} . 64 \sin(1.875^c)$

$$= 60 - 32 \times 0.9541$$

$\therefore$ area of segment $= 29.5 \text{ cm}^2$ (to 3 s.f.)

Exercise 10.3

1 A circle has centre O; an arc PQ has length 4.3 cm, and the angle POQ is 1.65 radians. Calculate the radius of the circle correct to 2 s.f.

2 A circle has centre O and radius 15 cm; an arc PQ has length 24 cm. Calculate the angle POQ in radians, and also in degrees to 3 s.f.

3 A circle has centre O and radius 9 cm. The area of the sector AOB is 25 cm^2. Calculate the radian measure of the angle AOB and the length of the arc AB. Give each answer correct to 2 s.f.

4 A circle has centre O and radius 10 cm; the chord AB has length 15 cm. Calculate the radian measure of the angle AOB and the area of the sector AOB. Give each answer correct to 3 s.f.

5 A circle has centre O and radius 4 cm; AB is a minor arc and the area of the triangle AOB is 6.4 cm^2. Calculate

a the length of the arc AB

b the area of the minor segment bounded by the arc AB and the chord AB.

Give each answer correct to 2 s.f.

6 Using the same axes for both graphs, and the same scales on each axis, draw accurate graphs for $-1 \leqslant \theta \leqslant 1$ of

a $\sin(\theta \text{ radians})$ **b** $\tan(\theta \text{ radians})$.

Estimate the gradient of the tangent to each graph at the origin.

10.4 Trigonometric functions of real numbers

The domain of the trigonometric functions was given in **4.1** as the set of all angles. Trigonometric functions of real numbers will now be defined.

An angle may be measured either in degrees or in radians—or in other units with which we are not concerned here. The degree measure of an angle is the number of degrees in the angle; the radian measure is the number of radians in the angle. The cosine of the number x could be defined either as the cosine of an angle of $x°$ or as the cosine of an angle of x radians. Since the use of radians greatly simplifies work in calculus, the second definition is used.

The cosine function with domain $\mathbb{R}$ is the function which maps the number x to the cosine of the angle of x radians, i.e. for all x in $\mathbb{R}$:

$$\cos x = \cos(x \text{ radians}).$$

Similarly for all x in $\mathbb{R}$:

$$\sin x = \sin(x \text{ radians}).$$

The tangent function is defined for all real x except odd multiples of $\frac{\pi}{2}$ by

$$\tan x = \tan(x \text{ radians}).$$

The other trigonometric functions of real numbers are defined similarly.

Note: It follows from these definitions that when a calculator is used in connection with trigonometric functions of real numbers, *it should always be set to radians.*

Relations involving trigonometric functions

The main results of **4.2** are given here in terms of trigonometric functions of real numbers, for ease of reference.

$\cos(-x) = \cos x$, $\sin(-x) = -\sin x$, $\tan(-x) = -\tan x$

$\cos(\pi - x) = -\cos x$, $\sin(\pi - x) = \sin x$, $\tan(\pi - x) = -\tan x$

$\cos\left(\frac{\pi}{2} - x\right) = \sin x$, $\sin\left(\frac{\pi}{2} - x\right) = \cos x$, $\tan\left(\frac{\pi}{2} - x\right) = \frac{1}{\tan x} = \cot x$

$\cos(x + \pi) = -\cos x$, $\sin(x + \pi) = -\sin x$, $\tan(x + \pi) = \tan x$

$\cos(x + 2n\pi) = \cos x$, $\sin(x + 2n\pi) = \sin x$, $\tan(x + n\pi) = \tan x$

The graphs of the trigonometric functions of real numbers

The graphs of $\cos x$, $\sin x$ and $\tan x$ are shown below, for values of x between $-\pi$ and π.

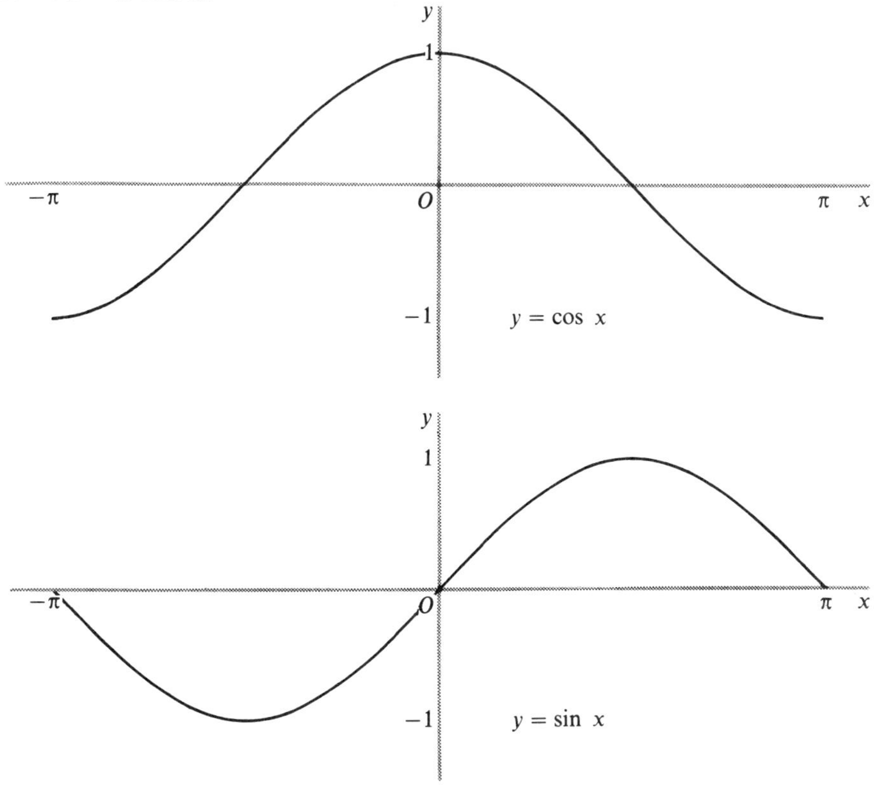

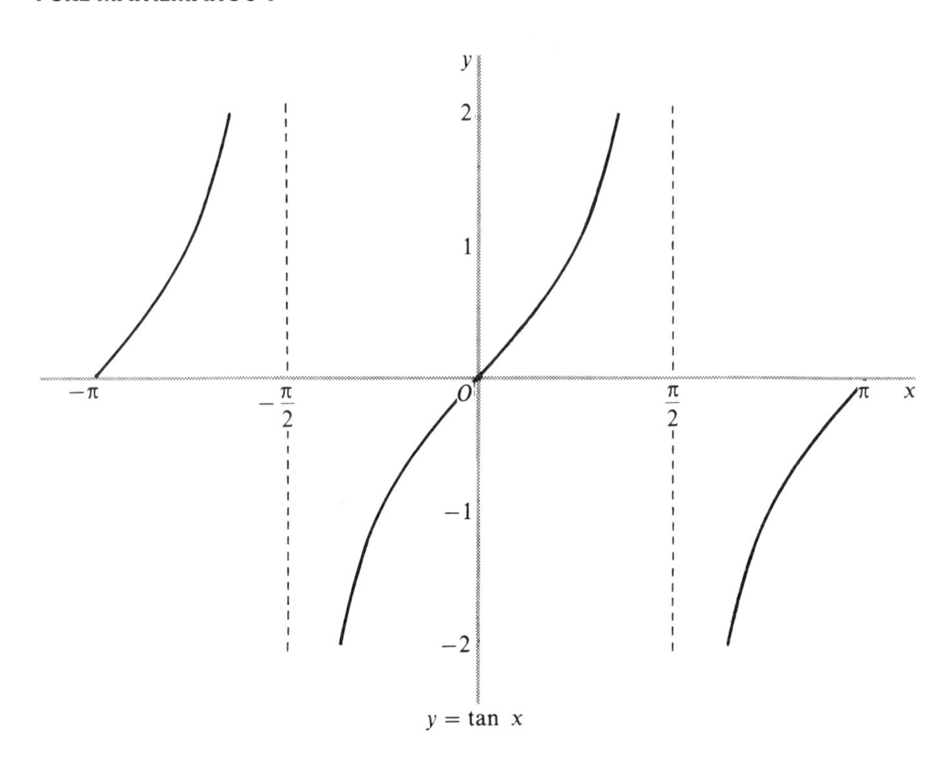

$y = \tan x$

The inverse trigonometric functions

These were defined in **4.1** in terms of angles measured in degrees; the angles could instead be measured in radians. To define inverses of the cosine, sine and tangent functions of real numbers, the domain must be restricted, as before, to give one-one functions. This leads to the following definitions:

The inverse cosine function and the inverse sine function each have the domain $-1 \leqslant x \leqslant 1$, and

$$y = \cos^{-1}x \text{ means } x = \cos y \text{ and } 0 \leqslant y \leqslant \pi$$

$$y = \sin^{-1}x \text{ means } x = \sin y \text{ and } -\frac{\pi}{2} \leqslant y \leqslant \frac{\pi}{2}.$$

The inverse tangent function has domain $\mathbb{R}$ and

$$y = \tan^{-1}x \text{ means } x = \tan y \text{ and } -\frac{\pi}{2} < y < \frac{\pi}{2}.$$

The graphs of these functions are shown in Fig. 1, Fig. 2, Fig. 3.

The graph of $y = \cos^{-1}x$ in Fig. 1 is obtained by reflecting in the line $y = x$ the graph of $y = \cos x$ for $0 \leqslant x \leqslant \pi$. The other graphs are obtained similarly. It is of course essential when this method is used that the scales are the same on both axes.

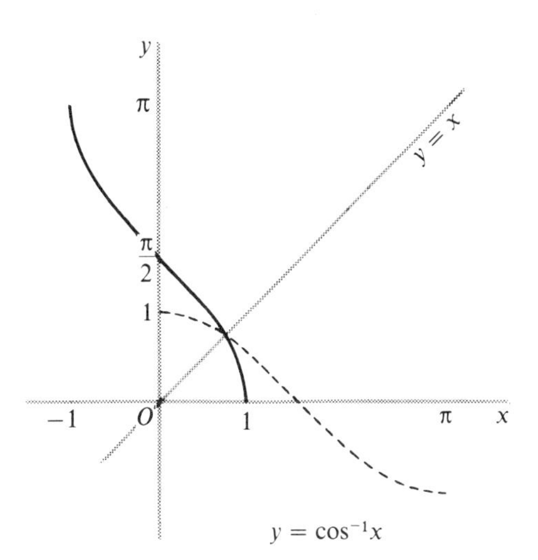

Fig. 1 $y = \cos^{-1}x$

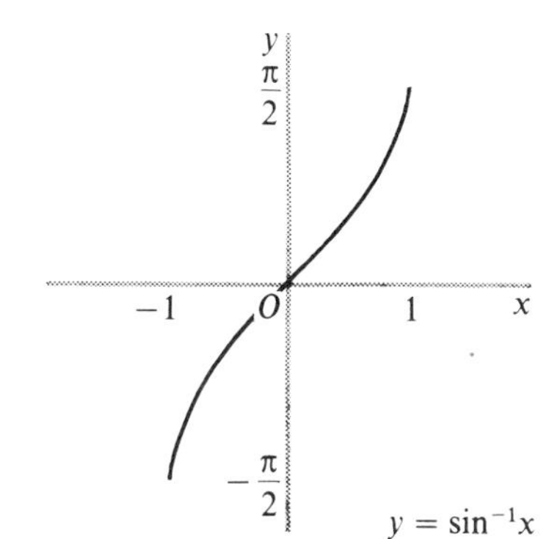

Fig. 2 $y = \sin^{-1}x$

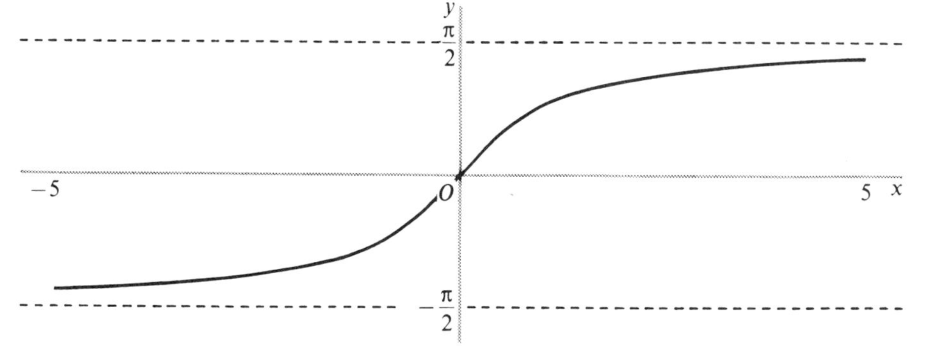

Fig. 3 $y = \tan^{-1}x$

The solution of equations

Equations involving trigonometric functions of real numbers may be solved b the same methods as are used for equations involving angles. The results of **4.2** are replaced by the following.

For solutions in the interval $-\pi < x \leqslant \pi$:

if $\cos x = y$, the solutions are $x = \cos^{-1}y$ and $x = -\cos^{-1}y$
if $\sin x = y$, then $x = \sin^{-1}y$ and either $x = \pi - \sin^{-1}y,\ y > 0$
or $x = -\pi - \sin^{-1}y,\ y < 0$
if $\tan x = y$, then $x = \tan^{-1}y$ and either $x = \tan^{-1}y - \pi,\ y > 0$
or $x = \tan^{-1}y + \pi,\ y < 0$.

For solutions in the interval $0 \leqslant x < 2\pi$, add 2π to any negative solutions in the interval $-\pi < x \leqslant \pi$.

For the *general solutions* of the equations $\cos x = y$ and $\sin x = y$, add $2n\pi$ to each of the two solutions in either of the above intervals. The general solution of $\tan x = y$ is $x = \tan^{-1}y + n\pi$.

Examples 10.4

1 Given that $-\pi < x \leqslant \pi$, solve the following equations. Give the solutions correct to 3 d.p. when not exact.

a $\cos x = 0.324$ **b** $\sin x = -\dfrac{1}{\sqrt{2}}$ **c** $\tan x = 2.643$

a $\cos x = 0.324,\ x = \pm 1.241$

b $\sin x = -\dfrac{1}{\sqrt{2}},\ x = -\dfrac{\pi}{4},\ -\dfrac{3\pi}{4}$

c $\tan x = 2.643,\ x = 1.209,\ 1.209 - \pi = 1.209,\ -1.933$

2 Find the general solutions of the following equations.

a $\cos 2x = \dfrac{\sqrt{3}}{2}$ **b** $\sin 3x = -\dfrac{1}{2}$ **c** $\tan 4x = -1$

a $\cos 2x = \dfrac{\sqrt{3}}{2}$

$$2x = \pm\frac{\pi}{6} + 2n\pi \quad \therefore \quad x = \pm\frac{\pi}{12} + n\pi$$

b $\sin 3x = -\dfrac{1}{2}$

$$3x = -\frac{\pi}{6} + 2n\pi \text{ or } 3x = -\frac{5\pi}{6} + 2n\pi$$

$$\therefore \quad x = -\frac{\pi}{18} + \frac{2n\pi}{3} \text{ or } x = -\frac{5\pi}{18} + \frac{2n\pi}{3}$$

c $\tan 4x = -1$

$$4x = -\frac{\pi}{4} + n\pi \quad \therefore \quad x = -\frac{\pi}{16} + \frac{n\pi}{4}$$

3 Given that $-\pi < x \leqslant \pi$, solve the equations

a $4 \sin 2x = 3 \sin x$ **b** $3 \cos 2x + \sin x = 2$.

Give the solutions correct to 3 d.p. when not exact.

a $4 \sin 2x = 3 \sin x$

$8 \sin x \cos x = 3 \sin x$

$\therefore \sin x = 0$ or $\cos x = \frac{3}{8}$

$\therefore x = 0, \pi, \pm 1.186$

b $3 \cos 2x + \sin x = 2$

$3(1 - 2 \sin^2 x) + \sin x = 2$

or $6 \sin^2 x - \sin x - 1 = 0$

$(3 \sin x + 1)(2 \sin x - 1) = 0$

$\therefore \sin x = -\frac{1}{3}$ or $\frac{1}{2}$

$x = -0.340, -2.802, \frac{\pi}{6}, \frac{5\pi}{6}$

4 A particle moves along a line through a point O. At time t seconds its displacement from O is x cm, where

$x = 2 \sin t + 3, \qquad 0 \leqslant t \leqslant 2\pi.$

a Find the maximum and minimum displacement and the corresponding values of t.

b Find the times at which the displacement is 4.5 cm, giving them correct to 2 d.p.

a $\sin t$ lies between -1 and 1, $\therefore$ $2 \sin t$ lies between -2 and 2

$\therefore$ the maximum and minimum values of x are 5 and 1 respectively.

$\therefore$ the maximum displacement is 5 cm and the minimum is 1 cm.

The corresponding values of t are the values of t for which $\sin t$ has the values 1 and -1.

$\therefore$ for maximum displacement $t = \frac{\pi}{2}$, for minimum displacement $t = \frac{3\pi}{2}$.

b when $x = 4.5$, $2 \sin t = 1.5$ and $\sin t = 0.75$

$\therefore t = 0.848$ or $\pi - 0.848$

$\therefore$ the required times are 0.85 seconds and 2.29 seconds, to 2 d.p.

5 A particle moves along a line through a point O. At time t seconds its displacement from O is x cm where

$$x = 7 \sin t - 2 \cos 2t, \qquad 0 \leqslant t \leqslant 2\pi.$$

a Find the displacement at $t = 0, 1.5, \pi, 5, 2\pi$. Give answers correct to 2 d.p. when not exact.

b Find the times at which the particle is at O, giving them correct to 2 d.p.

c Find the times at which $x = -5$, giving them correct to 2 d.p.

a the displacements are -2 cm, 8.96 cm, -2 cm, -5.03 cm, -2 cm.

b when the particle is at O, $x = 0$,

$$\therefore\ 7 \sin t - 2(1 - 2 \sin^2 t) = 0$$
$$4 \sin^2 t + 7 \sin t - 2 = 0$$
$$(4 \sin t - 1)(\sin t + 2) = 0$$
$$\therefore\ \sin t = 0.25$$
$$\therefore\ t = 0.253 \text{ or } \pi - 0.253$$

$\therefore$ the required times are 0.25 seconds and 2.89 seconds, correct to 2 d.p.

c when $x = -5$, $4 \sin^2 t + 7 \sin t + 3 = 0$

$$(4 \sin t + 3)(\sin t + 1) = 0$$
$$\sin t = -0.75 \text{ or } -1.$$

For $0 \leqslant t \leqslant 2\pi$, the only solution of $\sin t = -1$ is $t = \dfrac{3\pi}{2} = 4.71$.

The solutions of $\sin t = -0.75$ are $t = -0.848 + 2\pi = 5.44$
and $t = -(\pi - 0.848) + 2\pi = 3.99$.

$\therefore$ the required times are 3.99 seconds, 4.71 seconds and 5.44 seconds, correct to 2 d.p.

Exercise 10.4A

Give answers correct to 3 d.p. when not exact.

1 Solve the following equations for $-\pi < x \leqslant \pi$.

a $\cos x = -0.246$ **b** $\sin x = 0.348$ **c** $\tan x = -3.672$

2 Find the general solution of the following equations.

a $\cos 3x = -1$ **b** $\sin 2x = \dfrac{1}{\sqrt{2}}$ **c** $\tan \dfrac{x}{2} = \sqrt{3}$

3 Given that $-\pi < x \leqslant \pi$, solve the equations

a $4 \sin^2 x + 11 \cos x = 10$ **b** $4 \sec^2 x - 9 \tan x = 2$ **c** $5 \sin 2x = \cos x$.

4 A particle is attached to the end of a spring and oscillates in a vertical line. The height of the particle above a fixed point O at time t seconds is y cm, where

$$y = 4 \sin 2t + 10, \qquad 0 \leqslant t \leqslant 2\pi.$$

a Find the maximum and minimum values of y and the corresponding values of t.

b Find the values of t for which y is the mean of the maximum and minimum values.

c Find the values of t for which $y = 8$.

d Find the values of t for which $y = 13$.

5 The functions f and g each have domain $\mathbb{R}$; $f(x) = \cos x$, $g(x) = x^3$.
Calculate **a** fg(1) **b** gf(1) **c** ff(1) **d** fff(1).

6 The functions f and g each have domain $\mathbb{R}$; $f(x) = \sin x$, $g(x) = 2(x + \pi)$.

a Find fg(x) and give the range of fg.

b Find gf(x) and give the range of gf.

Exercise 10.4B

Give answers correct to 3 d.p. when not exact.

1 Find the general solution of the following equations.

a $\cos 2x = \frac{1}{2}$ **b** $\sin \frac{x}{2} = -1$ **c** $\tan 3x = -\frac{1}{\sqrt{3}}$

2 Given that $-\pi < x \leqslant \pi$, solve the equations

a $4\cos^2 x + 7\sin x = 7$ **b** $3\cos 2x + \cos x + 1 = 0$ **c** $\tan 2x = 8\tan x$.

3 A particle moves along a line through a point O. At time t seconds its displacement from O is x cm, where

$$x = \cos 2t - 5\cos t + 3, \qquad 0 \leqslant t \leqslant \pi.$$

a Find the displacement at $t = 0, 2, \pi$.

b Find the time at which the particle is at O.

c Find the time at which $x = 5$.

4 The function f is defined for $0 \leqslant x \leqslant \pi$ by $f(x) = \sin x$; the function g is defined for $x \geqslant 0$ by $g(x) = \sqrt{x}$.

a Find fg(x) and state the domain and range of fg.

b Find gf(x) and state the domain and range of gf.

10.5 Sketch graphs of trigonometric functions

The transformations described in Chapter 9 may now be used to sketch graphs of trigonometric functions. The use of a stretch parallel to the x-axis is particularly useful for graphs such as $y = \cos nx$. This may be obtained by applying to the graph of $y = \cos x$ a stretch of scale factor $\frac{1}{n}$ parallel to the x-axis. The graph of $y = \cos x$ is periodic with period 2π; the graph of $y = \cos nx$ is periodic with period $\frac{2\pi}{n}$. Similarly the graph of $y = \sin nx$ has period $\frac{2\pi}{n}$ and the graph of $y = \tan nx$ has period $\frac{\pi}{n}$.

Examples 10.5

1 Sketch the graph of $y = 2\cos\left(x - \frac{\pi}{3}\right)$ for $-\pi \leqslant x \leqslant \pi$ by applying to the graph of $y = \cos x$ a translation followed by a stretch parallel to the y-axis.

The translation $\begin{pmatrix} \pi/3 \\ 0 \end{pmatrix}$ maps $y = \cos x$ to $y = \cos\left(x - \frac{\pi}{3}\right)$. A stretch of scale factor 2 parallel to the y-axis gives the required graph.

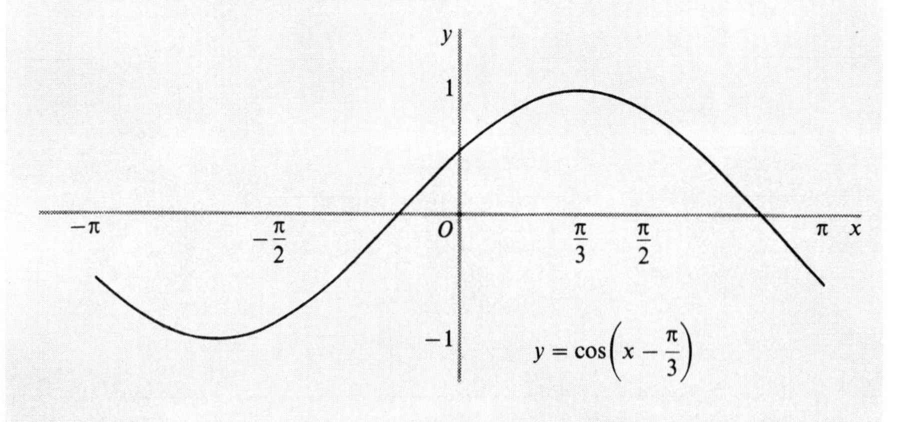

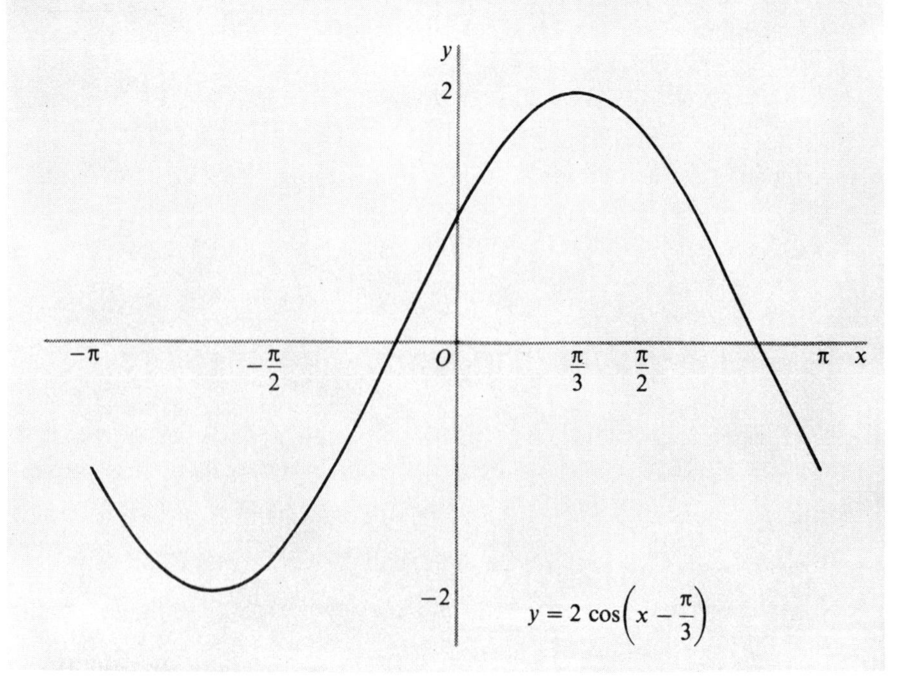

2 Sketch the graph of $y = 2 \sin 3x$ for $-\pi \leqslant x \leqslant \pi$ by applying to the graph of $y = \sin x$ a stretch parallel to each axis.

A stretch parallel to the x-axis of scale factor $\frac{1}{3}$ maps $y = \sin x$ to $y = \sin 3x$. A stretch parallel to the y-axis of scale factor 2 gives the required graph. The stretches may be applied in either order.

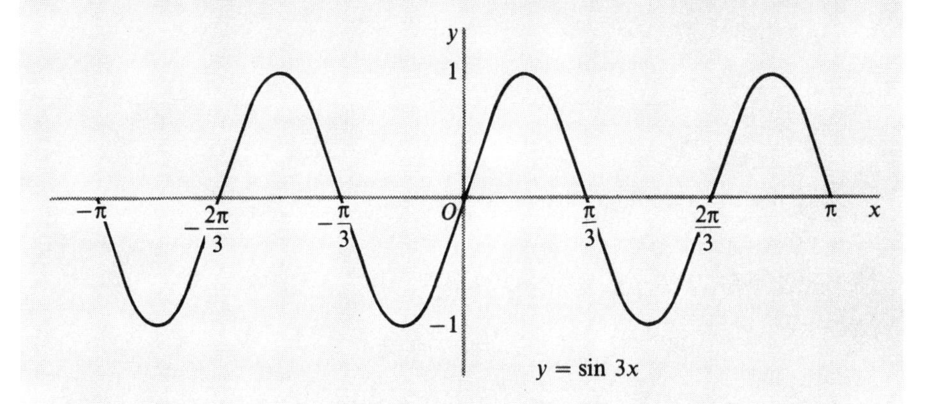

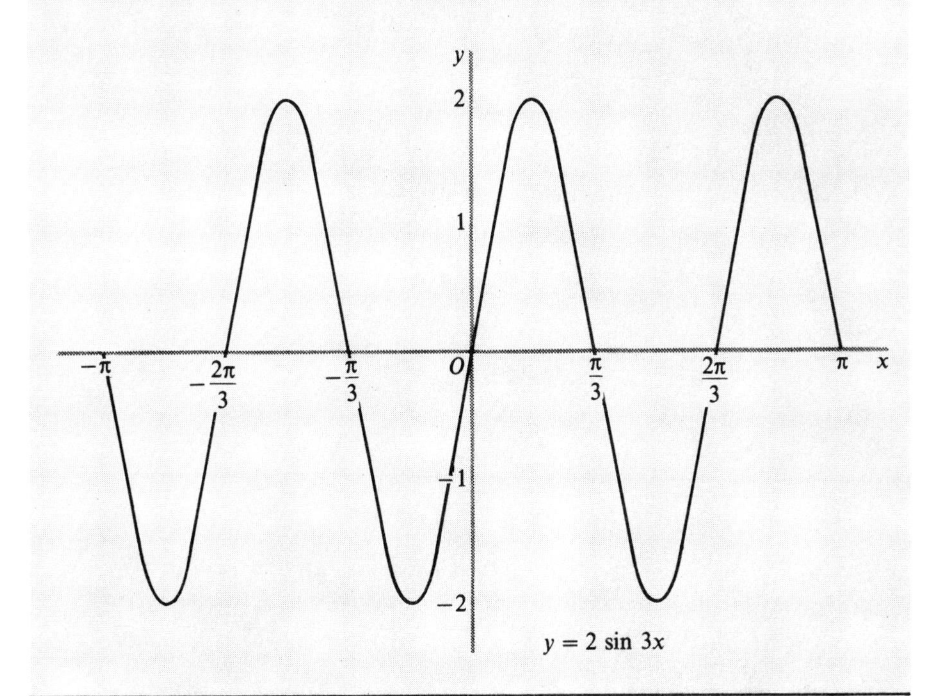

Exercise 10.5

Sketch the graph of each of the following by applying transformations to a suitable graph. Describe the transformations used, in the order in which you have used them.

1 $y = 3\tan\left(x - \dfrac{\pi}{4}\right), \qquad -\pi \leqslant x \leqslant \pi$

2 $y = 2\cos 3x, \qquad 0 \leqslant x \leqslant 2\pi$

3 $y = 2\sin\left(x + \dfrac{\pi}{6}\right), \qquad -\pi \leqslant x \leqslant \pi$

4 $y = 4\tan\dfrac{x}{2}, \qquad 0 \leqslant x \leqslant 2\pi$

5 $y = 3\left[\cos\left(x - \dfrac{\pi}{3}\right) + 1\right], \qquad 0 \leqslant x \leqslant 2\pi$

Miscellaneous Exercise 10

1 The angles A and B are acute and A is greater than B.

Given that $\cos A \cos B = \sin A \sin B = \dfrac{1}{4}$, find the values of $\cos(A + B)$ and $\cos(A - B)$, and hence obtain the values of A and B.

2 Prove that, for all values of x,

$$\frac{1 + \cos x}{1 - \cos x} - \frac{1 - \cos x}{1 + \cos x} = \frac{4}{\sin x \tan x}.$$

3 Given that $\sin\theta = \dfrac{2}{3}$, find the possible values of

(i) $\cos\theta$ (ii) $\cos 2\theta$ (iii) $\cos 3\theta$.

Give each answer as a fraction or in surd form, as appropriate.

4 Find the common ratio of the geometric sequence

$$\sin 2\alpha, \quad -\sin 2\alpha \cos 2\alpha, \quad \sin 2\alpha \cos^2 2\alpha, \quad \ldots$$

Prove that for $0 < \alpha < \dfrac{\pi}{2}$ the series

$$\sin 2\alpha - \sin 2\alpha \cos 2\alpha + \sin 2\alpha \cos^2 2\alpha + \ldots$$

has a sum to infinity and show that the sum to infinity is $\tan\alpha$. (S)

5 Given that $\tan(\alpha + \beta) = t$ and $\tan\alpha = 1$, express $\tan\beta$ in terms of t.

Use this result to show that

$$\tan 15° = \frac{\sqrt{3} - 1}{\sqrt{3} + 1}.$$

6 Show that, for all values of θ,

$$\frac{\cot^2\theta}{1+\cot^2\theta} = \cos^2\theta.$$

Hence, or otherwise, find the solutions in the interval $-180° \leqslant \theta \leqslant 180°$ of the equation

$$\frac{\cot^2\theta}{1+\cot^2\theta} = 2\cos 2\theta.$$

Give the solutions correct to 1 d.p.

7 Express $\tan 2\theta$ in terms of $\tan\theta$.

Hence show that one of the roots of the quadratic equation $2t = 1 - t^2$ is $\tan 22\tfrac{1}{2}°$ and find the value of $\tan 22\tfrac{1}{2}°$, leaving your answer in surd form.

The other root of the quadratic equation is $\tan\alpha$ where α is an obtuse angle. Obtain the value of α.

8 Given that $t = \tan\theta$, write down an expression for $\tan 2\theta$ in terms of t.

Show that $\tan 3\theta = \dfrac{3t - t^3}{1 - 3t^2}$.

Using the above results, show that the equation $2\tan 3\theta = 3\tan 2\theta$ simplifies to $t^5 + 5t^3 = 0$. Hence solve the equation $2\tan 3\theta = 3\tan 2\theta$ in the interval $0° \leqslant \theta \leqslant 180°$.

9 **a** Given that $\cos A = \dfrac{3}{4}$ find, without using tables or calculators, the value of

(i) $\cos 2A$ (ii) $\cos 4A$.

b If $\tan B = 3\tan C$ prove that $\tan(B - C) = \dfrac{\sin 2C}{2 - \cos 2C}$. (*C*)

10 Triangle PQR and rectangle $PQXY$ are drawn on opposite sides of the line PQ which is 15 cm long. In the triangle PQR, angle PRQ is a right angle and $PR = 12$ cm. In the rectangle $PQXY$, $PY = 8$ cm.
Angle $XPQ = \alpha$ and angle $QPR = \beta$. Express in fraction form the value of $\sin(\alpha + \beta)$ without calculating the values of α and β.

Hence, or otherwise, calculate the perpendicular distance of X from PR.

11 (i) Given that a, b and c are successive terms in a geometric progression, show that $ac = b^2$.

(ii) Express $\sin 2\theta$ in terms of $\sin\theta$ and $\cos\theta$, and express $\cos 2\theta$ in terms of $\cos\theta$.

Hence prove that $\cos 3\theta = 4\cos^3\theta - 3\cos\theta$.

(iii) Let $a = \cos\theta$, $b = \sin 2\theta$, $c = \cos 3\theta$ and use the results obtained in parts (i) and (ii) to find the positive value of $\cos\theta$ such that $\cos\theta$, $\sin 2\theta$ and $\cos 3\theta$ are in geometric progression.

Leave your answer in surd form.

12 By using identities for $\cos(A-B)$ and $\cos(A+B)$, prove that

$$1+\cos(A-B)\cos(A+B)=\cos^2 A+\cos^2 B.$$

Hence prove that

a $1+\cos 2\theta = 2\cos^2\theta$

b $3+\cos(P-Q)\cos(P+Q)+\cos(Q-R)\cos(Q+R)+\cos(R-P)\cos(R+P)$
$=2(\cos^2 P+\cos^2 Q+\cos^2 R).$

(*AEB* 1984)

13 Express $\sin 3\theta$ in terms of $\sin\theta$.

Hence solve the equation

$$\sin 3\theta = \sin^2\theta$$

for $-180° < \theta \leqslant 180°$.

14 (i) Solve, for $0 \leqslant \theta \leqslant 2\pi$, the equation

$$\sin\left(\theta+\frac{\pi}{4}\right)=2\cos\left(\theta-\frac{\pi}{6}\right).$$

(ii) Figure 1 shows a chord BD of a circle of radius 12 cm. The line ABC is the tangent to the circle at B and $\angle DBC = 30°$. Taking π as 3.14, calculate the area of the shaded region. (*L*)

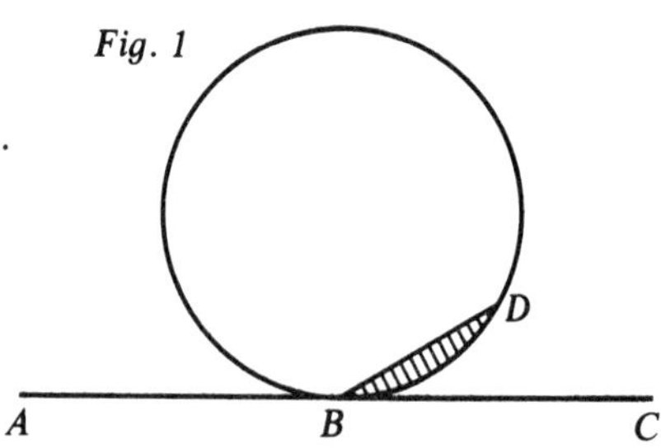

15

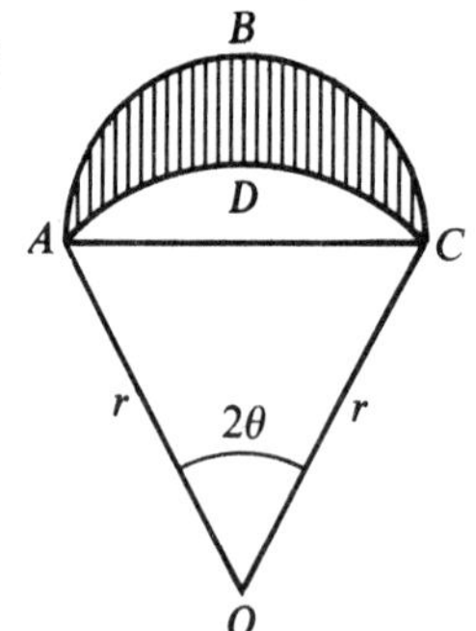

In the figure ADC is an arc of a circle, centre O, radius r and the angle $AOC = 2\theta$ radians. ABC is a semicircle on AC as diameter. Show that $AC = 2r\sin\theta$.

Find expressions, in terms of r and θ, for the areas of

(i) the sector $OADC$

(ii) the segment ADC

(iii) the shaded region. (*C*)

16 The figure shows an arc AB of a circle, centre O, radius 20 cm and an arc CD of a circle, centre O and radius r cm.

The angle AOB is $\frac{4}{5}$ radians.

Calculate the area of the region P.

Given that the areas of the regions P and Q are in the ratio 4 : 5, calculate

(i) the value of r

(ii) the length of the perimeter of the region Q. (*C*)

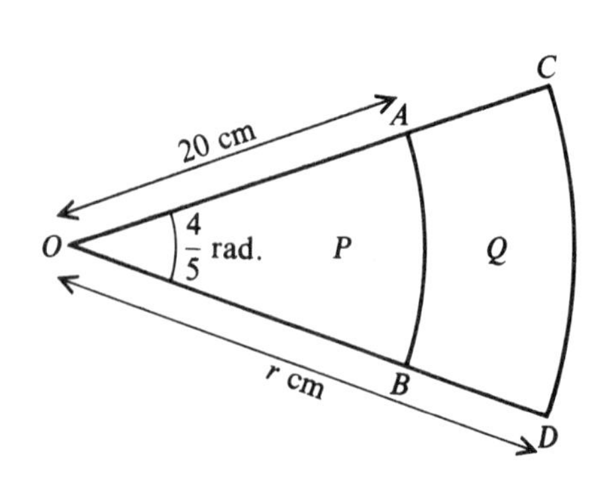

17 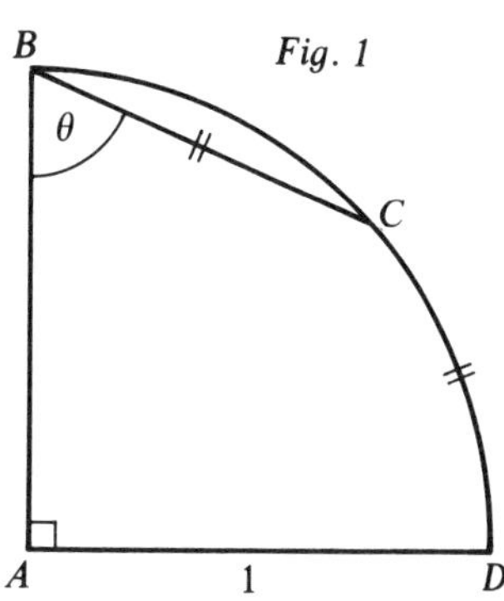

Figure 1 shows one quadrant of a circle of unit radius, centre A. The point C on the circumference is such that the length of the *chord BC* equals the length of the *arc CD*. If angle $ABC = \theta$ radians, prove that

$$\cos \theta = \theta - \frac{\pi}{4}.$$

By drawing on graph paper the cosine graph for $0 \leqslant \theta \leqslant \frac{\pi}{2}$ and a suitable straight line, estimate, to 2 significant figures, the solution of this equation. (*L*)

18 In the diagram ABC is a straight line with $AB = BC = 3$ cm; CD is perpendicular to ABC. On the semicircle with centre B and radius 2 cm is a variable point P, with angle $CBP = \theta$ radians. The line AP is produced to meet CD at Q, and $QC = y$ cm.

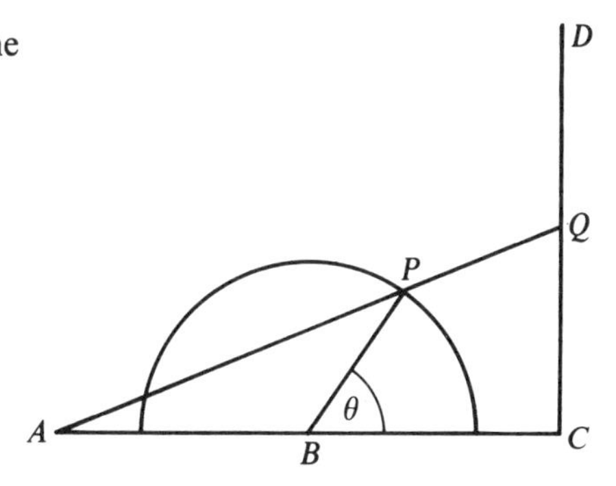

Prove that

$$y = \frac{12 \sin \theta}{3 + 2 \cos \theta}.$$

Sketch the diagram for the case when Q is as far as possible from C.

Without using calculus, calculate the maximum value of $\dfrac{12 \sin \theta}{3 + 2 \cos \theta}$, giving to two decimal places the value of θ between 0 and π for which this occurs. (*L*)

19 At time t hours after midnight the velocity v of the water flowing into an estuary is given by

$$v = 10 \cos\left(\frac{\pi}{6}t + \frac{\pi}{2}\right) \text{ km/h}.$$

Sketch the graph of v against t for $0 \leqslant t \leqslant 12$.

Calculate to the nearest minute the times during this interval when the speed of the current is 8 km/h. (*SMP*)

20 The depth of water at the entrance to a harbour t hours after high tide is D metres, where

$$D = p + q \cos(rt°)$$

for suitable constants p, q, r. At high tide the depth is 7 m; at low tide 6 hours later the depth is 3 m.

a Show that $r = 30$ and find the values of p and q.

b Sketch the graph of D against t for $0 \leqslant t \leqslant 12$.

c Find how soon after low tide a ship which requires a depth of at least 4 m of water will be able to enter harbour. (*L*)

Chapter 11

Inequalities

11.1 Introduction

On the number line, the point A represents a and the point B represents b, where $a < b$.

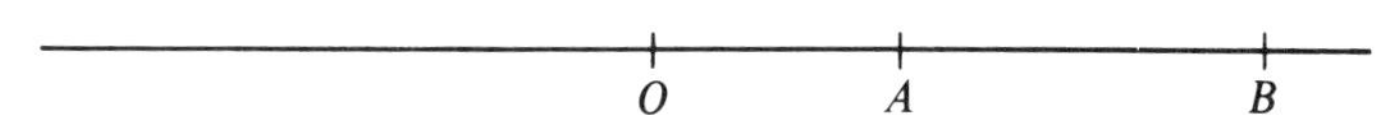

Then the following statements are all equivalent:

$a < b$, $a - b < 0$, $b > a$, $b - a > 0$,

A is on the left of B, B is on the right of A.

The statement $a < b < c$ means that $a < b$ *and* $b < c$.

The positions of the corresponding points A, B, C on the number line are as shown. From the diagram it is apparent that

$a < b$ and $b < c$ together give $a < c$,

i.e. $a < b$ and $b < c \Rightarrow a < c$.

This shows that the relation $<$ is *transitive*. The following is a formal proof of this result:

$a < b \Leftrightarrow a - b < 0$

$b < c \Leftrightarrow b - c < 0$

$\therefore$ $a - b + b - c$ is the sum of two negative numbers

$\therefore$ $a - c < 0$ and this is equivalent to $a < c$.

Solving inequalities: the basic rules

Examples of inequalities are

$$x + 1 \geqslant 3,\ (x - 1)(x + 2) > 0,\ \frac{x - 1}{x - 2} < 3,\ a^2 + b^2 \geqslant 2ab.$$

The first three of these examples are true for some values of x; finding these values is called 'solving' the inequality. The last inequality is true for all values of a and b, as the reader will find by considering $a^2 + b^2 - 2ab$.

Solving inequalities is in general harder than solving equations. If the inequality signs in the above examples are replaced by '=' the resulting equations provide easy examples for fourth formers. The reader may like to try to solve the inequalities above, before reading on.

The first two methods used in the solution of *equations* are:

Any number, positive or negative, may be added to each side.
Each side may be multiplied by any non-zero number.

For the solution of *inequalities*, the first of these remains unchanged. For if $a < b$, then $a + c < b + c$; for example, $3 < 5$, $6 < 8$, $-4 < -2$. The points A and B representing a and b are each moved the same distance on the number line, to the right for $c > 0$, to the left for $c < 0$.

The order of the translated pair of points is unchanged, each A being on the left of the corresponding B.

The second method remains unchanged *when the multiplying number is positive*, but only then.

Multiplication of the numbers a and b by a positive number moves the corresponding points A and B on the number line to new positions which are each on the same side of the origin O as before, and are in the same order:

e.g. $-1 < 3$, $-2 < 6$,

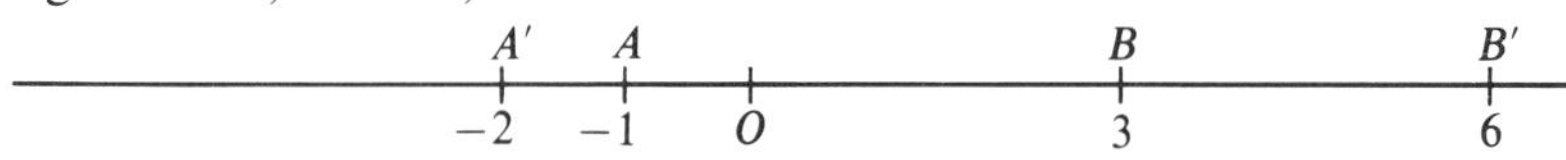

But when the multiplying number is negative, the points A and B each move to the opposite side of O and their order on the line is therefore reversed:

e.g. $-1 < 3$, $2 > -6$,

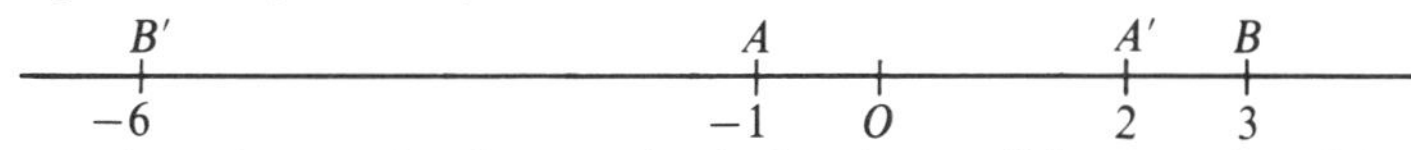

The first three rules for manipulating inequalities are therefore:

I Any number, positive or negative, may be added to each side of an inequality.

II Each side of an inequality may be multiplied by a positive number.

III Each side of an inequality may be multiplied by a negative number provided the inequality sign is reversed.

Writing the solution of an inequality

The solution of an inequality consists of all the numbers which satisfy one or more *simpler* inequalities, e.g. all numbers less than 3 *or* all numbers between 1 and 3 inclusive. To avoid excessive verbosity it is conventionally accepted that the solution 'all numbers less than 3' may be written as '$x < 3$', etc.

If the solution consists of all values of x such that $x \leqslant 1$ together with all values of x such that $x \geqslant 3$, then $x \leqslant 1$ *or* $x \geqslant 3$ and this will be written as '$x \leqslant 1$, $x \geqslant 3$'.

The *solution set* of an inequality is the set of all values of x which satisfy it. If the solution is given by $x < 3$, then the solution set is $\{x : x < 3\}$. If the solution is given by $1 \leqslant x \leqslant 3$, the solution set is $\{x : 1 \leqslant x \leqslant 3\}$.

If the solution is given by $x \leqslant 1$ or $x \geqslant 3$, the solution set may be written $\{x : x \leqslant 1\} \cup \{x : x \geqslant 3\}$.

Linear inequalities

An inequality is linear when it can be written in the form $ax + b > 0$ (or $\geqslant 0$). The examples which follow are all linear.

Examples 11.1

Solve the inequalities in questions **1**–**6**. In question **6**, give the solution set.

1 $2x - 1 < x + 3$

2 $4 - x \geqslant x - 5$

3 $2x + 7 \leqslant 3x - 4$

4 $x + 3 \leqslant 3x - 1 \leqslant 4x - 8$

5 $4 - x \leqslant x + 2 \leqslant 6 - 3x$

6 $3 - x \leqslant x + 5 \leqslant 7 - x$

1 $2x - 1 < x + 3$

$\therefore\ x < 4$ (by I)

2 $4 - x \geqslant x - 5$

$\therefore\ 9 \geqslant 2x$ (by I)

$x \leqslant \frac{9}{2}$ (by II)

3 $2x + 7 \leqslant 3x - 4$

$-x \leqslant -11$ (by I)

$x \geqslant 11$ (by III)

4 $x + 3 \leqslant 3x - 1 \leqslant 4x - 8$

First: $x + 3 \leqslant 3x - 1$

$-2x \leqslant -4$ (by I)

$x \geqslant 2$ (by III)

Then: $3x - 1 \leqslant 4x - 8$

$-x \leqslant -7$ (by I)

$x \geqslant 7$ (by III)

Since *both* inequalities must be true, the solution is $x \geqslant 7$.

5 $4 - x \leqslant x + 2 \leqslant 6 - 3x$

The left-hand pair give $-2x \leqslant -2$, $x \geqslant 1$.

The right-hand pair give $4x \leqslant 4$, $x \leqslant 1$.

So the solution is $x = 1$.

6 $3 - x \leqslant x + 5 \leqslant 7 - x$

The left-hand pair give $-2x \leqslant 2$, $x \geqslant -1$.

The right-hand pair give $2x \leqslant 2$, $x \leqslant 1$.

So the solution is $-1 \leqslant x \leqslant 1$.

The solution set is $\{x\colon -1 \leqslant x \leqslant 1\}$.

Exercise 11.1A

Solve the inequalities in questions **1**–**5**. In question **5** give the solution set.

1 $3x - 2 \leqslant 2x + 5$

2 $4x - 3 \geqslant 6 - 2x$

3 $5 - x < 2x - 1$

4 $8 - 3x > x + 4$

5 $2x + 5 \leqslant 3x + 4 \leqslant 5x + 6$

Exercise 11.1B

Solve the inequalities in questions **1**–**5**. In question **5** give the solution set.

1 $4x + 3 \leqslant x - 2$

2 $5x - 4 \geqslant 2 - x$

3 $7 - 2x \leqslant 4 + x$

4 $2x - 3 \leqslant x - 1 \leqslant 3x + 2$

5 $x - 4 \leqslant 2x + 1 \leqslant x + 6$

11.2 Quadratic inequalities

An inequality is quadratic when it can be written in the form $ax^2 + bx + c > 0$, (or $\geqslant 0$). One of the main methods for solving quadratic *equations* (and many others) is to use the important principle:

If $pq = 0$ then either $p = 0$ or $q = 0$.

For example, given $(x - 1)(x - 3) = 0$, then either $x - 1 = 0$ or $x - 3 = 0$ so $x = 1$ or $x = 3$.

It is *not* true that this principle extends at once to inequalities; it is obvious nonsense to assert that if $pq > 0$ then either $p > 0$ or $q > 0$. Instead we have the more complicated principle:

If $pq > 0$ then **either** $p > 0$ *and* $q > 0$ **or** $p < 0$ *and* $q < 0$.

A quadratic inequality in which the quadratic can easily be factorised may be solved by using this principle or by using a sketch graph.

Every quadratic inequality may be solved by the method of completing the square, with or without the use of a sketch graph.

Examples 11.2

1 Solve $(x - 1)(x - 3) > 0$.

Method 1 The graph of $y = (x - 1)(x - 3)$ may be sketched by the methods of **9.4**.

From the graph $y > 0$ for $x < 1$, $x > 3$.

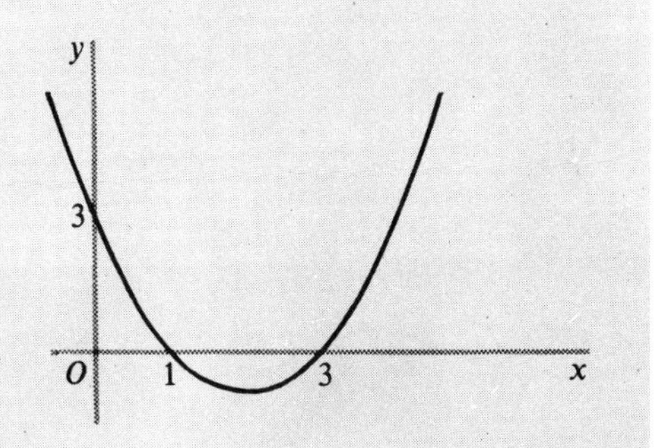

Method 2 Either $x - 1 > 0$ and $x - 3 > 0$, so $x > 3$
or $x - 1 < 0$ and $x - 3 < 0$, so $x < 1$.

$\therefore$ The solution is $x < 1$, $x > 3$.

The working may be shown by using the number line:

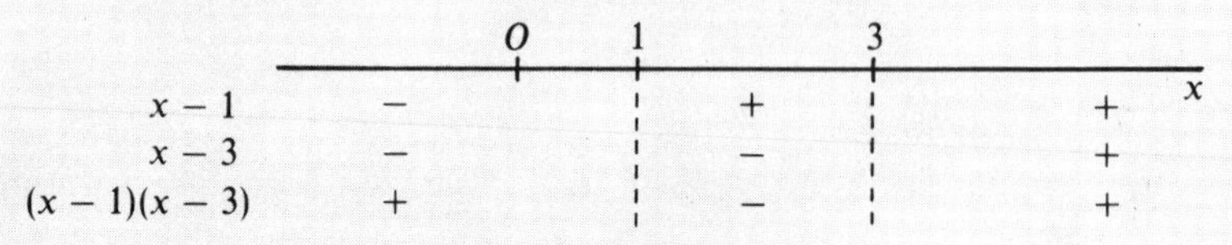

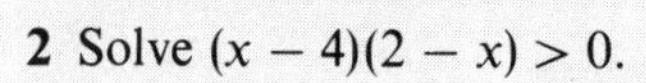

2 Solve $(x - 4)(2 - x) > 0$.

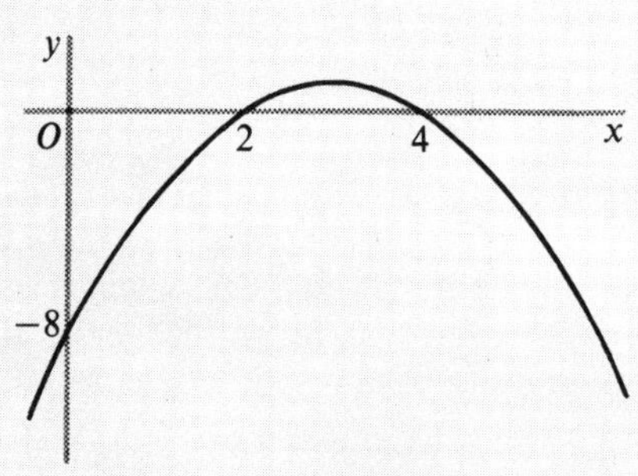

Method 1 Let $y = (x - 4)(2 - x)$ and sketch the graph.

From the graph $y > 0$ for $2 < x < 4$.

Method 2 Use the number line to show the signs of the factors.

	$x<2$	$2<x<4$	$x>4$
$x - 4$	−	−	+
$2 - x$	+	−	−
$(x - 4)(2 - x)$	−	+	−

$\therefore$ the solution is $2 < x < 4$.

3 Find the solution set of $x^2 - 6x + 10 > 0$.

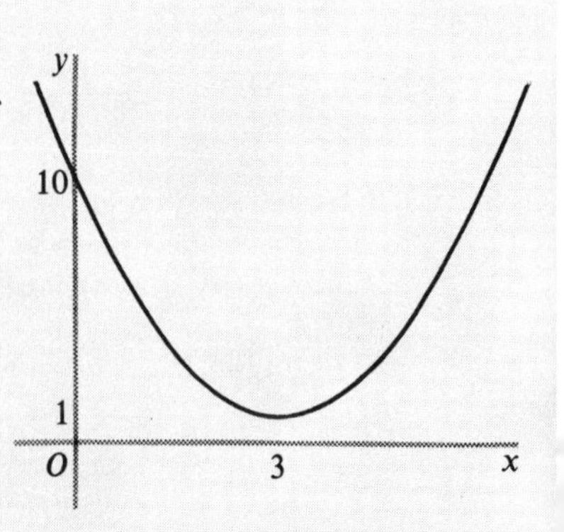

The quadratic cannot be factorised. Let $y = x^2 - 6x + 10$.

By completing the square, $y = (x - 3)^2 + 1$.

By inspection $y > 0$ for all values of x; since $(x - 3)^2 \geqslant 0$ for all x, the minimum value of y is 1.

$\therefore$ the solution set is $\mathbb{R}$. This can be shown on a sketch graph, but the graph is not necessary.

4 Find the solution set of $x^2 + 4x + 7 \leqslant 0$.

The quadratic cannot be factorised; let $y = x^2 + 4x + 7$.
By completing the square, $y = (x + 2)^2 + 3$, and so the minimum value of y is 3. It follows that no value of x satisfies the inequality.

$\therefore$ the solution set is empty.

5 Solve $(x - 2)^2 \leqslant 3$.

Method 1 Let $y = (x - 2)^2$. The line $y = 3$ meets the graph of y where

$(x - 2)^2 = 3$

$x - 2 = \pm\sqrt{3}$, $x = 2 \pm \sqrt{3}$.

From the graph the solution is $2 - \sqrt{3} \leqslant x \leqslant 2 + \sqrt{3}$.

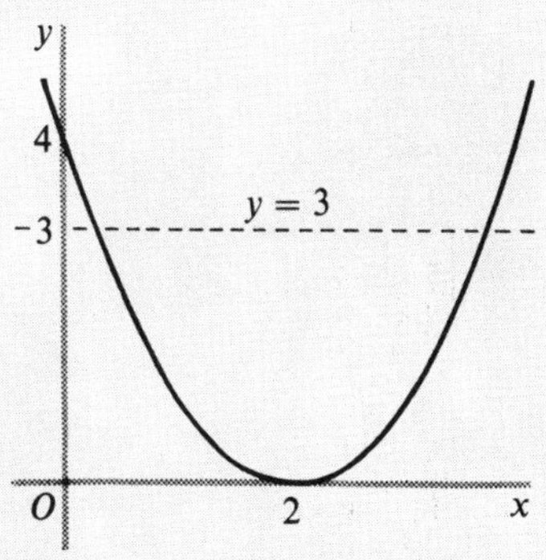

Method 2 $(x - 2)^2 \leqslant 3$

$\Leftrightarrow |x - 2| \leqslant \sqrt{3}$

$\Leftrightarrow -\sqrt{3} \leqslant x - 2 \leqslant \sqrt{3}$

$\Leftrightarrow 2 - \sqrt{3} \leqslant x \leqslant 2 + \sqrt{3}$

6 Find the solution set of $x^2 - 8x + 6 \geqslant 0$.

The quadratic does not factorise; let $y = x^2 - 8x + 6$.
By completing the square, $y = (x - 4)^2 - 10$

Method 1 $y \geqslant 0$ when $(x - 4)^2 \geqslant 10$

$|x - 4| \geqslant \sqrt{10}$

$\therefore\ x - 4 \leqslant -\sqrt{10}$ or $x - 4 \geqslant \sqrt{10}$

$\therefore$ the solution set is $\{x : x \leqslant 4 - \sqrt{10}\} \cup \{x : x \geqslant 4 + \sqrt{10}\}$.

Method 2 the solution may be found using Method 1 of Q5.

Exercise 11.2A

Solve the inequalities in questions **1**–**4**.

1 $x^2 - 4x - 5 \geqslant 0$

2 $9x - 4 - 2x^2 > 0$

3 $x^2 + 6x + 12 \geqslant 0$

4 $(x + 1)^2 \leqslant 9$

5 Find the solution set of $x^2 - 2x - 4 \leqslant 0$.

Exercise 11.2B

Solve the inequalities in questions **1–4**.

1 $3x^2 + 10x - 8 \geqslant 0$

2 $x^2 - 8x < 9$

3 $x^2 + 20 < 8x$

4 $(x - 4)^2 \geqslant 25$

5 Find the solution set of $x^2 - 6x + 3 \geqslant 0$.

11.3 More inequalities

Examples 11.3

1 Solve $(x + 2)(x - 1)(x - 3) > 0$.

Method 1 Sketch the graph of $y = (x + 2)(x - 1)(x - 3)$.

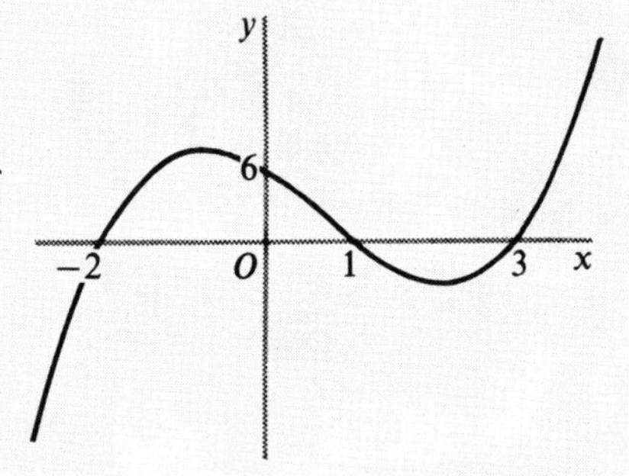

From the graph the solution is $-2 < x < 1$, $x > 3$.

Method 2 Use the number line to show the signs of the factors.

	$x < -2$	$-2 < x < 1$	$1 < x < 3$	$x > 3$
$x + 2$	−	+	+	+
$x - 1$	−	−	+	+
$x - 3$	−	−	−	+
$(x + 2)(x - 1)(x - 3)$	−	+	−	+

The solution is $-2 < x < 1$, $x > 3$.

2 Solve $\dfrac{x - 1}{(x - 3)(x + 2)} > 0$.

Method 1 It is not so easy to sketch the graph of the left-hand side here.
But both sides of the inequality may be multiplied by the *positive* number $(x - 3)^2(x + 2)^2$ and the resulting inequality solved instead. This inequality has been solved in Example 1.

Note: The number $(x - 3)^2(x + 2)^2$ is positive *in the context of this question*, since the factors $x - 3$ and $x + 2$ in the denominator imply that $x - 3$ and $x + 2$ are not zero.

Method 2 Use the signs of the factors as in Example 1, Method 2.

3 Solve $\dfrac{x-1}{(x-3)(x+2)} \geqslant 0.$

Method 1 This inequality differs from Example 2 only in the inclusion of '='.

It is essential to solve the *equation* before multiplying by $(x-3)^2(x+2)^2$ since the *equations* $\dfrac{x-1}{(x-3)(x+2)} = 0$ and $(x-1)(x-3)(x+2) = 0$ do not have the same solutions.

The solution of the given equation is $x = 1$.

The solution of the given inequality is $-2 < x \leqslant 1$, $x > 3$.

Method 2 Solve the *equation* first and then use the signs of the factors as in Example 1, Method 2.

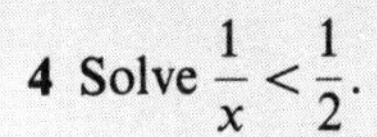

4 Solve $\dfrac{1}{x} < \dfrac{1}{2}.$

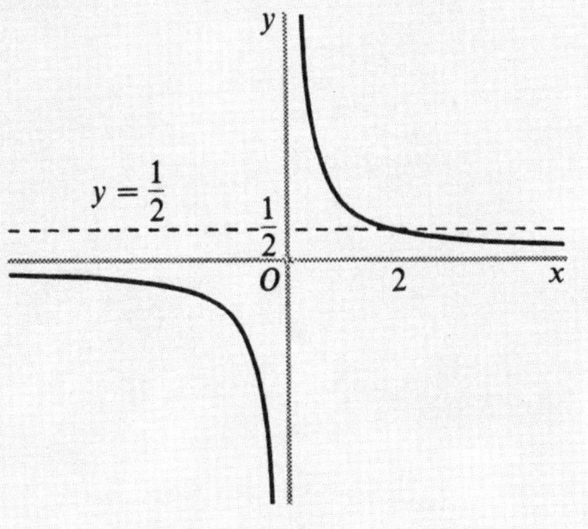

Method 1 Let $y = \dfrac{1}{x}$ and use a sketch graph.

The line $y = \dfrac{1}{2}$ meets the graph at $x = 2$.

We need the values of x for which the graph lies below the line $y = \dfrac{1}{2}$.

The solution can be read from the graph: $x < 0$, $x > 2$.

Method 2 Multiply both sides of the inequality by $2x^2$, which is positive for all non-zero x, and x cannot be zero here.

This gives $2x < x^2$ or $x^2 - 2x > 0$.

This may now be solved by any of the methods of **11.2**.

Method 3 Multiply both sides by $2x$, in each of the cases $x > 0$, $x < 0$:

$x > 0$ gives $2 < x$ or $x > 2$

$x < 0$ gives $2 > x$ or $x < 2$, but also $x < 0$

$\therefore$ the solution is $x < 0$, $x > 2$.

Method 4 Rearrange the inequality to make the right-hand side zero:

$$\frac{1}{x} < \frac{1}{2} \Leftrightarrow \frac{1}{x} - \frac{1}{2} < 0 \Leftrightarrow \frac{2-x}{2x} < 0 \Leftrightarrow \frac{2-x}{x} < 0$$

Complete the solution by using a sketch graph of $y = \dfrac{2-x}{x}$ or by using the number line to show the signs of $2 - x$ and x.

5 Solve $\dfrac{3}{x-1} > -2.$

Method 1 Let $y = \dfrac{3}{x-1}$ and sketch the graph.

The line $y = -2$ meets the graph where
$3 = -2(x-1)$ or $1 = -2x$

$$x = -\frac{1}{2}.$$

The solution can be read from the graph:

$x < -\frac{1}{2}$, $x > 1$.

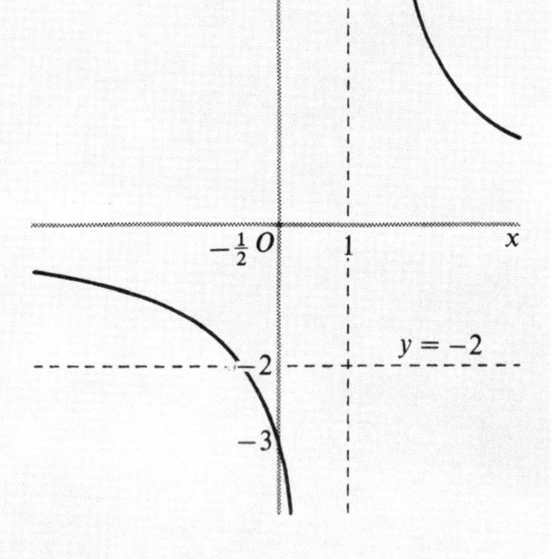

Method 2 Multiply both sides by $(x-1)^2$ to give
$3(x-1) > -2(x-1)^2$.
Remove the *common factor* $x - 1$:
$(x-1)[3 + 2(x-1)] > 0$
$(x-1)(2x+1) \quad > 0.$
Complete the solution by any of the methods of **11.2**.

Method 3 Rearrange the inequality to make the right-hand side zero:

$$\frac{3}{x-1} + 2 > 0$$

$$\frac{3 + 2(x-1)}{x-1} > 0$$

$$\frac{2x+1}{x-1} > 0$$

Complete the solution by using the number line to show the signs of $2x + 1$ and $x - 1$.

6 Solve $\dfrac{x-2}{x-1} < 2$.

Method 1 Multiply both sides by $(x-1)^2$ to give

$(x-2)(x-1) < 2(x-1)^2$.

$(x-1)[x-2-2(x-1)] < 0$

$x(x-1) > 0$

Using a sketch graph of $y = x(x-1)$, or otherwise, the solution is $x < 0$, $x > 1$.

Method 2 Rearrange

$$\frac{x-2-2(x-1)}{x-1} < 0 \quad \text{or} \quad \frac{x}{x-1} > 0$$

Complete by using the signs of x and $x-1$.

Method 3 Let $y = \dfrac{x-2}{x-1}$ and use a sketch graph.

The line $y = 2$ meets the graph where $x = 0$.

The solution can be read as $x < 0$, $x > 1$.

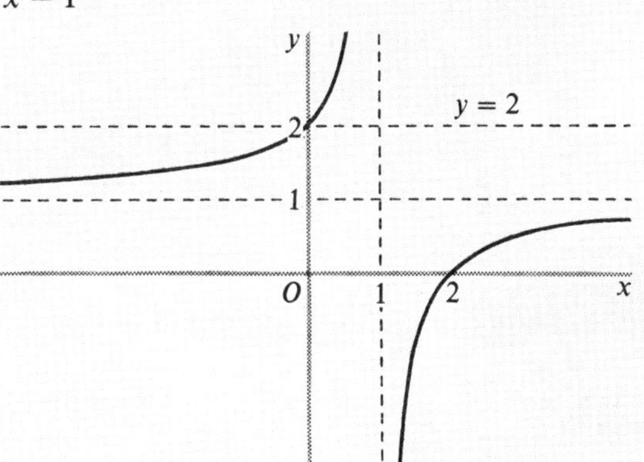

7 Solve $\dfrac{2x-1}{x^2+1} < \dfrac{1}{2}$.

Since $x^2 + 1 > 0$ for all x, both sides may be multiplied by $2(x^2+1)$ to give

$4x - 2 < x^2 + 1$

$x^2 - 4x + 3 > 0$

$(x-1)(x-3) > 0$

Using a sketch graph of $y = (x-1)(x-3)$ or otherwise, the solution is $x < 1$, $x > 3$.

8 Find the solution set for $\dfrac{x^2+1}{2x-1} > 2$.

Note: The reader may be tempted to argue that this is the same inequality as in Q7, as it 'results' from inverting both sides and reversing the inequality. But this is not a valid process if negative numbers are involved,

e.g. $-\frac{4}{3} < \frac{1}{2}$ but $-\frac{3}{4} < \frac{2}{1}$ also.

If $2x - 1$ is negative the inequality cannot be satisfied since the left-hand side is then negative. So only the case $2x - 1 > 0$ need be considered.

Multiply both sides by $2x - 1$ to give $x^2 + 1 > 4x - 2$

$$x^2 - 4x + 3 > 0$$

$$(x-1)(x-3) > 0.$$

By the usual methods, this is true for $x < 1$, $x > 3$.

But also $2x - 1 > 0$ so $x > \frac{1}{2}$

$\therefore$ the solution is $\frac{1}{2} < x < 1$, $x > 3$.

The solution set is $\left\{x : \frac{1}{2} < x < 1\right\} \cup \{x : x > 3\}$.

Summary of methods

The methods used for the solution of inequalities have involved the following techniques:

A The application of the basic rules I, II, III.

B The use of sketch graphs.

C The use of a number line to show the signs of factors, numerators, denominators, etc., after rearranging the inequality if necessary to give the form $f(x) > 0$, or an equivalent form.

A method which seems to one person to be the simplest may seem to someone else to be the hardest. There is NO necessity for every student to master all the methods suggested.

Exercise 11.3A

In questions **1**–**4** solve the inequality.

1 $(x+1)(2x-3)(x-4) \geqslant 0$

2 $\dfrac{x+2}{(2x+3)(x-1)} \leqslant 0$

3 $x(x+4)^2 \geqslant 0$

4 $\dfrac{1}{x+1} < 2$

In questions **5** and **6** find the solution set.

5 $\dfrac{7}{x} < x - 6$

6 $\dfrac{7}{x-6} < x$

Exercise 11.3B

In questions **1**–**6** solve the inequality.

1 $(x+3)(x+2)(3x-5) < 0$

2 $\dfrac{x-3}{(x-4)(2x+1)} > 0$

3 $(x-2)(x-3)^2 \leqslant 0$

4 $\dfrac{2}{x-1} > 3$

5 $\dfrac{2}{x-1} > -1$

6 $\dfrac{x-2}{x+1} < 4$

In questions **7** and **8** find the solution set.

7 $\dfrac{5x-2}{x^2+4} > 1$

8 $\dfrac{x^2+4}{5x-2} < 1$

11.4 Inequalities involving the modulus function

The modulus function was discussed in **1.4**. It was shown that there are three ways of describing the interval between A and B shown in the diagram. This interval could be described by any of the three inequalities

$$|x| < 3, \qquad -3 < x < 3, \qquad x^2 < 9.$$

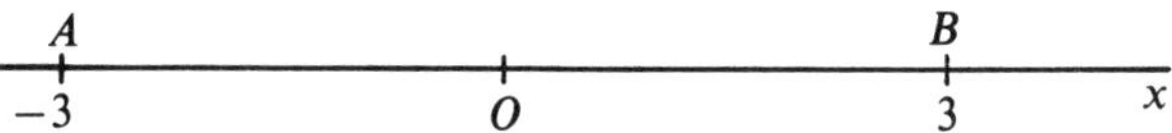

In general

$|f(x)| < a$ is equivalent to $-a < f(x) < a$ and to $[f(x)]^2 < a^2$,

$|f(x)| < |g(x)|$ is equivalent to $[f(x)]^2 < [g(x)]^2$.

Examples 11.4

1 Solve $|x-1| < 4$.

Method 1 From the definition of the modulus function in **1.4**, $|x-1|$ is the distance of the point representing x on the number line from the point representing 1. The given inequality states that this distance must be less than 4. It follows from the diagram that the solution is $-3 < x < 5$.

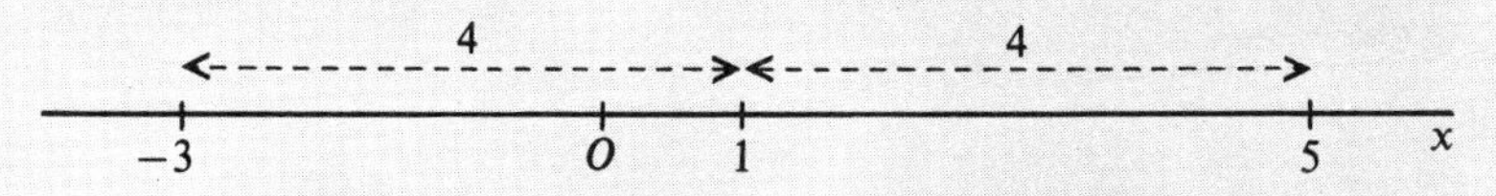

Method 2 The inequality can be written

$$-4 < x - 1 < 4$$

or $\qquad -3 < x < 5.$

2 Solve $|x-2| < |x-4|$.

Method 1 The inequality states that the distance of x from 2 is less than the distance of x from 4, i.e. x is nearer to 2 than to 4. It follows from the diagram that the solution is $x < 3$.

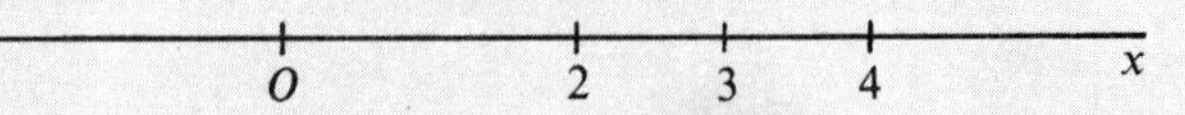

Method 2 Rewrite the inequality as

$$(x-2)^2 < (x-4)^2$$

or $$x^2 - 4x + 4 < x^2 - 8x + 16$$

$$4x < 12$$

$$x < 3.$$

Method 3 Use sketch graphs of $y = |x-2|$ and $y = |x-4|$ (see Examples **1.4**, Q3).

The graphs meet where $x = 3$ by symmetry.

From the graphs the solution is $x < 3$.

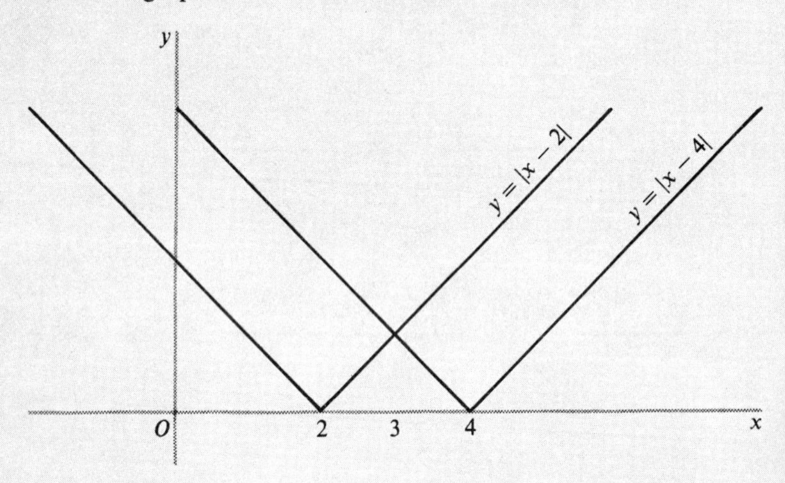

3 Solve $\left|\dfrac{x-2}{x-1}\right| < 2$.

Method 1 Rewrite as

$$\left(\frac{x-2}{x-1}\right)^2 < 4$$

$$x^2 - 4x + 4 < 4(x^2 - 2x + 1)$$

$$3x^2 - 4x > 0$$

$$x(3x-4) > 0.$$

By using a sketch graph or otherwise the solution is $x < 0$, $x > \frac{4}{3}$.

Method 2 Rewrite as $|x-2| < 2|x-1|$ and use sketch graphs of $y = |x-2|$ and $y = 2|x-1|$.

The graphs meet where $x = 0$ and where

$$2 - x = 2(x-1)$$

$$x = \frac{4}{3}.$$

From the graph the solution is $x < 0$, $x > \frac{4}{3}$.

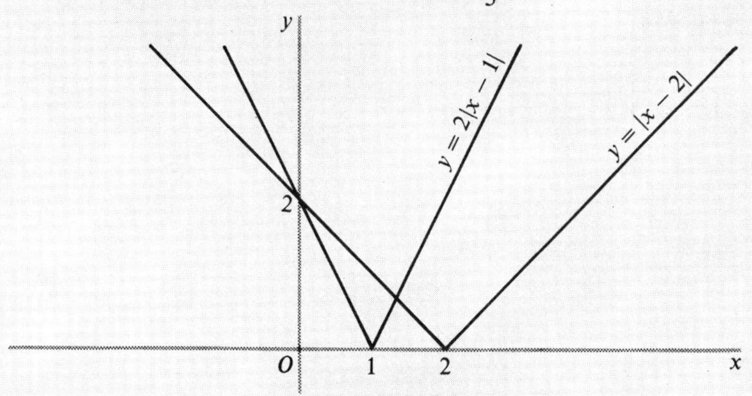

4 Solve $x^2 - 4|x| + 3 \geqslant 0$.

Method 1 Since $x^2 = |x|^2$, the left-hand side may be written $|x|^2 - 4|x| + 3$, and this is $f(|x|)$ where $f(x) = x^2 - 4x + 3$.

Using the method of **9.9** the graph of the left-hand side is the reflection in the y-axis of the graph of $y = x^2 - 4x + 3$ for $x \geqslant 0$.

From the graph the solution is $x \leqslant -3$, $-1 \leqslant x \leqslant 1$, $x \geqslant 3$.

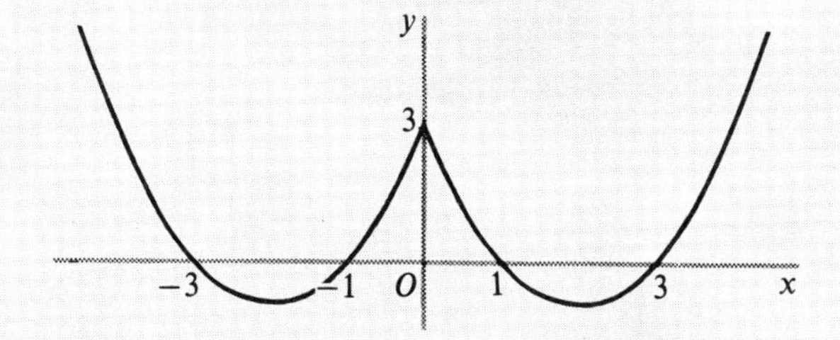

Method 2 Since $x^2 = |x|^2$, the inequality may be written

$t^2 - 4t + 3 \geqslant 0$, where $t = |x|$.

This gives $(t-1)(t-3) \geqslant 0$ and $t \geqslant 0$.

Solution is $0 \leqslant t \leqslant 1$, $t \geqslant 3$

or $|x| \leqslant 1$, $|x| \geqslant 3$.

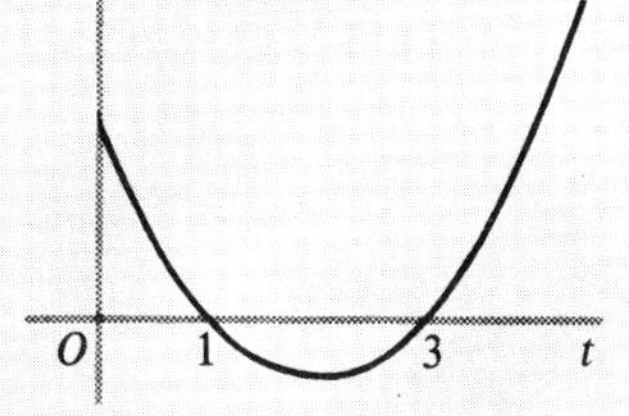

Exercise 11.4A

Solve the given inequalities.

1 $|x + 4| < |x - 6|$

2 $|2x - 3| \geqslant 2|x - 2|$

3 $\left|\dfrac{x - 5}{x + 1}\right| < 3$

4 $x^2 - 5|x| - 6 \leqslant 0$

5 $\left|\dfrac{x + 3}{x - 2}\right| < 4$

6 $x > |x - 1|$

7 $3x < |x - 2|$

Exercise 11.4B

Solve the given inequalities.

1 $|x - 3| > |x + 1|$

2 $\left|\dfrac{2x - 1}{x - 3}\right| < 2$

3 $\left|\dfrac{x + 2}{x - 1}\right| < 2$

4 $x^2 - 6|x| + 8 \geqslant 0$

5 $(|x| - 1)(|x| - 2)(|x| - 3) \geqslant 0$

6 $4x < |x + 3|$

7 $|2x - 1| \geqslant 2|3x - 2|$

Miscellaneous Exercise 11

1 Find the set of values of x for which

$$x^2 + x - 3 > 3x.$$

(*L*)

2 Sketch the curve $y = \dfrac{1}{x}$.

By using the graph, or otherwise, solve the inequality

$$\frac{1}{x} > \frac{x - 1}{2}.$$

(*AEB* 1983)

3 Find the ranges of values of x which satisfy the inequalities

a $x^2 - 3x - 3 > 1$ **b** $\dfrac{3}{x + 2} > x$.

(*AEB* 1984)

4 Find the ranges of values of x which satisfy the inequalities

a $x^2 - 7x + 6 > 0$ **b** $\dfrac{1}{6x - 1} < x$.

(*AEB* 1984

5 Solve the inequality

$$\frac{x + 2}{x - 1} < 3.$$

(*JMB*

6 Find the set of values of x for which

$$\frac{2x+3}{3x+4} < 1. \qquad (L)$$

7 Using the same axes sketch the curves

$$y = \frac{1}{x-1},\ y = \frac{x}{x+3},$$

giving the equations of the asymptotes. Hence, or otherwise, find the set of values of x for which

$$\frac{1}{x-1} > \frac{x}{x+3}. \qquad (L)$$

8 Obtain the set of values of x for which

$$\frac{1}{x-2} > \frac{1}{x+2}. \qquad (L)$$

9 Find the set of real values of x for which

$$|x+4| < |x+3|. \qquad (L)$$

10 Find the set of real values of x for which

$$|x-2| > 2|x+1|. \qquad (L)$$

11 Obtain the three sets of values of x for which

a $x > \dfrac{1}{x}$ **b** $\dfrac{1}{x-1} > \dfrac{x}{2-x}$ **c** $3|x-1| > |x+1|$. (L)

12 Given that $p(x) = 2x^3 - 7x^2 - 5x + 4$, use the factor theorem to find one factor of $p(x)$ and hence express $p(x)$ as the product of three linear factors. Sketch a graph of $y = p(x)$.

Solve **a** $p(x) > 0$ **b** $p(|x|) > 0$.

13 Find the solution set of $2x^2 + x \leqslant 1$. Hence find the solution set of

$$2\sin^2\theta + \sin\theta \leqslant 1$$

given that $-\pi \leqslant \theta \leqslant \pi$.

14 Given that the geometric series

$$1 + \frac{x-1}{x+3} + \left(\frac{x-1}{x+3}\right)^2 + \ldots$$

is convergent, find the set of possible values of x.

15 Given that the equation

$$kx^2 + 4(k-3)x + 2(k-1) = 0$$

has real roots, find the set of possible values of k.

16 Find the set of values of m for which the line $y = m(x-4)$ meets the curve $y = x^2 + 4$ in two distinct points. Find also the gradients of the tangents to the curve from the point (4, 0). Show the curve and the tangents in a sketch.

Chapter 12

Calculus 1

12.1 Introduction

Calculus is a branch of mathematics with many applications, for example in science, engineering and economics. One of the first applications is to problems involving the rate at which one quantity changes with respect to another.

The student has probably already solved some problems of this type by graphical methods; the following example provides a reminder.

Exercise 12.1

1 The table gives the number of bacteria, x, which were present in a solution at time t hours after noon, where $0 \leqslant t \leqslant 7$. Draw a graph of x against t.

t	0	1	2	3	4	5	6	7
x	130	180	250	360	500	700	980	1370

Label the points on the graph given by $t = 0$, $t = 3$, $t = 7$ as A, B, C respectively. Draw the lines AB and BC, and calculate the gradient of each line, correct to the nearest unit. State, to the nearest unit, the average rate at which the number of bacteria increased

a over the interval $0 \leqslant t \leqslant 3$ **b** over the interval $0 \leqslant t \leqslant 7$.

Estimate the rate at which the number of bacteria were increasing at $t = 3$.

12.2 The average gradient of a graph

A line which intersects a graph at two distinct points A and B is called a *secant*. The line segment between A and B is called a *chord*.

Given a secant AB on the graph of a function f, let $x = a$ at A and $x = b$ at B. Then the average gradient of the graph for $a \leqslant x \leqslant b$ is defined as the gradient of the line AB, i.e.

$$\text{average gradient} = \frac{f(b) - f(a)}{b - a}.$$

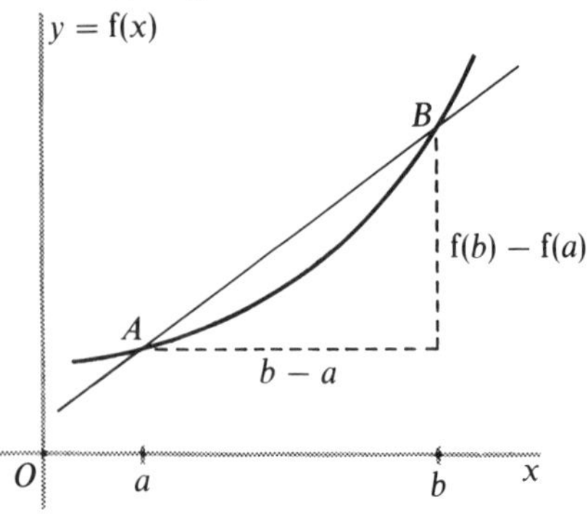

This gradient gives the average rate of increase of f(x) with respect to x for $a \leqslant x \leqslant b$.

In the special case when f(x) is linear, the average gradient is the same for any two numbers a, b. In all other cases, the average gradient varies according to the numbers a, b used.

Exercise 12.2

1

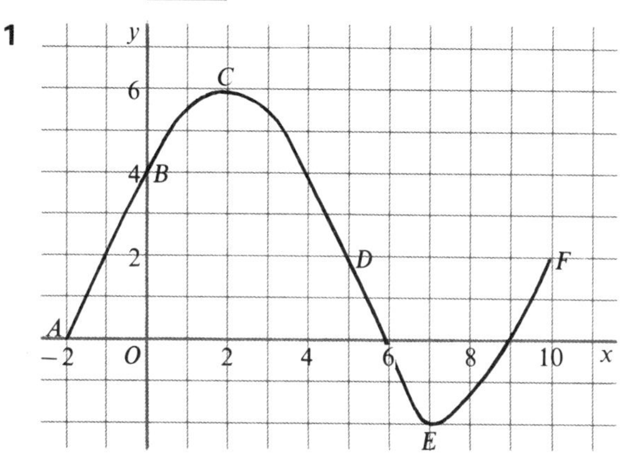

Calculate the average gradient of the graph for

a $-2 \leqslant x \leqslant 0$

b $0 \leqslant x \leqslant 2$

c $2 \leqslant x \leqslant 5$

d $5 \leqslant x \leqslant 7$

e $7 \leqslant x \leqslant 10$

f $5 \leqslant x \leqslant 10$

g $6 \leqslant x \leqslant 10$

2 In the graph for question **1**, name two points between which

a y is increasing

b y is decreasing

c y first increases and then decreases

d y first decreases and then increases.

12.3 The gradient of a graph at a point

The gradient of the graph of f(x) at the point A is defined as the gradient of the tangent to the graph at A. This gradient measures the rate at which f(x) is changing with respect to x at the point A.

Exercise 12.3

1 Draw an accurate graph of $f(x) = x^2$ for $0 \leqslant x \leqslant 9$.

Draw the tangents to the graph at each integer value of x for $1 \leqslant x \leqslant 7$. Find by measurement the gradient of each tangent, to the nearest unit.

Complete the following table.

x	1	2	3	4	5	6	7
gradient							

Use the pattern of your results to suggest a possible value for the gradient of the tangent at the point where $x = a$.

2 Draw an accurate graph of $f(x) = x^3$ for $0 \leqslant x \leqslant 4$.

Draw tangents to the graph at $x = 1, 2, 3$. Find by measurement the gradient of each tangent, to the nearest unit.

Complete the following table.

x	1	2	3
gradient			
$\frac{\text{gradient}}{3}$			

Use the pattern of your results to suggest a possible value for the gradient of the tangent at the point where $x = a$.

3 The table shows the x-coordinate of each of the points A and B on the graph of $y = x^2$, for various positions of A and B. Copy and complete the table to show the gradient, $g(AB)$, of the secant AB in each case.

x_A	3	2	-1	-2	1	2	3	3	3	3	3
x_B	5	6	3	4	5	4	4	3.5	3.3	3.1	3.001
y_A											
y_B											
$g(AB)$											

a Is there a secant through $A(3, 9)$ with gradient 6? What line through A has gradient 6?

b Find and simplify the gradient of the secant through the points $A(a, a^2)$, $B(b, b^2)$. Is there a secant through A with gradient $2a$? What line through A has gradient $2a$?

12.4 The gradient of the graph of x^2

To calculate the gradient of a graph, i.e. the gradient of the tangent to a graph, at a point A given by $x = a$, we first find the gradient of a secant through the point A and a different point B, given by $x = b$.

We then consider what happens to this gradient as A remains fixed and B moves closer to A along the graph.

The closer B is to A, the closer the secant AB is to the tangent at A.

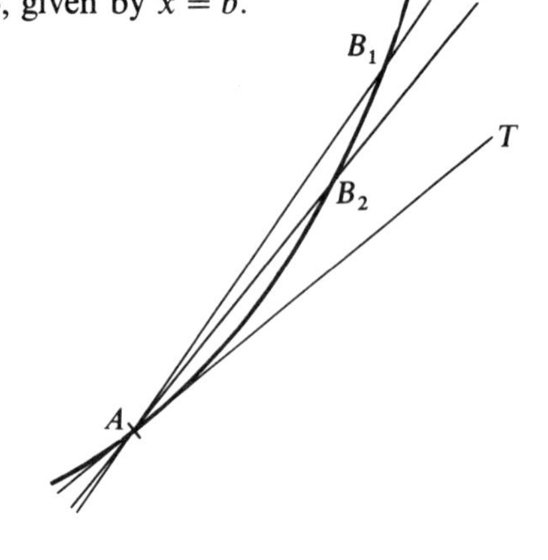

On the graph of $y = x^2$,
A is (a, a^2), B is (b, b^2)

$\therefore$ the gradient of the secant AB is

$$\frac{b^2 - a^2}{b - a} = \frac{(b - a)(b + a)}{b - a}$$
$$= b + a.$$

The closer B is to A, the closer b is to a, and the closer the gradient $b + a$ is to $a + a = 2a$.

$\therefore$ the gradient of the tangent at A is $2a$.

The gradient of the graph of x^3

The gradient of the secant AB through $A(a, a^3)$ and $B(b, b^3)$ is

$$\frac{b^3 - a^3}{b - a} = \frac{(b - a)(b^2 + ba + a^2)}{b - a}$$
$$= b^2 + ba + a^2.$$

The closer b is to a, the closer the gradient of AB is to

$$a^2 + a^2 + a^2 = 3a^2.$$

$\therefore$ the gradient of the tangent at A is $3a^2$.

It is convenient to use an abbreviated form of the phrases used above. Instead of 'the closer b is to a, the closer the gradient of AB is to' we may say 'as b tends to a, the gradient of AB tends to'; this may further be shortened by using '$\rightarrow$' as an abbreviation for 'tends to'. Using this notation, we may write

as $b \rightarrow a$, the gradient of $AB \rightarrow a^2 + a^2 + a^2 = 3a^2$.

The gradient of the tangent is the *limit* as $b \rightarrow a$ of the gradient of the secant AB.

The gradient of the graph of $\frac{1}{x}$

The gradient of the secant AB through $A\left(a, \frac{1}{a}\right)$ and $B\left(b, \frac{1}{b}\right)$ is

$$\frac{\frac{1}{b} - \frac{1}{a}}{b - a} = \frac{\frac{a - b}{ab}}{b - a} = -\frac{1}{ab}.$$

As $b \rightarrow a$, the gradient of $AB \rightarrow -\frac{1}{a^2}$.

$\therefore$ the gradient of the tangent at A is $-\frac{1}{a^2}$.

The gradient of the graph of $\sqrt{x}$

The gradient of the secant AB through $A(a, \sqrt{a})$ and $B(b, \sqrt{b})$ is

$$\frac{\sqrt{b} - \sqrt{a}}{b - a} = \frac{\sqrt{b} - \sqrt{a}}{(\sqrt{b} - \sqrt{a})(\sqrt{b} + \sqrt{a})} = \frac{1}{\sqrt{b} + \sqrt{a}}.$$

As $b \rightarrow a$, the gradient of $AB \rightarrow \frac{1}{2\sqrt{a}}$.

$\therefore$ the gradient of the tangent at A is $\frac{1}{2\sqrt{a}}$.

The derived function: differentiation

We have seen in several cases that the gradient of the graph of $f(x)$ at the point where $x = a$ depends on a. The function which maps a to the gradient at a is called the derived function of f; it is written f′. The process of obtaining f′ from f is called the 'differentiation' of f. If y is written for $f(x)$, then y' may be written for $f'(x)$; the name *derivative* is used for $f'(x)$.

The results so far found for the gradients of various graphs at the point where $x = a$ lead to the following table of derivatives:

$f(x)$	c	mx	x^2	x^3	$\frac{1}{x}$	$\sqrt{x}$
$f'(x)$	0	m	$2x$	$3x^2$	$-\frac{1}{x^2}$	$\frac{1}{2\sqrt{x}}$

The reader may have noticed a pattern emerging.

Differentiation of x^n, where n is a positive integer

Given that $f(x) = x^n$, where $n \in \mathbb{N}$, we have to find $f'(x)$, i.e. we have to find the gradient of the tangent. Using the same notation as before, the gradient of the secant AB is

$$\frac{b^n - a^n}{b - a} = b^{n-1} + ab^{n-2} + \ldots + a^{n-1}$$ (See **2.6**)

As $b \to a$, the gradient of $AB \to a^{n-1} + a^{n-1} + \ldots + a^{n-1}$

$$= na^{n-1}$$

$$\therefore f'(x) = nx^{n-1}$$

This result agrees with the pattern shown in the table.

It will later be proved that for all rational k, if $f(x) = x^k$, then $f'(x) = kx^{k-1}$. This result will meanwhile be used without proof.

Differentiation of $pf(x) + qg(x)$

If p and q are constants and $y = pf(x) + qg(x)$, then $y' = pf'(x) + qg'(x)$. The proof of this result is left to the reader. It may be extended to any number of terms.

Examples 12.4

1 Given that $y = 5x^3 + 4x^2 + 6x + 2$, find y'.

Using the known gradients of x^3, x^2, $6x$ and 2, the answer may be written down as

$$y' = 5 \,.\, 3x^2 + 4 \,.\, 2x + 6$$
$$= 15x^2 + 8x + 6$$

2 Given that $y = x^3 + \frac{5}{\sqrt{x}}$, find y'.

$$y = x^3 + 5x^{-\frac{1}{2}}$$
$$\therefore y' = 3x^2 - \frac{5}{2}x^{-\frac{3}{2}}$$

3 Given that $f(x) = (4x - 3)(2x + 5)$, find $f'(x)$.

The brackets must be removed first.

$$f(x) = 8x^2 + 14x - 15$$
$$\therefore f'(x) = 16x + 14$$

Exercise 12.4A

In each of questions **1**–**9**, differentiate to find y'.

1 $y = 5x^2 + 7x + 6$

2 $y = x^3 + 6x^2 - 9x + 2$

3 $y = 4x^3 + \frac{5}{x}$

4 $y = 3x^2 + \frac{4}{x^2}$

5 $y = 2\sqrt{x} + \frac{6}{\sqrt{x}}$

6 $y = (3x + 2)^2$

7 $y = \left(x^2 + \frac{3}{x}\right)^2$

8 $y = (1 + 2x)\sqrt{x}$

9 $y = \frac{x^2 + 4x}{\sqrt{x}}$

10 By considering the limit as $B \to A$ of the gradient of a secant AB, show that the derivative of x^4 is $4x^3$.

Exercise 12.4B

In each of questions **1**–**9**, find the derivative of the given $f(x)$.

1 $4x^2 - 3x + 5$

2 $x^3 + 7x^2 - 6x + 3$

3 $6x^2 - \frac{2}{x}$

4 $(4x - 5)(2x + 3)$

5 $\left(x + \frac{1}{2x}\right)^2$

6 $4x^{\frac{1}{2}} + 2x^{-\frac{1}{2}}$

7 $\frac{x^3 - 6x^2 + 2}{x^2}$

8 $x^2\left(\frac{2}{\sqrt{x}} + \frac{3}{x}\right)$

9 $\frac{(2x + 1)(3x - 5)}{x^2}$

10 By considering the limit as $B \to A$ of the gradient of a secant AB, show that the derivative of $\frac{1}{x^2}$ is $-\frac{2}{x^3}$.

12.5 Tangents and normals

For the curve given by the equation $y = f(x)$, the gradient of the tangent to the curve at the point A, where $x = a$, is $f'(a)$. The line through the point (x_1, y_1) with gradient m has the equation $y - y_1 = m(x - x_1)$, $\therefore$ the tangent at A to the curve has the equation

$$y - f(a) = f'(a)(x - a).$$

The *normal* to the curve at A is defined as the line through A perpendicular to the tangent at A; the gradient of the normal is therefore $-\dfrac{1}{f'(a)}$.
The equation of the normal at A is therefore

$$y - f(a) = -\frac{1}{f'(a)}(x - a).$$

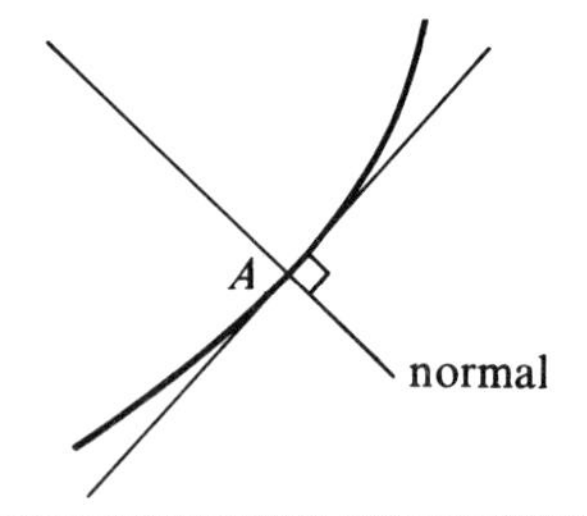

Examples 12.5

1 Find the equation of the tangent and the normal to the curve

$$y = f(x) = x^3 + 4x^2 - 8x + 2$$

at the point A where $x = 2$.

$y = f(x) = x^3 + 4x^2 - 8x + 2$
At A, $y = f(2) = 10$
$y' = f'(x) = 3x^2 + 8x - 8$
At A, $y' = f'(2) = 20$
$\therefore$ the equation of the tangent at A is $y - 10 = 20(x - 2)$
i.e. $y = 20x - 30$.

The equation of the normal at A is $y - 10 = -\dfrac{1}{20}(x - 2)$
i.e. $x + 20y = 202$.

2 A curve has the equation $y = f(x) = x^2 - 6x + 5$. Find the equation of the tangent to the curve which is parallel to the line $L: y = 2x + 1$.

The gradient of L is 2; the gradient of the tangent to the curve at $P(x, y)$ is $2x - 6$, $\therefore$ the point of contact of the required tangent is given by $2x - 6 = 2$, $x = 4$, $\therefore$ the point of contact is $(4, -3)$ and the equation of the tangent is $y + 3 = 2(x - 4)$ or $y = 2x - 11$.

Exercise 12.5A

1 Find the equation of the tangent and the normal to the given curves at the point for which x has the given value.

a $y = x^2 + 4x + 5$, $x = 1$ **b** $y = x + \dfrac{1}{x}$, $x = 2$

2 A curve has the equation $y = x^2 - 3x + 6$. Find the equation of the tangent which is perpendicular to the line $x + 3y = 6$.

3 Find the equations of the tangents to the curve

$$y = x^3 - 9x^2 + 21x - 10$$

which are parallel to the line $y = 6x + 3$.

4 Find the equation of the normal at the point (2, 3) on the curve $xy = 6$. Find also the coordinates of the point at which this normal meets the curve again. Illustrate by a sketch.

Exercise 12.5B

1 Find the equation of the tangent and the normal to the given curves at the point for which x has the given value.

a $y = x^3 - 5x^2 + 20,\ x = 3$ **b** $y = x^2 - \dfrac{2}{x^2},\ x = -1$

2 A curve has the equation $y = 3x^2 - 4x + 5$. Find the equation of the tangent which is parallel to the line $y = 8x + 3$.

3 Find the equations of the tangents to the curve

$$y = x^3 - 3x^2 - 3x + 6$$

which are parallel to the line $y = 6x - 7$.

4 Find the equation of the normal at the point (2, 3) on the curve $y = x + \dfrac{2}{x}$.

Find also the coordinates of the point where this normal meets the curve again.

5 The point A, given by $x = a$, lies on the curve $y = x^2 - 4x + 9$. Find the equation of the tangent at A. Deduce the equations of the two tangents to the curve from the origin O.

12.6 Stationary points, turning points and points of inflexion

Let A be the point given by $x = a$ on the graph of a function f.

If $f'(a) > 0$, f is increasing at A; the tangent at A has positive gradient.

If $f'(a) < 0$, f is decreasing at A; the tangent at A has negative gradient.

If $f'(a) = 0$, f is neither increasing nor decreasing at A and f is then said to be *stationary* at A; the tangent at A has zero gradient; A is called a stationary point on the graph of f.

Near a stationary point the graph may look like any one of the following four sketches. The tangent at A is shown in each case.

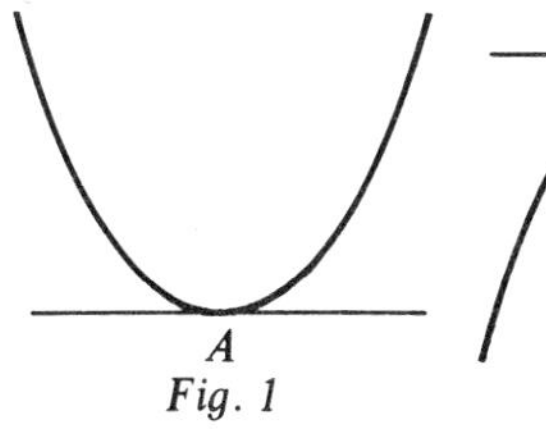

Fig. 1

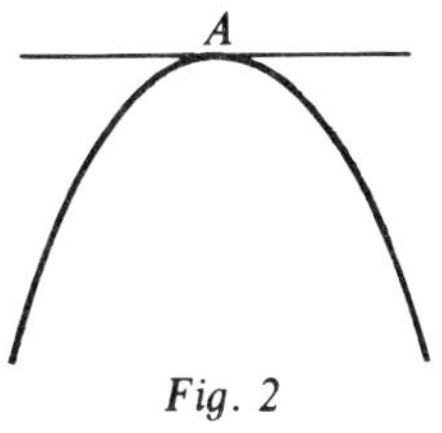

Fig. 2

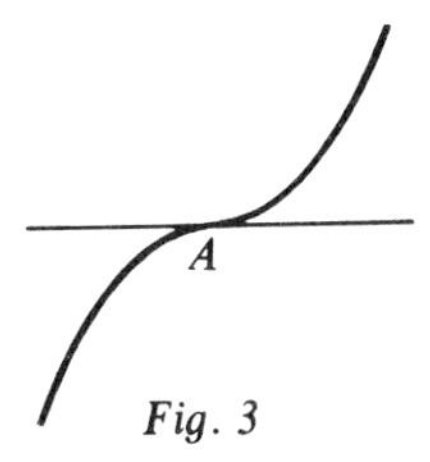

Fig. 3

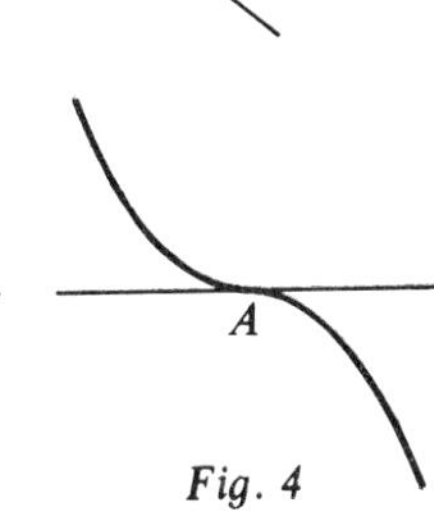

Fig. 4

In Fig. 1 $f(x)$ decreases until A is reached and then increases; the sign of $f'(x)$ changes from negative to positive as x increases through the value a; f has a 'local minimum' at A, and A is a *minimum point*.

In Fig. 2 $f(x)$ increases until A is reached and then decreases; the sign of $f'(x)$ changes from positive to negative as x increases through the value a; f has a 'local maximum' at A, and A is a *maximum point*.

In each of Fig. 1 and Fig. 2 the graph 'turns' at A, either from coming down to going up or vice versa, and in both these cases A is called a *turning point*.

In Fig. 3 $f(x)$ increases until A is reached and increases again on the right of A; the tangent at A crosses the graph at A.

In Fig. 4 $f(x)$ decreases until A is reached and decreases again on the right of A; again the tangent at A crosses the graph at A.

A point at which the tangent crosses the graph is called a *point of inflexion*; in Figs. 3 and 4 the point A is both a stationary point and a point of inflexion.

The gradient at a point of inflexion need not be zero; it may have any value, as illustrated in Figs. 5 and 6. Thus a point of inflexion need not be a stationary point.

Fig. 5 *Fig. 6*

Note that at B in Fig. 5 the gradient of the tangent has a minimum value; at C in Fig. 6 it has a maximum value.

Note also that a smooth curve must have at least one point of inflexion between two consecutive turning points, since the tangent at a maximum point is above the curve, and at a minimum point the tangent is below the curve; it must therefore cross the curve at some point. The cosine and sine curves have inflexions at each intersection with the x-axis. Points of inflexion will be discussed more fully in Book 2.

It is often important to find maximum and minimum values of a function; these are found by first looking for stationary points on the graph.

Examples 12.6

1 The function f is defined for all x by $f(x) = x^3 - 6x^2 + 9x + 2$.

Calculate the coordinates of the stationary points on the graph of $f(x)$ and determine the nature of these points. Sketch the graph.

$$f(x) = x^3 - 6x^2 + 9x + 2$$
$$\therefore f'(x) = 3x^2 - 12x + 9$$
$$= 3(x^2 - 4x + 3) = 3(x - 1)(x - 3)$$

At the stationary points, $f'(x) = 0$,
$\therefore x = 1$ or 3, $f(1) = 6$,
$f(3) = 2$
$\therefore$ the stationary points are $A(1, 6)$, $B(3, 2)$.

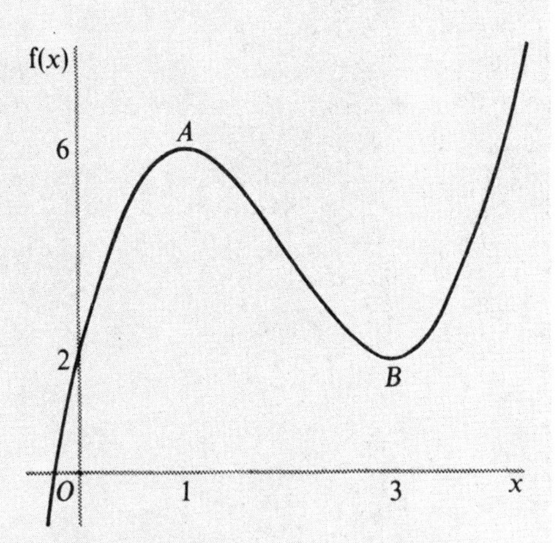

To determine the nature of these points, consider the signs of $f'(x)$, which is $3(x-1)(x-3)$; $f'(x) > 0$ for $x < 1$ and for $x > 3$, and $f'(x) < 0$ for $1 < x < 3$, so the signs on the left and right of $x = 1$ are $+$, then $-$, and on the left and right of $x = 3$ are $-$, then $+$.

$\therefore A$ is a maximum point and B is a minimum point.

To sketch the graph, the point $(0, 2)$ is useful; also $f(x) \approx x^3$ for large x. The graph is as shown.

2 The function f is defined for all x by $f(x) = x^3 - 6x^2 + 12x - 5$.

Calculate the coordinates of the stationary point on the graph of $f(x)$ and determine the nature of this point. Sketch the graph.

$$f(x) = x^3 - 6x^2 + 12x - 5$$
$$\therefore f'(x) = 3x^2 - 12x + 12$$
$$= 3(x^2 - 4x + 4)$$
$$= 3(x-2)^2$$

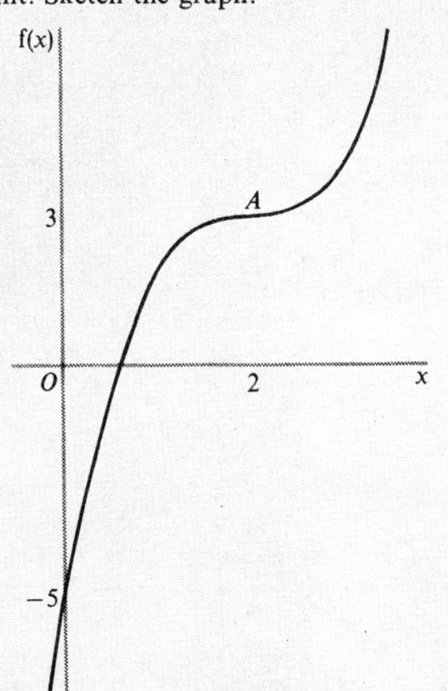

$\therefore f'(x) = 0$ at $x = 2$ only, and for $x \neq 2$, $f'(x) > 0$.

$\therefore f(x)$ has a stationary point at $x = 2$, and $f(x)$ increases for all other values of x, so that $x = 2$ is a point of inflexion. Since $f(2) = 3$, the point is $A(2, 3)$.

Another point on the graph is $(0, -5)$; also $f(x) \approx x^3$ for large x. The graph is as shown.

It may be verified that $f(x) = (x-2)^3 + 3$, and the graph may therefore be sketched by the methods of **9.8**. It is the result of applying the translation $\begin{pmatrix} 2 \\ 3 \end{pmatrix}$ to the graph of $y = x^3$.

3 The function f is defined for all non-zero x by $f(x) = x + \frac{1}{x}$.

Calculate the coordinates of all stationary points on the graph of f(x) and determine the nature of these points. Sketch the graph.

$$f(x) = x + \frac{1}{x} = x + x^{-1}$$

$$\therefore f'(x) = 1 - x^{-2}$$

$$= 1 - \frac{1}{x^2} = \frac{x^2 - 1}{x^2}$$

$$\therefore f'(x) = 0 \text{ at } x = \pm 1$$

$\therefore$ the stationary points are $A(1, 2)$ and $B(-1, -2)$.

To determine the nature of the stationary points, consider the sign of $f'(x)$; this is the same as the sign of $x^2 - 1$, since the denominator x^2 is positive for all non-zero x.

$\therefore f'(x) < 0$ for $x^2 < 1$, i.e. for $0 < x < 1$ and for $-1 < x < 0$
and $f'(x) > 0$ for $x^2 > 1$, i.e. for $x > 1$ and for $x < -1$

$\therefore f'(x)$ changes from $-$ to $+$ at A and from $+$ to $-$ at B, showing that A is a minimum point and B is a maximum point.

In this case $x = 0$ cannot be used to give another point on the graph since f is not defined for $x = 0$.

For x near $x = 0$, x is small and $f(x) \approx \frac{1}{x}$.

For x large, $\frac{1}{x}$ is small and $f(x) \approx x$.

Since $f(x) = x + \frac{1}{x}$, $f(x) > x$ for $x > 0$ and $f(x) < x$ for $x < 0$.

The line $y = x$ and the y-axis are both asymptotes to the graph.

Using these facts gives the framework on the left below, and the graph may be completed as shown on the right.

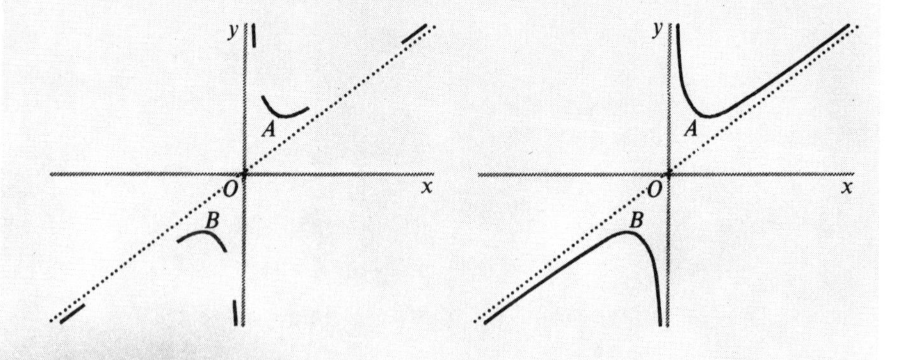

Exercise 12.6A

1 The function f is defined for all x by $f(x) = x^3 - 3x^2 + 2$.

Calculate the coordinates of the stationary points on the graph of $f(x)$ and determine the nature of these points. Sketch the graph.

2 Repeat question **1** given that $f(x) = x^3 - 9x^2 + 24x - 6$.

3 Repeat question **1** given that $f(x) = 2 - 3x + 3x^2 - x^3$.

4 The function f is defined for all non-zero x by $f(x) = x^2 + \frac{2}{x}$.

Show that the graph of $f(x)$ has one stationary point and state its coordinates. Sketch the graph.

Exercise 12.6B

1 The function f is defined for all x by $f(x) = x^3 - 12x + 6$.

Calculate the coordinates of the stationary points on the graph of $f(x)$ and determine the nature of these points. Sketch the graph.

2 Repeat question **1** given that $f(x) = 1 + x^2 - 2x^3$.

3 Repeat question **1** given that $f(x) = x^3 + 6x^2 + 12x + 12$.

4 The function f is defined for all non-zero x by $f(x) = x - \frac{1}{x}$.

Show that the graph of $f(x)$ has no stationary points and sketch the graph.

12.7 Integration

Integration is the reverse of differentiation. It is the process of finding a function f when the function f′ has been given. For example, given that $f'(x) = 2x$, what can be said about $f(x)$? We have found in **12.4** that if $f(x) = x^2$ then $f'(x) = 2x$. Therefore $f(x)$ could be x^2. But $f(x)$ could also be $x^2 + 3$, since in this case also $f'(x) = 2x$. Any constant can be added to x^2, since its derivative is zero. So if $f'(x) = 2x$, then $f(x) = x^2 + C$, where C is any constant.

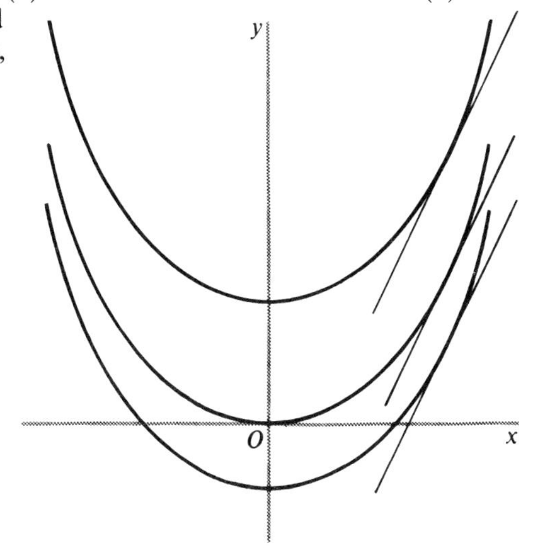

By giving C various values an unlimited number of curves $y = x^2 + C$ can be drawn. For a given value of x, all these curves have the same gradient; the tangents in the diagram are parallel. Any one of these curves may be transformed into any other by a translation parallel to the y-axis.

The following table may be verified by differentiating f(x) in each case; the constant C is called the *arbitrary constant of integration.*

f′(x)	0	a	x	x^2	x^k $(k \neq -1)$
f(x)	C	$ax + C$	$\frac{x^2}{2} + C$	$\frac{x^3}{3} + C$	$\frac{x^{k+1}}{k+1} + C$

(Note that the third and fourth entries are special cases of the fifth.)

Each entry in the bottom row is called the *integral* of the corresponding entry in the top row. If ambiguity is possible, it should be called 'the integral with respect to x'.

The following examples illustrate a simple application of integration; many other applications will be met later.

Examples 12.7

1 A curve passes through the point (2, 9) and $y' = 3x^2 + 8x - 6$. Find the equation of the curve.

$$y' = 3x^2 + 8x - 6$$

$$\therefore\ y = x^3 + 4x^2 - 6x + C$$

Since (2, 9) satisfies this equation, $9 = 12 + C$, $C = -3$

$\therefore$ the equation of the curve is $y = x^3 + 4x^2 - 6x - 3$.

2 A curve passes through the point (2, 5) and $y' = 2x + \frac{1}{x^2}$. Find the equation of the curve.

$$y' = 2x + \frac{1}{x^2} = 2x + x^{-2}$$

$$\therefore\ y = x^2 - x^{-1} + C$$

Since (2, 5) satisfies this equation, $5 = 4 - \frac{1}{2} + C$, $C = \frac{3}{2}$

$\therefore$ the equation of the curve is $y = x^2 - \frac{1}{x} + \frac{3}{2}$.

Exercise 12.7A

1 In each of the following, f′(x) is given. Find f(x).

a $2x + 5$ **b** $3x - 4$ **c** $3x^2 - 4x + 5$

d $x^2 - 6x - 7$ **e** $2x + \sqrt{x}$ **f** $x^3 + \frac{1}{x^2}$

g $x^4 + \frac{1}{x^4}$ **h** $3x^2 + \frac{1}{\sqrt{x}}$

2 The curve $y = $ f(x) passes through the point (4, 2), and f′(x) $= 4x + 5$. Find the equation of the curve.

3 The curve $y = f(x)$ passes through the point (0, 4) and $f'(x) = 3x^2 - 6x + 2$.
Find the equation of the curve.

4 A curve passes through the point (1, 5) and $y' = 4x + \dfrac{1}{x^2}$.
Find the equation of the curve.

Exercise 12.7B

1 In each of the following, $f'(x)$ is given. Find $f(x)$.

a $4x - 5$ **b** $6x^2 + 3x - 2$ **c** $x^2 - 10x + 3$

d $\dfrac{(x+1)^2}{x^4}$ **e** $\left(x^3 + \dfrac{1}{x^3}\right)^2$

2 A curve passes through the point (4, 3) and $y' = 2x + 1$.
Find the equation of the curve.

3 A curve passes through the point (0, 6) and $y' = 6x^2 + 4x - 5$.
Find the equation of the curve.

4 A curve passes through the point $(-1, 2)$ and $y' = x^2 - \dfrac{1}{x^4}$.
Find the equation of the curve and find also the equation of the tangent to the curve at the given point.

12.8 The Leibniz notation

So far, all the functions used in this chapter have been written in terms of the same letter x; y has been used for $f(x)$ and y' for $f'(x)$. In many applications of calculus more than one variable may be in use in one problem, and it is then more convenient to use the Leibniz notation; this notation has other advantages also in certain contexts.

As an illustration of the use of this notation, the result found at the start of **12.4** is now found again.

The gradient of the graph of x^2

Let P be the point (x, y) on the graph of $y = x^2$; let Q be a point on the curve near to P, and use the symbol δx for the x-step from P to Q. The Greek letter δ here is pronounced 'delta'. Use the symbol δy for the corresponding y-step from P to Q, so that Q has coordinates $(x + \delta x, y + \delta y)$.

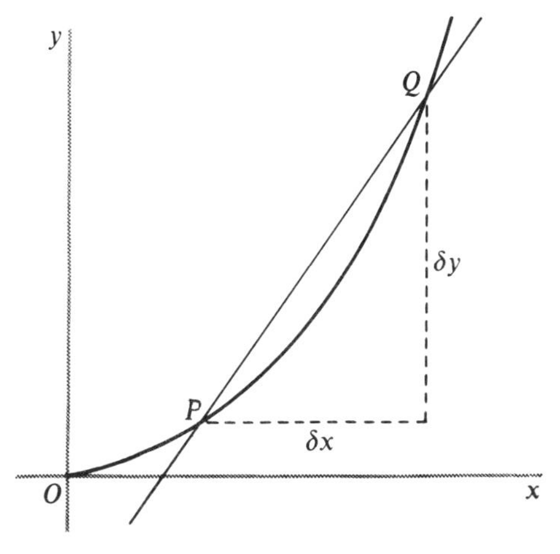

Since Q lies on the curve $y = x^2$,

$$y + \delta y = (x + \delta x)^2$$

$$\begin{aligned}\therefore \delta y &= (x + \delta x)^2 - x^2 \\ &= (x + \delta x + x)(x + \delta x - x) \\ &= (2x + \delta x)(\delta x).\end{aligned}$$

The gradient of the secant $PQ = \frac{\delta y}{\delta x} = 2x + \delta x$.

As $Q \to P$, $\delta x \to 0$, and the gradient of $PQ \to 2x$

$\therefore$ the gradient of the tangent at P is $2x$.

In Leibniz notation, the gradient of the tangent is written $\frac{dy}{dx}$, so the conclusion is:

$$\text{for } y = x^2, \frac{dy}{dx} = 2x.$$

The notation $\frac{dy}{dx}$

The symbol $\frac{dy}{dx}$ is defined by the statements:

On the graph of $y = f(x)$ the gradient of a secant is $\frac{\delta y}{\delta x}$.

As $\delta x \to 0$, $\frac{\delta y}{\delta x} \to \frac{dy}{dx}$, the gradient of the tangent.

Thus $\frac{dy}{dx} = f'(x)$.

The symbols dx and dy separately have no meaning; $\frac{dy}{dx}$ is not a fraction.

The second derived function

Differentiation of the function f gives the first derived function f′; this function may itself be differentiated to give the second derived function of f, which is written f″. If $y = f(x)$, the first derivative is written y' or $f'(x)$ or, in Leibniz notation, $\frac{dy}{dx}$. The second derivative is written y'' or $f''(x)$ or, in Leibniz notation, $\frac{d}{dx}\left(\frac{dy}{dx}\right)$; this last form is abbreviated to $\frac{d^2y}{dx^2}$. Thus

$$y = f(x) \Rightarrow \frac{dy}{dx} = f'(x) \Rightarrow \frac{d^2y}{dx^2} = f''(x).$$

The second derivative may in some cases be used to distinguish between the different types of stationary point. If at a stationary point $y'' > 0$, then y' has positive gradient and is therefore increasing; it must be changing from negative values to positive values, so the stationary point is a minimum point.

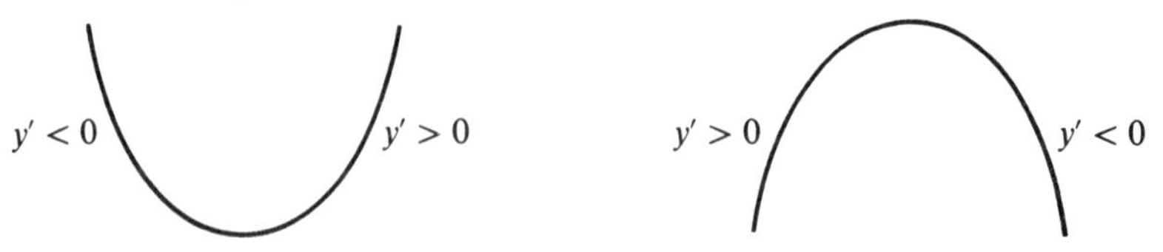

Similarly if at a stationary point $y'' < 0$, then y' is decreasing and the stationary point is a maximum.

It is not however true that at a minimum point y'' is necessarily positive or that at a maximum point y'' is necessarily negative; y'' can be zero at any type of stationary point. Consider for example $y = x^4$, $y = -x^4$.

Summarising these facts:

if at $x = a$, $y' = 0$ and $y'' > 0$, then $x = a$ gives a minimum point;

if at $x = a$, $y' = 0$ and $y'' < 0$, then $x = a$ gives a maximum point;

if at $x = a$, $y' = 0$ and $y'' = 0$, then $x = a$ may give a minimum point or a maximum point or a point of inflexion.

Examples 12.8

1 A sector of a circle is to have an area of $100\,\text{cm}^2$ and the least possible perimeter. Find the angle of the sector.

Let the radius of the sector be r cm, the angle be θ radians, and the perimeter be p cm. Then

$$\frac{1}{2}r^2\theta = 100 \qquad \text{and} \qquad p = 2r + r\theta.$$

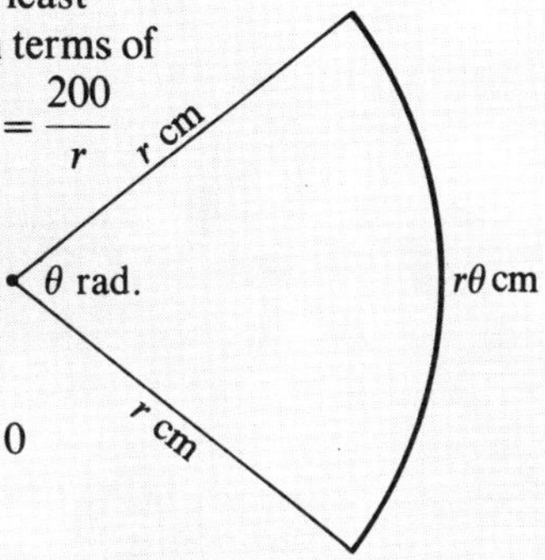

Before we can use calculus to find the least possible perimeter, we must express p in terms of one variable only. Since $r^2\theta = 200$, $r\theta = \dfrac{200}{r}$

$$\therefore\quad p = 2r + \frac{200}{r} = 2r + 200r^{-1}$$

$$\therefore\quad \frac{dp}{dr} = 2 - 200r^{-2} = 2 - \frac{200}{r^2}.$$

r cm

θ rad.

rθ cm

r cm

For the least possible perimeter, $\dfrac{dp}{dr} = 0$

$\therefore\ r^2 = 100$, $r = 10$, since $r > 0$.

Using the sign of the second derivative to determine the nature of the stationary point at $r = 10$:

$\dfrac{d^2p}{dr^2} = 400r^{-3} > 0$ for $r = 10$, so $r = 10$ gives a minimum point.

When $r = 10$, $\theta = 2$, and the angle of the sector is 2 radians.

Exercise 12.8

1 Given that $y = x^3 + 6x^2 - 3x - 2$, find $\dfrac{dy}{dx}$ and $\dfrac{d^2y}{dx^2}$.

2 Given that $v = t^3 - 4t^2 + 8$, find $\dfrac{dv}{dt}$ and $\dfrac{d^2v}{dt^2}$.

3 Given that $a = 9(t^2 - 5)$, find $\dfrac{da}{dt}$ and $\dfrac{d^2a}{dt^2}$.

4 Given that $\theta = 4t^2(t + 2)$, find $\dfrac{d\theta}{dt}$ and $\dfrac{d^2\theta}{dt^2}$.

5 A box without a lid is to be in the form of a cuboid with a square base. The total surface area of the box is to be $300\,\text{cm}^2$. Given that the side of the box is x cm and the volume is $V\,\text{cm}^3$, show that

$$V = \frac{1}{4}(300x - x^3).$$

Find the side of the base for which the volume of the box is as large as possible.

6 An open metal box is to be made in the form of a cuboid with a square base and a volume of $4000\,\text{cm}^3$. Find the measurements of the box for which the area of metal used is as small as possible.

12.9 Displacement, velocity and acceleration

There are two particularly important applications of the ideas of average rate of change over an interval and rate of change at a point, which were discussed in **12.2** and **12.3**.

Suppose a particle P is moving along the x-axis and that the displacement of P from the origin O is x metres after t seconds, where $x = f(t)$. Then the average velocity of P for $t_1 \leqslant t \leqslant t_2$ is the average rate of change of the displacement with respect to time, and is therefore given by the gradient of the secant AB in the diagram. Let $x_1 = f(t_1)$ and $x_2 = f(t_2)$. Then

$$\text{average velocity} = \frac{x_2 - x_1}{t_2 - t_1}\,\text{ms}^{-1}.$$

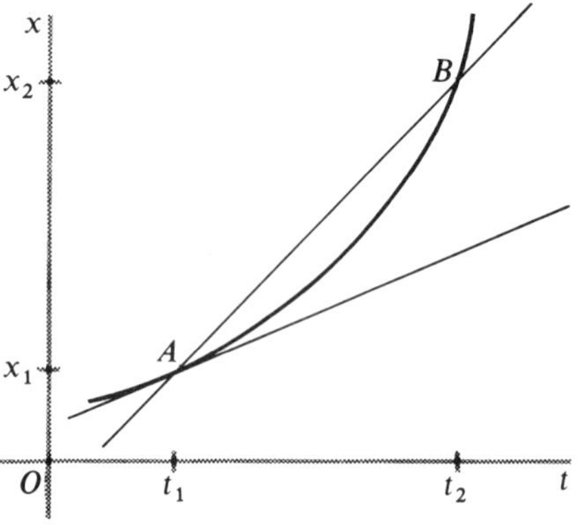

The velocity of P *at the instant* $t = t_1$ is given by the gradient of the tangent at A, which is $f'(t_1)$. If the velocity after t seconds is $v\,\text{ms}^{-1}$, then

$$v = \frac{dx}{dt} = f'(t).$$

If $v > 0$, x is increasing and the particle P is moving in the positive direction along the x-axis. If $v < 0$, then x is decreasing and P is moving in the negative direction. If $v = 0$, the particle is stationary; the direction of motion may, or may not, be about to change.

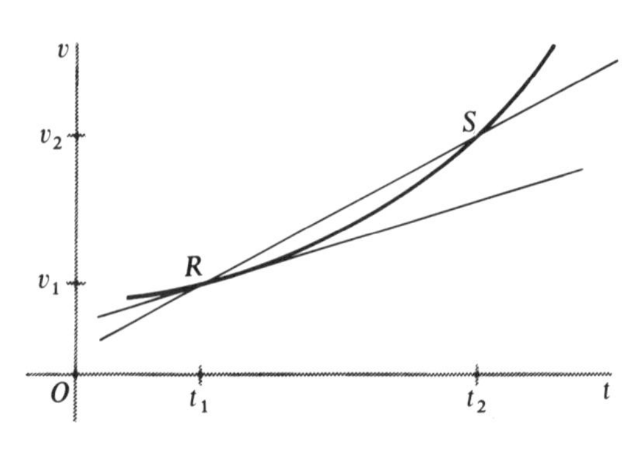

The *speed* of P at an instant is the magnitude of the velocity, i.e. it is given by $|v|$.

The *average acceleration* over the interval $t_1 \leqslant t \leqslant t_2$ is the average rate of change of the velocity with respect to time; in the diagram it is given by the gradient of the secant RS

The acceleration *at the instant* $t = t_1$ is given by the gradient of the tangent at R; $\therefore$ if the acceleration after t seconds is a ms^{-2} then $a = \frac{dv}{dt}$.

Summarising: $x = f(t)$, $\quad v = \frac{dx}{dt} = f'(t)$, $\quad a = \frac{dv}{dt} = \frac{d^2x}{dt^2} = f''(t)$.

Examples 12.9

The questions in these examples refer to a particle P moving along an x-axis. After t seconds the displacement of P from O is x m, the velocity is v ms^{-1} and the acceleration is a ms^{-2}.

1 Given that $x = t^3 - 12t + 6$, calculate the displacement of P at $t = 1$ and at $t = 4$. Hence find the average velocity of P for $1 \leqslant t \leqslant 4$. Calculate the velocity of P at $t = 1$ and at $t = 4$. Hence find the average acceleration for $1 \leqslant t \leqslant 4$. Find also the acceleration at $t = 1$ and at $t = 4$.

At $t = 1$, displacement $= -5$ m; at $t = 4$, it is 22 m

$\therefore$ for $1 \leqslant t \leqslant 4$, average velocity $= \frac{22 - (-5)}{4 - 1}$ ms^{-1} $= 9$ ms^{-1}.

Since $x = t^3 - 12t + 6$, $v = \frac{dx}{dt} = 3t^2 - 12$

$\therefore$ at $t = 1$, velocity $= -9$ ms^{-1}; at $t = 4$, velocity $= 36$ ms^{-1}

$\therefore$ for $1 \leqslant t \leqslant 4$, average acceleration $= \frac{36 - (-9)}{3}$ ms^{-2} $= 15$ ms^{-2}.

Since $v = 3t^2 - 12$, $a = \frac{dv}{dt} = 6t$

$\therefore$ at $t = 1$ acceleration $= 6$ ms^{-2}, at $t = 4$ acceleration $= 24$ ms^{-2}.

2 Given that $x = (t - 2)(t - 4)$ for $0 \leqslant t \leqslant 6$, sketch the graph of x. Hence write down the least and greatest displacements of P from O. Find the total distance the particle travels.

Find v and sketch the graph of v. Sketch also the graph of the speed of the particle.

The least displacement is given by the minimum on the graph at $t = 3$ and is -1 m.

The greatest displacement is at the beginning and end of the interval and is 8 m.

The total distance the particle travels is from 8 m on the positive side of 0 to 1 m on the negative side, and back to the starting position, so the total distance is 2×9 m $= 18$ m.

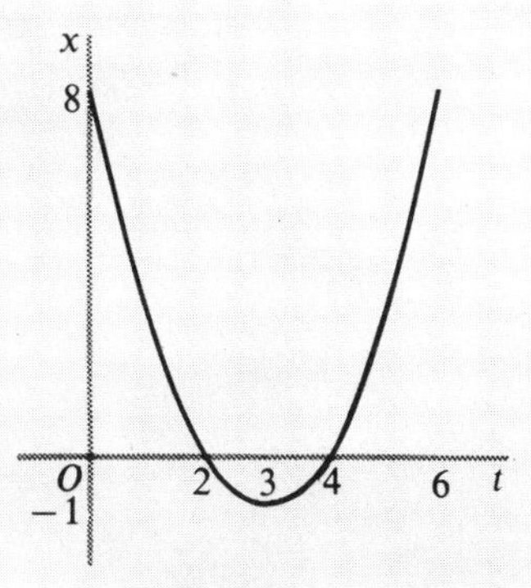

Since $x = (t - 2)(t - 4) = t^2 - 6t + 8$

$$v = \frac{dx}{dt} = 2t - 6.$$

The graphs are as shown.

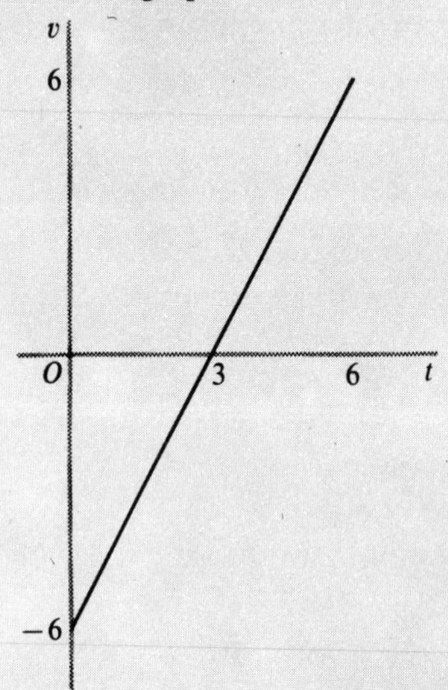

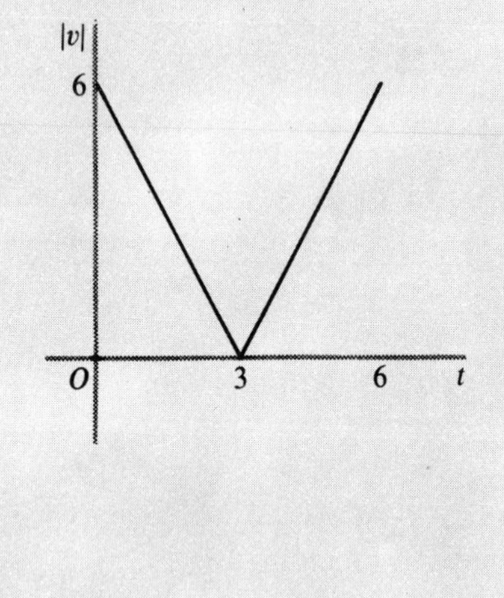

3 Given that $v = 4t + 3$ and that when $t = 2$, $x = 16$, find x in terms of t.

$$v = 4t + 3 \qquad \therefore \frac{dx}{dt} = 4t + 3$$

$$\therefore \text{ by integration } x = 2t^2 + 3t + C \qquad (1)$$

where C is some constant. If no more information was given, no more would be known about x. But it is also given that when $t = 2$, $x = 16$. Substituting in (1):

$$16 = 8 + 6 + C \qquad \therefore C = 2$$

$$\therefore x = 2t^2 + 3t + 2$$

4 Given that $a = 6t^2 + 8t + 1$ and that when $t = 1$, $v = 10$, find v in terms of t.

$$a = 6t^2 + 8t + 1 \qquad \therefore \frac{dv}{dt} = 6t^2 + 8t + 1$$

$$\therefore \text{ by integration } v = 2t^3 + 4t^2 + t + C \qquad (2)$$

where C is some constant. Since it is given that when $t = 1$, $v = 10$, C can be found by substituting in (2):

$$10 = 2 + 4 + 1 + C \qquad \therefore C = 3$$

$$\therefore v = 2t^3 + 4t^2 + t + 3$$

5 Given that $a = 6t - 12$ for $0 \leqslant t \leqslant 5$, and that when $t = 0$, $v = 9$ and $x = 2$, find v and x in terms of t.

Find the times at which the direction of motion of P is reversed and find the displacement at each of these times.

$$a = \frac{dv}{dt} = 6t - 12$$

$$\therefore v = 3t^2 - 12t + C$$

when $t = 0$, $v = 9$ $\quad\therefore C = 9$

$$\therefore v = \frac{dx}{dt} = 3t^2 - 12t + 9$$

$$\therefore x = t^3 - 6t^2 + 9t + k$$

when $t = 0$, $x = 2$ $\quad\therefore k = 2$

$$\therefore x = t^3 - 6t^2 + 9t + 2$$

When the direction of motion is reversed, $v = 0$, and

$$v = 3(t^2 - 4t + 3)$$
$$= 3(t - 1)(t - 3)$$
$$= 0 \text{ when } t = 1 \text{ and when } t = 3.$$

At each of these values of t, v changes sign, and so the direction of motion is reversed.

$\therefore$ the times are 1 s and 3 s, and the corresponding displacements are 6 m and 2 m respectively.

All the questions in Exercise **12.9** refer to a particle P moving along an x-axis through a point O. After t seconds the displacement of P from O is x m, the velocity is v ms^{-1} and the acceleration is a ms^{-2}.

Exercise 12.9A

1 Given that $x = t^3 - 6t^2 + 5t$, find the velocity at the times when the particle is at O. Find also the velocity when the acceleration is zero.

2 Given that $v = 3t(t - 4)$ and that when $t = 0$, $x = 3$, find x at $t = 4$.

3 Given that $a = 6t + 4$, and that when $t = 0$, $v = 5$ and $x = 2$, find the velocity and the displacement when $t = 2$.

4 Given that $x = t^3 + 4t + 3$ for $0 \leqslant t \leqslant 5$, calculate x at $t = 2$ and at $t = 4$. Hence find the average velocity of P for $2 \leqslant t \leqslant 4$. Find also the velocity of P at $t = 2$ and at $t = 4$, and calculate the average of these two velocities.

5 Given that $x = (2 - t)(t + 1)$ for $0 \leqslant t \leqslant 5$, sketch the graph of x. Find the greatest and least displacement of P from O and the corresponding velocities. Find also the total distance travelled.

6 Given that $v = 4t - 9$ and that when $t = 0$, $x = 10$, find x in terms of t. Hence find the times at which the particle passes through O, and calculate the velocity at each of these times.

Exercise 12.9B

1 Given that $v = t^2 - 9$ for $0 \leqslant t \leqslant 5$, sketch the graph of v. State the least and greatest velocities. Calculate the average acceleration for $1 \leqslant t \leqslant 3$. Find also the acceleration at $t = 1$ and at $t = 3$.

2 Given that $v = 6t^2 - 4t + 3$ and that when $t = 1$, $x = 7$, find x in terms of t.

3 Given that $a = 6t - 4$ and that when $t = 1$, $v = 5$ and $x = 9$, find v and x in terms of t.

4 Given that $x = t(t - 3)^2$ for $0 \leqslant t \leqslant 6$, find the times at which P is stationary and sketch the velocity–time graph. State the time at which the displacement has a local maximum and calculate its value. Sketch the distance–time graph. State the greatest displacement of P and calculate the total distance travelled.

5 Given that $x = t^3 - 6t^2 + 12t - 7$, show that P passes through O when $t = 1$ and for no other value of t. Show that P is stationary for one value of t only, and show that for all other values of t, P moves in the positive direction along the x-axis.

12.10 Differentiation of composite functions: the chain rule

Given that $h(x) = gf(x)$, the derived function of h may be found by a method called the *chain rule*, if the derived functions of f and g are known.

As an example, suppose $f(x) = x^3 + 2$ and $g(x) = x^2$. Then $h(x) = g(x^3 + 2) = (x^3 + 2)^2$. In this simple case, $h(x)$ may be differentiated by first removing the brackets, giving

$$h(x) = x^6 + 4x^3 + 4$$
$$h'(x) = 6x^5 + 12x^2$$

and the chain rule is not needed. The rule will now be stated, and used to obtain $h'(x)$ in the above example.

The chain rule states that if $y = g(t)$ and $t = f(x)$, so that $y = gf(x)$, then

$$\frac{dy}{dx} = \frac{dy}{dt}\frac{dt}{dx}.$$

In the above example, let $y = h(x) = (x^3 + 2)^2$.

Let $\quad y = t^2$ where $t = x^3 + 2$, $\quad$ then $\dfrac{dy}{dt} = 2t$ $\quad$ and $\quad \dfrac{dt}{dx} = 3x^2$

$$\therefore \frac{dy}{dx} = 2t \,.\, 3x^2$$
$$= 2(x^3 + 2) \,.\, 3x^2$$
$$= 6x^5 + 12x^2 \quad \text{as obtained above.}$$

In this example the chain rule was not needed, but consider the example $h(x) = (x^3 + 2)^{10}$. Here the method of removing brackets is not attractive.

To use the chain rule,

let $\quad y = t^{10}$ where $t = x^3 + 2$

then $\dfrac{dy}{dt} = 10t^9 \quad$ and $\quad \dfrac{dt}{dx} = 3x^2 \qquad \therefore \dfrac{dy}{dx} = 10t^9 \,.\, 3x^2$

$$= 30x^2(x^3 + 2)^9.$$

A satisfactory proof of the chain rule is not within the scope of this text, but the following argument indicates the method in outline.

Let $y = g(t)$ where $t = f(x)$, so that $y = h(x)$ where $h = gf$. Suppose an increase δx in x causes an increase δt in t, which in turn causes an increase δy in y.

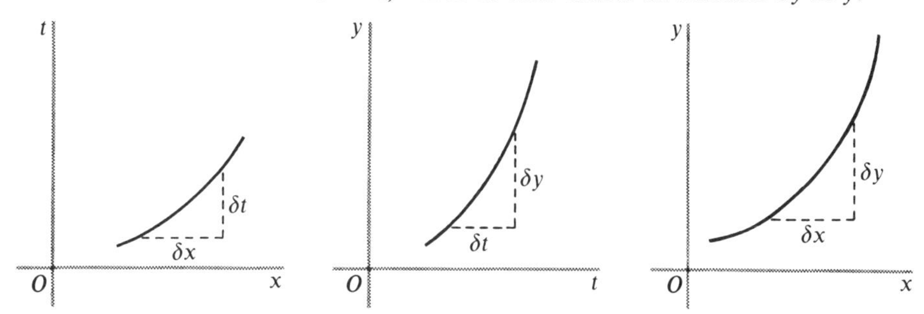

Then $\dfrac{\delta y}{\delta x} = \dfrac{\delta y}{\delta t}\dfrac{\delta t}{\delta x}$

Let $\quad \delta x \to 0$; 'then' $\delta t \to 0 \quad$ and $\quad \delta y \to 0$, $\quad \dfrac{\delta y}{\delta x} \to \dfrac{dy}{dx}$, $\quad \dfrac{\delta y}{\delta t} \to \dfrac{dy}{dt}$, $\quad \dfrac{\delta t}{\delta x} \to \dfrac{dt}{dx}$

which suggests that $\dfrac{dy}{dx} = \dfrac{dy}{dt}\dfrac{dt}{dx}$.

The derivative of x^n, where n is a negative integer

In **12.4** it was proved that when n is a positive integer, the derivative of x^n is nx^{n-1}. It will now be proved that the same result is true when n is a negative integer.

Given that $y = x^n$, where n is a negative integer, let $n = -k$, so that k is a positive integer. Then $y = x^{-k}$.

Let $\quad t = x^k$, then $y = t^{-1}$, $\qquad \dfrac{dt}{dx} = kx^{k-1}$ since k is a positive integer,

and $\dfrac{dy}{dt} = -t^{-2}$ using the result proved in **12.4**,

$$\therefore \frac{dy}{dx} = \frac{dy}{dt}\frac{dt}{dx} = -\frac{1}{t^2} \,.\, kx^{k-1}$$

$$= -\frac{1}{x^{2k}} \,.\, kx^{k-1}$$

$$= -kx^{-k-1}$$

$$= nx^{n-1}, \text{ since } n = -k.$$

Examples 12.10

Use the chain rule to differentiate y.

1 $y = (5x^2 + 1)^4$ **2** $y = \sqrt{(x^3 + 4)}$ **3** $y = \dfrac{1}{x^5 + 4x}$

1 $y = (5x^2 + 1)^4$; then $y = t^4$ where $t = 5x^2 + 1$

$$\frac{dy}{dt} = 4t^3, \quad \frac{dt}{dx} = 10x$$

$$\therefore \frac{dy}{dx} = 4t^3 \,.\, 10x \quad = 40x(5x^2 + 1)^3$$

2 $y = \sqrt{(x^3 + 4)}$; $y = t^{\frac{1}{2}}$ where $t = x^3 + 4$

$$\frac{dy}{dt} = \frac{1}{2}t^{-\frac{1}{2}}, \quad \frac{dt}{dx} = 3x^2$$

$$\therefore \frac{dy}{dx} = \frac{1}{2}t^{-\frac{1}{2}} \,.\, 3x^2 \quad = \frac{3}{2}x^2(x^3 + 4)^{-\frac{1}{2}} = \frac{3x^2}{2\sqrt{(x^3 + 4)}}$$

3 $y = \dfrac{1}{x^5 + 4x}$; $y = t^{-1}$ where $t = x^5 + 4x$

$$\frac{dy}{dt} = -t^{-2}, \quad \frac{dt}{dx} = 5x^4 + 4$$

$$\therefore \frac{dy}{dx} = -(x^5 + 4x)^{-2}(5x^4 + 4) = -\frac{5x^4 + 4}{(x^5 + 4x)^2}$$

Exercise 12.10A

Use the chain rule to differentiate y.

1 $y = (3x + 1)^2$

2 $y = (1 - 4x)^5$

3 $y = \dfrac{1}{2x - 3}$

4 $y = (x^2 + 4)^3$

5 $y = \sqrt{(2x + 1)}$

6 $y = \dfrac{1}{(x^2 + 3)^2}$

7 $y = \left(x^2 - \dfrac{1}{x}\right)^3$

8 $y = \dfrac{1}{\sqrt{(4x^2 - 1)}}$

9 $y = \dfrac{1}{(3x^2 + 5x + 2)^3}$

Exercise 12.10B

Use the chain rule to differentiate y.

1 $y = (4x - 5)^3$

2 $y = (2 - 3x)^4$

3 $y = \dfrac{1}{5x - 2}$

4 $y = (x^2 + 2x + 3)^2$

5 $y = \sqrt{(4 - 3x)}$

6 $y = \dfrac{1}{2x^2 - 5}$

7 $y = \sqrt{(3x^4 - 2)}$

8 $y = (x^3 + 4x)^5$

9 $y = \left(\sqrt{x} + \dfrac{1}{\sqrt{x}}\right)^4$

12.11 Differentiation of products

Given the product $y = x^2(3x + 2)$, there is no difficulty about differentiating y, as the brackets can easily be removed, giving $y = 3x^3 + 2x^2$, $y' = 9x^2 + 4x$.

Given $y = (x + 1)^6(x + 2)^8$, this method would not be possible, and a method of differentiating products will now be discussed.

The rule for differentiating a product is

$$\text{if } y = uv \text{ then } \frac{dy}{dx} = u\frac{dv}{dx} + v\frac{du}{dx} \text{ or more shortly } y' = uv' + vu'.$$

Applying this in the first example above:

$$y = x^2(3x + 2) = uv \text{ where } u = x^2,\ v = 3x + 2$$
$$u' = 2x,\ v' = 3$$
$$\therefore \text{ by the rule } y' = x^2 \,.\, 3 + (3x + 2)2x$$
$$= 9x^2 + 4x, \text{ as found above.}$$

The following argument indicates the reasons for the product rule:

It is given that $y = uv$ where $u = f(x)$ and $v = g(x)$.

Let x increase by δx and let the resulting increases in u, v and y be δu, δv and δy respectively.

Then $y + \delta y = (u + \delta u)(v + \delta v)$

$$\therefore uv + \delta y = uv + u\delta v + v\delta u + \delta u\delta v$$

$$\therefore \frac{\delta y}{\delta x} = u\frac{\delta v}{\delta x} + v\frac{\delta u}{\delta x} + \frac{\delta u}{\delta x}\delta v \qquad (1)$$

Let $\delta x \to 0$; then $\delta u \to 0$, $\delta v \to 0$, $\delta y \to 0$.

Equating the limits of the two sides of (1) as $\delta x \to 0$ gives

$$\frac{dy}{dx} = u\frac{dv}{dx} + v\frac{du}{dx} + \frac{du}{dx}\,.\,0 \text{ and hence the rule as stated.}$$

Differentiation of quotients

If $y = \frac{u}{v}$, then y can be regarded as the product of u and $\frac{1}{v}$ and y' can be found by the product rule. It does however often give simpler algebra if this method is used to obtain a new rule for a quotient. The product rule will now be used to obtain the quotient rule.

Replacing v by w in the product rule gives:

$$\text{If } y = uw, \text{ then } \frac{dy}{dx} = u\frac{dw}{dx} + w\frac{du}{dx} \qquad (2)$$

Let $w = v^{-1}$, so that $y = \frac{u}{v}$ and $\frac{dw}{dv} = -v^{-2} = -\frac{1}{v^2}$

$$\therefore \text{ by the chain rule, } \frac{dw}{dx} = \frac{dw}{dv}\frac{dv}{dx} = -\frac{1}{v^2}\frac{dv}{dx}$$

$$\therefore \text{ by (2)} \quad \frac{dy}{dx} = u\left(-\frac{1}{v^2}\frac{dv}{dx}\right) + \frac{1}{v}\frac{du}{dx} = \frac{v\frac{du}{dx} - u\frac{dv}{dx}}{v^2}$$

which is the quotient rule. It can more briefly be stated as:

If $y = \frac{u}{v}$, then $y' = \frac{vu' - uv'}{v^2}$.

Note that the product rule is symmetrical in u and v, as is the product, but the quotient rule, like the quotient, is not symmetrical. It must carefully be noted that in applying the quotient rule the first term starts with v.

Examples 12.11

Differentiate **1** $x^3(4x+3)^2$ **2** $x^4\sqrt{(x^2+9)}$ **3** $\frac{x^2}{x^3+1}$

and simplify each answer.

1 Let $y = x^3(4x+3)^2$

$= uv$ where $u = x^3$, $v = (4x+3)^2$

$u' = 3x^2$, $v' = 8(4x+3)$ by the chain rule

$\therefore y' = x^3 . 8(4x+3) + (4x+3)^2 3x^2$

$= x^2(4x+3)[8x+3(4x+3)]$ (removing the common factors)

$= x^2(4x+3)(20x+9)$

2 Let $y = x^4\sqrt{(x^2+9)}$

$= uv$ where $u = x^4$, $v = (x^2+9)^{\frac{1}{2}}$

$u' = 4x^3$, $v' = \frac{1}{2}(x^2+9)^{-\frac{1}{2}}2x$ by the chain rule

$$\therefore y' = x^4 . \frac{x}{(x^2+9)^{\frac{1}{2}}} + (x^2+9)^{\frac{1}{2}} . 4x^3$$

$$= \frac{x^3}{(x^2+9)^{\frac{1}{2}}}[x^2 + 4(x^2+9)] = \frac{x^3(5x^2+36)}{\sqrt{(x^2+9)}}$$

3 Let $y = \frac{x^2}{x^3+1}$

$= \frac{u}{v}$ where $u = x^2$, $v = x^3+1$

$u' = 2x$, $v' = 3x^2$

$$\therefore y' = \frac{(x^3+1)2x - x^2 . 3x^2}{(x^3+1)^2}$$

$$= \frac{2x - x^4}{(x^3+1)^2}$$

Exercise 12.11A

In questions **1**–**9**, differentiate, and simplify each answer where possible.

1 $x(2x+1)^3$

2 $(3x-2)(4x+1)^2$

3 $(x^2+4x+3)(x+2)^2$

4 $(5x+2)^2(x^5+3)$

5 $(x-3)^2(x+3)^4$

6 $x\sqrt{(x^2+4)}$

7 $\dfrac{x^2}{3x+4}$

8 $\dfrac{x^2}{x^3+1}$

9 $\dfrac{2x-1}{3x+1}$

10 Find the coordinates of the stationary points on the graph of $y=(x-2)^2(x-5)$. Sketch the graph.

Exercise 12.11B

In questions **1**–**9**, differentiate, and simplify each answer where possible.

1 $x^3(3x-2)^2$

2 $(4x+1)(5x+3)^3$

3 $(x^2-5)(2x-1)^2$

4 $(3x+4)(2-x^4)$

5 $(x+1)^3(x-2)^2$

6 $2x\sqrt{(x^4+4)}$

7 $\dfrac{3x-2}{4x+3}$

8 $\dfrac{x^2-1}{x^2+2}$

9 $x(x^2+2)^{-\frac{1}{2}}$

10 Find the coordinates of the stationary points on the graph of $y=(x-2)(x+2)^3$ and sketch the graph.

Miscellaneous Exercise 12

1 Show that the equations of the tangent and normal at the point $P(4, 1)$ on the curve $y=\dfrac{4}{x}$ are $4y+x-8=0$ and $y-4x+15=0$ respectively.

The tangent at P intersects the x-axis at X and the y-axis at Y. The normal at P intersects the line $y=x$ at L and the line $y=-x$ at M. Find the coordinates of the points X, Y, L and M and prove that $LYMX$ is a square.

(*JMB*)

2 The function f is defined on the interval $-1 \leqslant x \leqslant 3$ by

$$f(x)=4x^3-15x^2+12x+4.$$

a Find the roots of $f(x)=0$.

b Find the stationary points of $f(x)$ and describe their nature, justifying your answers.

c Make a sketch of the graph of f.

d State the maximum and minimum values of the function f on the interval $-1 \leqslant x \leqslant 3$.

(*S*)

3 A function f is defined by the formula $f(x) = 2x^4 + 2x^3$, $x \in R$, where R is the set of real numbers.

a Find the stationary points of f(x) and determine their nature, justifying your answers.

b Find where the graph of f(x) meets the x and y axes and make a rough sketch of the graph.

(*S amended*)

4 Obtain the gradient function of the curve $y = 3x - x^3 - 2$. Hence find the x and y coordinates of points where the gradient of the curve is zero. Find also the x and y coordinates of the point at which the curve has the maximum positive gradient.

Sketch the curve in the interval $-3 \leqslant x \leqslant +3$, showing the points found above; indicate also which point is a 'local maximum' and which point has the greatest positive value of y, marking their coordinates on your sketch.

(*MEI*)

5 Find the coordinates of the stationary points on the curve $y = x^3 - 3x^2 - 9x$, stating with a reason whether y has a maximum or minimum value at each of these points. Sketch the curve.

By considering the intersections of this curve with suitable straight lines, determine the range of values of k for which the equation $x^3 - 3x^2 - 9x = k$ has three different real roots, of which two are negative and one is positive.

(*L*)

6 A particle moves in a straight line so that its velocity in metres per second at time t seconds after passing a point O is given by

$$v = 4 + 3t - t^2.$$

Calculate the positive value of t for which the particle is at rest, and calculate also the acceleration of the particle at this time.

Calculate the average velocity of the particle during the first four seconds after passing O.

Show that the particle passes O again between 6 and 7 seconds after it passed O.

(*OLE*

7 A particle moves along a line which passes through a point O; t seconds after passing through O the velocity is $v\,\mathrm{m\,s^{-1}}$, where $v = t^2 - 6t + 8$.

a Find the values of t for which the particle is at rest. Sketch the velocity–time graph for $0 \leqslant t \leqslant 6$. State the minimum velocity.

b Find the displacement of the particle from O at each of the times when it is at rest. Find the total distance travelled by the particle in the first four seconds.

c Prove that the particle does not pass through O again in the subsequent motion.

8 A solid right circular cylinder has volume $54\pi\,\text{cm}^3$. The radius of the cylinder is r cm, the height is h cm and the *total* surface area is $A\,\text{cm}^2$.

a Show that $r^2h = 54$.

b Show that $A = 2\pi\left(r^2 + \frac{54}{r}\right)$.

c Find the minimum value of A as r varies.

d Find the value of $\frac{\mathrm{d}h}{\mathrm{d}r}$ when $r = 1.5$. *(L)*

9 In making closed cylindrical tins of height h cm and radius r cm, the walls can be made from rectangular sheets of width h cm and length $2\pi r$ cm without waste, but stamping out each circular end of area $\pi r^2\,\text{cm}^2$ requires an area $4r^2\,\text{cm}^2$ of tinplate and some is wasted.

If the tins are to contain $1000\,\text{cm}^3$,

(i) find h in terms of r to give the correct volume;

(ii) find the area of tinplate required for each tin in terms of r.

If tinplate costs 0.01p per cm^2, find by a calculus method the radius, height and cost of the tin which will contain the required volume most cheaply.

(MEI)

10 a On the curve $y = 2x^2 + 3x$, A and B are the points with x coordinates a and $a + h$ respectively ($h > 0$).

Find, in terms of a and h, the gradient of the line AB.

Hence deduce the gradient of the tangent to the curve at the point A.

b A right circular cylinder of radius r and height h is inscribed in a sphere of fixed radius R so that the perimeter of each plane face of the cylinder lies on the surface of the sphere.

Prove that V, the volume of the cylinder, can be expressed in the form

$$V = \frac{\pi h}{4}(4R^2 - h^2).$$

Find the value of h, in terms of R, when V has its maximum value and show that in this case

$$r = \frac{R\sqrt{6}}{3}.$$

(JMB)

11 Find $\frac{\mathrm{d}y}{\mathrm{d}x}$ and simplify your answer to a product of factors or a single fraction.

a $y = (4x^3 + 1)^5$ **b** $y = \sqrt{(x^2 + 9)}$ **c** $y = \frac{1}{(3x^2 + 2)^4}$

d $y = x^2(x^5 + 2)^4$ **e** $y = \frac{x^2 + 3}{x - 5}$ **f** $y = \frac{x^3}{(x + 4)^2}$

12 Given that $y = \dfrac{x^2 - 1}{2x^2 + 1}$, find $\dfrac{dy}{dx}$ and state the set of values of x for which $\dfrac{dy}{dx}$ is positive.

Find the greatest and least values of y for $0 \leqslant x \leqslant 1$. *(L)*

13 **a** Differentiate with respect to x

$$\frac{x^2}{x + 4}.$$

b Find the coordinates of the points on the curve

$$y = \frac{x^2}{x + 4}$$

at which y has stationary values. Determine whether y has a maximum or minimum value at each of these points.

c Given that the line $y = c - 3x$ is a tangent to the curve $y = \dfrac{x^2}{x + 4}$, find the coordinates of the points of contact of the two tangents and the two possible values of c. *(L)*

14 The function f is defined for all real x by

$$f(x) = x^4 - 4x^3 - 12x^2 + 32x + 30.$$

Show that $f'(x)$ is zero for three integral values of x and sketch the graph of $f'(x)$. Hence write down the solution of $f'(x) > 0$.

Calculate the coordinates of the turning points on the graph of $f(x)$. Determine whether $f(x)$ has a maximum or a minimum value at each of the turning points. Sketch the graph of $f(x)$.

15 **a** Sketch the graph of

$$y = \frac{(x + 1)(x + 9)}{x}$$

showing clearly the coordinates of the turning points and the points of intersection with the axes, and the equations of the asymptotes.

b Use the graph obtained in **a** to sketch the graph of each of the following:

(i) $y = \dfrac{(x - 4)(x + 4)}{x - 5}$

(ii) $y = \dfrac{(x - 1)(x - 9)}{x}$

(iii) $y = \dfrac{x}{(x + 1)(x + 9)}$.

Show on all graphs the points of intersection with the axes and the equations of the asymptotes. *(S amended)*

Chapter 13

Vectors 2

13.1 Resolved parts

Definition The resolved part of a vector **a** in the direction of a vector **b** is $a \cos \theta$, where θ is the angle between **a** and **b**.

Since $\cos \theta$ may be positive, zero or negative, and a is positive, it follows that the resolved part may be positive, zero or negative.

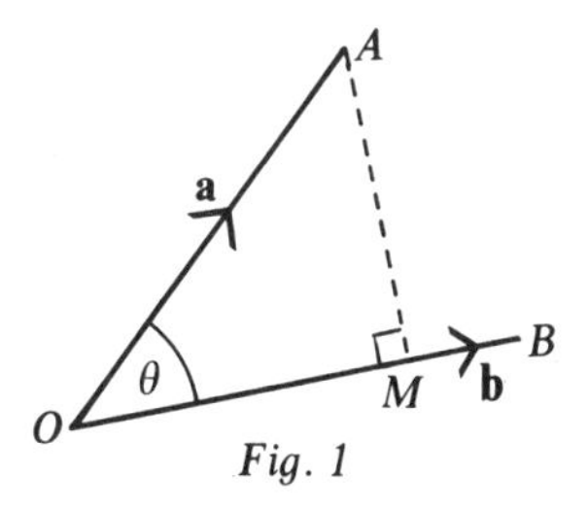

Fig. 1

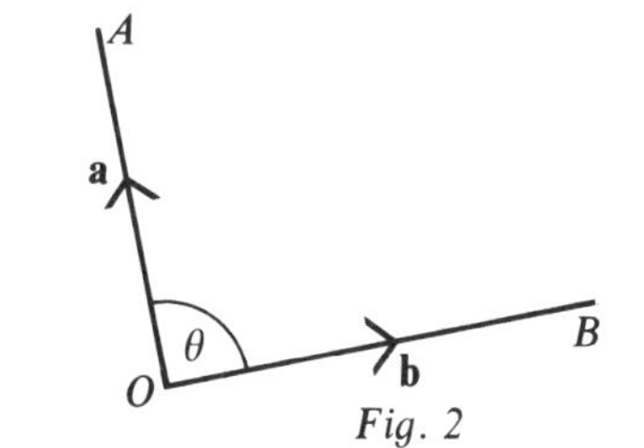

Fig. 2

In Fig. 1, where $0 < \theta < 90°$, $a \cos \theta > 0$.

In Fig. 2, where $\theta = 90°$, $a \cos \theta = 0$.

In Fig. 3, where $90° < \theta < 180°$, $a \cos \theta < 0$.

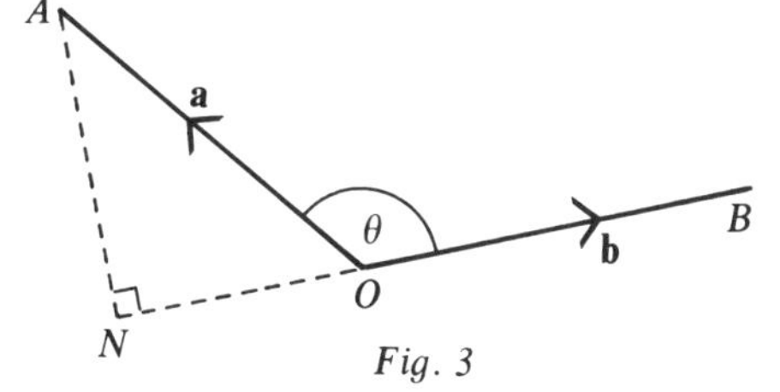

Fig. 3

From the definition it is evident that the resolved part can immediately be calculated if a and θ are known. If instead **a** and **b** are given in component form, then the resolved part may be calculated as $\frac{\mathbf{a} \cdot \mathbf{b}}{b}$, since this is

$\frac{ab \cos \theta}{b} = a \cos \theta$, as required.

Since $\frac{\mathbf{b}}{b} = \hat{\mathbf{b}}$, the resolved part of **a** in the direction of **b** is $\mathbf{a} \cdot \hat{\mathbf{b}}$.

An important application of the idea of a resolved part is in the case where the vector **a** is a force. The resolved part in the direction of the vector **b** measures the effect of the force in this direction.

The resolved part of a vector **a** in the direction of a vector **b** is also called the 'projection' of **a** on **b**. Fig. 1 helps to explain this usage.

Examples 13.1

1 Given the diagram, find the resolved part of **a** in the direction of **b**.

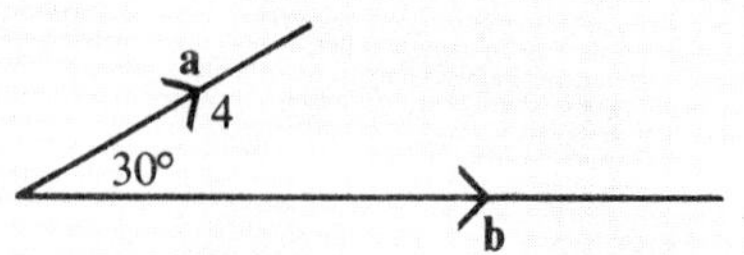

Resolved part $= 4\cos 30° = 2\sqrt{3}$.

2 Given that $\mathbf{a} = \begin{pmatrix} 1 \\ -3 \\ 2 \end{pmatrix}$ and $\mathbf{b} = \begin{pmatrix} 3 \\ 4 \\ -5 \end{pmatrix}$ find the resolved part of **a** in the direction of **b**.

$$b^2 = 50, \qquad b = 5\sqrt{2}, \qquad \hat{\mathbf{b}} = \frac{1}{5\sqrt{2}}\begin{pmatrix} 3 \\ 4 \\ -5 \end{pmatrix}$$

$$\therefore \text{ the resolved part } = \mathbf{a}\,.\,\hat{\mathbf{b}} = \frac{1}{5\sqrt{2}}(3 - 12 - 10) = -\frac{19\sqrt{2}}{10}.$$

Exercise 13.1A

1 Find the resolved part of **a** in the direction of **b** in each of the cases.

(i) (ii) (iii)

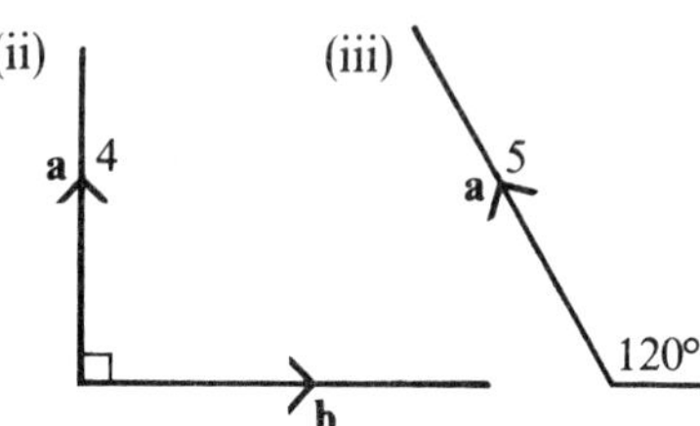

(i) a, 6, 45°, b (ii) a, 4, b (iii) a, 5, 120°, b

2 Find the resolved part of **a** in the direction of **b** in each of the cases.

(i) $\mathbf{a} = \begin{pmatrix} 2 \\ 3 \\ -1 \end{pmatrix}$, $\quad \mathbf{b} = \begin{pmatrix} 2 \\ 4 \\ 5 \end{pmatrix}$ $\qquad$ (ii) $\mathbf{a} = \begin{pmatrix} -4 \\ 2 \\ 3 \end{pmatrix}$, $\quad \mathbf{b} = \begin{pmatrix} 1 \\ 3 \\ -2 \end{pmatrix}$

3 Find the resolved part of the force $\begin{pmatrix} 3 \\ 5 \\ 4 \end{pmatrix}$N in the direction of the vector $\begin{pmatrix} 1 \\ 1 \\ 0 \end{pmatrix}$.

Exercise 13.1B

1 Giving each answer to 2 s.f., find the resolved part of **a** in the direction of **b** in each of the cases.

(i)

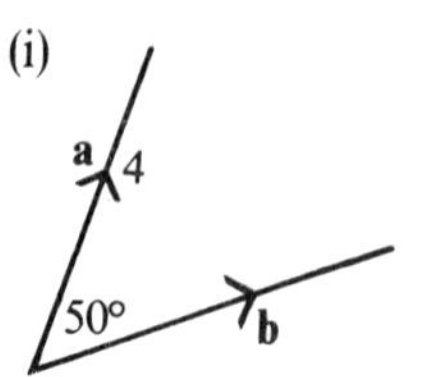

(ii)

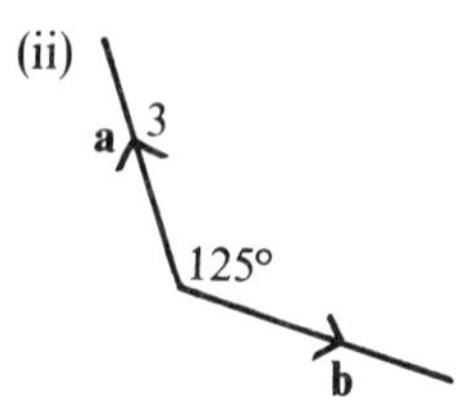

(iii)

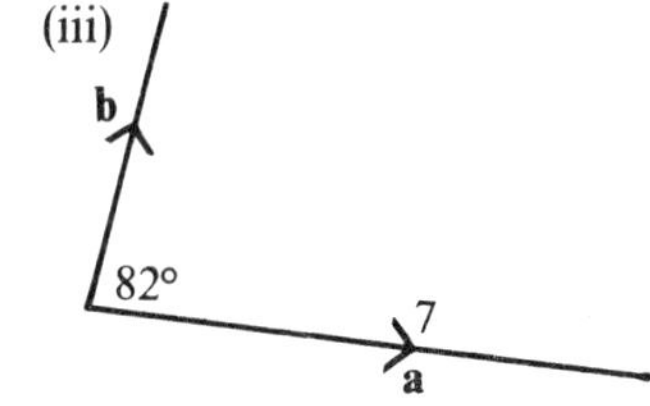

2 Find the resolved part of **a** in the direction of **b** in each of the cases.

(i) $\mathbf{a} = \begin{pmatrix} 1 \\ 2 \\ -3 \end{pmatrix}$, $\mathbf{b} = \begin{pmatrix} 3 \\ 1 \\ 4 \end{pmatrix}$ (ii) $\mathbf{a} = \begin{pmatrix} 1 \\ 0 \\ 2 \end{pmatrix}$, $\mathbf{b} = \begin{pmatrix} 2 \\ 1 \\ -1 \end{pmatrix}$

(iii) $\mathbf{a} = 5\mathbf{i} - 4\mathbf{j} + \mathbf{k}$, $\mathbf{b} = \mathbf{i} + 2\mathbf{j}$

3 Find the resolved part of the force $(2\mathbf{i} + 3\mathbf{k})$N in the direction of the vector $4\mathbf{i} + \mathbf{j} - 5\mathbf{k}$.

13.2 The vector equation of a line in two dimensions

In **6.3** the parametric equations of a line in the x–y plane were introduced. It was shown that a line passing through the point (x_1, y_1) with gradient $\frac{q}{p}$ may be represented by the parametric equations

$$x = x_1 + pt, \qquad y = y_1 + qt,$$

where t is a parameter. These two equations may be written as the single vector equation

$$\begin{pmatrix} x \\ y \end{pmatrix} = \begin{pmatrix} x_1 \\ y_1 \end{pmatrix} + t\begin{pmatrix} p \\ q \end{pmatrix}.$$

Writing **r** for $\begin{pmatrix} x \\ y \end{pmatrix}$, **a** for $\begin{pmatrix} x_1 \\ y_1 \end{pmatrix}$ and **d** for $\begin{pmatrix} p \\ q \end{pmatrix}$

gives the vector equation of the line in the form

$$\mathbf{r} = \mathbf{a} + t\mathbf{d}.$$

The vector **a** in this equation is the position vector of some point on the line; since this may be *any* point on the line, the vector equation is not unique.

The vector **d** gives the direction of the line; this vector is also not unique since any vector in the same or opposite direction to **d** gives the same line, so that any scalar multiple of **d** may be used instead of **d**.

In Fig. 1, A_1, A_2, A_3 are given by $t = 1$, $t = 2$, $t = 3$; A_{-1}, A_{-2} are given by $t = -1$, $t = -2$. Fig. 2 shows $\mathbf{r} = \mathbf{a} + t\mathbf{d}$ for a positive value of t.

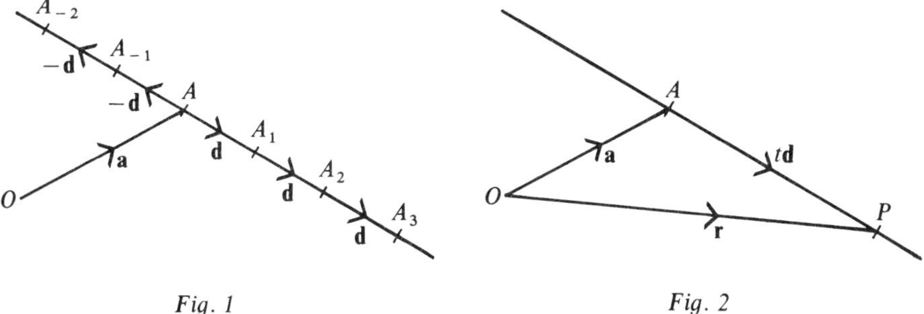

Fig. 1 *Fig. 2*

Examples 13.2

1 Find parametric equations and the Cartesian equation for the line L given by the vector equation

$$\mathbf{r} = \begin{pmatrix} 4 \\ 3 \end{pmatrix} + t\begin{pmatrix} 2 \\ 5 \end{pmatrix}.$$

Writing $\mathbf{r} = \begin{pmatrix} x \\ y \end{pmatrix}$ and equating components in the directions of $\mathbf{i}$ and $\mathbf{j}$ gives

$$x = 4 + 2t, \qquad y = 3 + 5t.$$

These are parametric equations for L. Equating the values of t given by these equations gives

$$\frac{y-3}{5} = \frac{x-4}{2}$$

or $5x - 2y = 14$, the Cartesian equation of L.

2 A line L passes through the points $P(3, 5)$ and $Q(1, 2)$. Find parametric equations and a vector equation for L.

The vector PQ is $\begin{pmatrix} -2 \\ -3 \end{pmatrix}$, $\therefore$ a direction vector for L is $\begin{pmatrix} 2 \\ 3 \end{pmatrix}$.

Parametric equations are

$$x = 3 + 2t, \qquad y = 5 + 3t.$$

A vector equation is $\mathbf{r} = \begin{pmatrix} 3 \\ 5 \end{pmatrix} + t\begin{pmatrix} 2 \\ 3 \end{pmatrix}$.

3 A line L has the vector equation $\mathbf{r} = \begin{pmatrix} -3 \\ 2 \end{pmatrix} + t\begin{pmatrix} 5 \\ 12 \end{pmatrix}$.

Find a unit direction vector for L. Hence find the two points on L which are 26 units from the point $(-3, 2)$.

A direction vector for L is $\begin{pmatrix} 5 \\ 12 \end{pmatrix}$ which has length 13.

$\therefore$ a unit direction vector is $\frac{1}{13}\begin{pmatrix} 5 \\ 12 \end{pmatrix}$. Moving along L through 26 units from the point $(-3, 2)$ given by $t = 0$ gives the points with position vectors

$$\begin{pmatrix} -3 \\ 2 \end{pmatrix} \pm 26 \cdot \frac{1}{13}\begin{pmatrix} 5 \\ 12 \end{pmatrix} = \begin{pmatrix} -3 \\ 2 \end{pmatrix} \pm \begin{pmatrix} 10 \\ 24 \end{pmatrix}.$$

$\therefore$ the required points are $(7, 26)$ and $(-13, -22)$.

4 Show that the equations

$$\mathbf{r} = \begin{pmatrix} 2 \\ 5 \end{pmatrix} + s\begin{pmatrix} -3 \\ 4 \end{pmatrix} \quad \text{and} \quad \mathbf{r} = \begin{pmatrix} 8 \\ -3 \end{pmatrix} + t\begin{pmatrix} 6 \\ -8 \end{pmatrix}$$

give the same line.

The lines are parallel since $\begin{pmatrix} 6 \\ -8 \end{pmatrix} = -2\begin{pmatrix} -3 \\ 4 \end{pmatrix}$.

The point (2, 5) is given by $s = 0$ in the first equation and by $t = -1$ in the second equation so the lines have a common point and are therefore the same line.

5 Calculate to the nearest degree the angle between the lines given by the equations

$$\mathbf{r} = \begin{pmatrix} 7 \\ -2 \end{pmatrix} + s\begin{pmatrix} 3 \\ 1 \end{pmatrix} \quad \text{and} \quad \mathbf{r} = \begin{pmatrix} -4 \\ 2 \end{pmatrix} + t\begin{pmatrix} 5 \\ -6 \end{pmatrix}.$$

The angle between the lines is the angle between their direction vectors. Let this angle be θ. Then

$$\sqrt{10}\sqrt{61}\cos\theta = \begin{pmatrix} 3 \\ 1 \end{pmatrix} \cdot \begin{pmatrix} 5 \\ -6 \end{pmatrix} = 15 - 6 = 9$$

$$\therefore \cos\theta = \frac{9}{\sqrt{10}\sqrt{61}}$$

$$\theta = 69^\circ \text{ to the nearest degree.}$$

Exercise 13.2A

1 Find parametric equations and the Cartesian equation for each of the lines.

a $\mathbf{r} = \begin{pmatrix} 3 \\ 5 \end{pmatrix} + t\begin{pmatrix} 4 \\ 1 \end{pmatrix}$ **b** $\mathbf{r} = \begin{pmatrix} -2 \\ 7 \end{pmatrix} + t\begin{pmatrix} 3 \\ 0 \end{pmatrix}$

2 A line L passes through the points (2, 5) and (4, 8). Find a vector equation and the Cartesian equation for L.

3 A line L is given by the vector equation $\mathbf{r} = \begin{pmatrix} 2 \\ -5 \end{pmatrix} + t\begin{pmatrix} 3 \\ 4 \end{pmatrix}$. Find a unit direction vector for L. Hence find the two points on L which are 15 units from the point (2, −5).

4 Calculate to the nearest degree the angle between the lines given by the equations $\mathbf{r} = \begin{pmatrix} 1 \\ 3 \end{pmatrix} + s\begin{pmatrix} 2 \\ 5 \end{pmatrix}$, $\mathbf{r} = \begin{pmatrix} -2 \\ 4 \end{pmatrix} + t\begin{pmatrix} 3 \\ -2 \end{pmatrix}$.

Exercise 13.2B

1 Find parametric equations and the Cartesian equation for each of the lines.

a $\mathbf{r} = \begin{pmatrix} 5 \\ -4 \end{pmatrix} + t\begin{pmatrix} -6 \\ 1 \end{pmatrix}$ **b** $\mathbf{r} = \begin{pmatrix} -3 \\ -5 \end{pmatrix} + t\begin{pmatrix} 0 \\ 2 \end{pmatrix}$

2 A line L passes through the point $(\frac{1}{2}, \frac{3}{4})$ and has gradient -4. Find a vector equation for L.

3 Show that the equations

$\mathbf{r} = \begin{pmatrix} -4 \\ 5 \end{pmatrix} + s\begin{pmatrix} 2 \\ -3 \end{pmatrix}$ and $\mathbf{r} = \begin{pmatrix} -2 \\ 2 \end{pmatrix} + t\begin{pmatrix} -6 \\ 9 \end{pmatrix}$ give the same line.

4 Calculate to the nearest degree the angle between the lines given by the equations

$\mathbf{r} = \begin{pmatrix} 2 \\ 5 \end{pmatrix} + s\begin{pmatrix} -4 \\ 3 \end{pmatrix}$ and $\mathbf{r} = \begin{pmatrix} -1 \\ 4 \end{pmatrix} + t\begin{pmatrix} 1 \\ 7 \end{pmatrix}$.

5 A line L is given by the equation $\mathbf{r} = \begin{pmatrix} -4 \\ 1 \end{pmatrix} + t\begin{pmatrix} 1 \\ -2 \end{pmatrix}$.

Find a unit direction vector for L. Hence find the coordinates of the points on L which are 10 units from the point $(-4, 1)$.

13.3 The vector equation of a line in three dimensions

In the vector equation $\mathbf{r} = \mathbf{a} + t\mathbf{d}$ which was introduced in **13.2**, each vector was in two dimensions. The vectors could instead be in three dimensions; the diagrams in **13.2** would be unchanged.

For example, the equation

$$\mathbf{r} = \begin{pmatrix} 2 \\ 3 \\ 4 \end{pmatrix} + t\begin{pmatrix} 5 \\ 6 \\ 7 \end{pmatrix}$$

represents a line L through the point A with position vector $\begin{pmatrix} 2 \\ 3 \\ 4 \end{pmatrix}$ and parallel to the vector $\begin{pmatrix} 5 \\ 6 \\ 7 \end{pmatrix}$. The vector $\begin{pmatrix} 5 \\ 6 \\ 7 \end{pmatrix}$ is one of an unlimited number of possible direction vectors for L.

Writing $\mathbf{r} = \begin{pmatrix} x \\ y \\ z \end{pmatrix}$ and equating components on both sides of the equation gives

$$x = 2 + 5t, \qquad y = 3 + 6t, \qquad z = 4 + 7t.$$

These are parametric equations for the line L.

Equating the values of t obtained from each of these equations gives

$$\frac{x-2}{5}=\frac{y-3}{6}=\frac{z-4}{7}.$$

These are Cartesian equations for the line L.

Note that in three dimensions a line has one vector equation, three parametric equations and two Cartesian equations.

Note also that each point P on the line L is defined by its position vector $\overrightarrow{OP}$ pointing from O to P, but the line L does not carry an arrow, unless for some reason it is convenient to give it one; the line L could be given the direction of either the vector $\begin{pmatrix}5\\6\\7\end{pmatrix}$ or of the vector $\begin{pmatrix}-5\\-6\\-7\end{pmatrix}$.

It is essential to distinguish clearly between

1 a direction vector $\mathbf{d}$ of a line and the vector $\mathbf{r}$ from O to a point P on the line,

2 the vector $\overrightarrow{AB}$ and the vector *equation* of the line AB.

It is also essential to remember that a vector equation of a line is an *equation*, requiring the sign = and a vector on each side of it.

Examples 13.3

1 Determine whether the points $P(61, 52, 43)$ and $Q(-5, -3, 1)$ lie on the line $\mathbf{r}=\begin{pmatrix}1\\2\\3\end{pmatrix}+t\begin{pmatrix}6\\5\\4\end{pmatrix}$.

For P to lie on the line, we require a value of t satisfying all three equations $1+6t=61$, $2+5t=52$ and $3+4t=43$. Clearly, $t=10$ is the common solution and so P lies on the line.

For Q, we require $1+6t=-5$, $2+5t=-3$ and $3+4t=1$. The first two equations are satisfied by $t=-1$, and the third by $t=-\frac{1}{2}$, so there is no common solution and therefore Q does not lie on the line.

2 Determine whether the equations

$$\mathbf{r}=\begin{pmatrix}5\\2\\5\end{pmatrix}+s\begin{pmatrix}6\\-2\\8\end{pmatrix} \quad\text{and}\quad \mathbf{r}=\begin{pmatrix}2\\3\\1\end{pmatrix}+t\begin{pmatrix}3\\-1\\4\end{pmatrix}$$

give the same line.

Clearly the lines given by the two equations are parallel, since $\begin{pmatrix}6\\-2\\8\end{pmatrix}=2\begin{pmatrix}3\\-1\\4\end{pmatrix}$, $\therefore$ if the lines have a common point they are the same line. In the first equation $s=0$ gives the point $(5, 2, 5)$, and in the second equation $t=1$ gives the same point. $\therefore$ the equations give the same line.

3 Show that each of the points $B(2, 16, 5)$ and $C(-13, -19, -5)$ lies on the line

$$L\colon \mathbf{r} = \begin{pmatrix} -4 \\ 2 \\ 1 \end{pmatrix} + t\begin{pmatrix} 3 \\ 7 \\ 2 \end{pmatrix}.$$

State the corresponding values of t. Given that A is the point $(-4, 2, 1)$, state the ratio of AB to AC.

The x-coordinates show that for B and C to lie on L, the corresponding values of t must be 2 and -3 respectively.

Checking the y-coordinates and the z-coordinates shows that $t = 2$ gives B and $t = -3$ gives C. So B and C lie on opposite sides of A, and $AB{:}AC = 2{:}3$.

4 Find a vector equation for the line AB, where A and B have coordinates $(1, 2, 3)$ and $(3, 5, 7)$ respectively. Find also the point P on AB such that $\overrightarrow{PA} = \overrightarrow{AB}$.

The vector $\mathbf{d} = \overrightarrow{AB} = \begin{pmatrix} 2 \\ 3 \\ 4 \end{pmatrix}$ is a direction vector for the line AB, so the required equation is $\mathbf{r} = \begin{pmatrix} 1 \\ 2 \\ 3 \end{pmatrix} + t\begin{pmatrix} 2 \\ 3 \\ 4 \end{pmatrix}$.

The point B is given by $t = 1$, hence P is given by $t = -1$ and so P has coordinates $(-1, -1, -1)$.

Exercise 13.3A

1 Find parametric equations and Cartesian equations for the lines

a $\mathbf{r} = \begin{pmatrix} 3 \\ 2 \\ 5 \end{pmatrix} + t\begin{pmatrix} 1 \\ -4 \\ 7 \end{pmatrix}$ **b** $\mathbf{r} = \begin{pmatrix} 2 \\ -5 \\ 6 \end{pmatrix} + t\begin{pmatrix} 4 \\ 3 \\ -1 \end{pmatrix}$.

2 Find a vector equation for the line through the point $(3, -1, 4)$ in the direction $\begin{pmatrix} 4 \\ 5 \\ -2 \end{pmatrix}$.

3 Find a vector equation for the line AB in each of the cases.

a $A(2, -4, 1)$, $B(1, -5, 7)$ **b** $A(-3, 2, 4)$, $B(6, 2, 5)$

4 Determine whether the point $(-6, 5, -2)$ lies on the line

$$\mathbf{r} = \begin{pmatrix} 2 \\ 3 \\ -5 \end{pmatrix} + t\begin{pmatrix} -4 \\ 1 \\ 2 \end{pmatrix}.$$

5 Determine whether the following vector equations represent the same line.

$$\mathbf{r} = \begin{pmatrix} -3 \\ 2 \\ 5 \end{pmatrix} + t\begin{pmatrix} 1 \\ 3 \\ -4 \end{pmatrix} \quad \text{and} \quad \mathbf{r} = \begin{pmatrix} 0 \\ 11 \\ -7 \end{pmatrix} + s\begin{pmatrix} -1 \\ -3 \\ 4 \end{pmatrix}$$

6 The line L has the equation $\mathbf{r} = \begin{pmatrix} 2 \\ 7 \\ 3 \end{pmatrix} + t\begin{pmatrix} 1 \\ 3 \\ 6 \end{pmatrix}$. The points A and B on L are given by $t = 0$ and $t = 1$ respectively. Determine the coordinates of the point C on L such that A lies between B and C and $CA:AB = 2:1$.

Exercise 13.3B

1 Find a vector equation for the line through the point $(4, 5, -2)$ in the direction $\begin{pmatrix} 3 \\ -1 \\ 4 \end{pmatrix}$.

2 Find a vector equation for the line AB in each of the cases.

a $A(1, -3, 2)$, $B(5, -2, 4)$ **b** $A(-7, 3, -1)$, $B(2, -3, 5)$

3 Determine whether the following equations represent the same line.

$$\mathbf{r} = \begin{pmatrix} 2 \\ -1 \\ 4 \end{pmatrix} + s\begin{pmatrix} \frac{1}{2} \\ \frac{1}{3} \\ \frac{1}{4} \end{pmatrix} \quad \text{and} \quad \mathbf{r} = \begin{pmatrix} 8 \\ 3 \\ 6 \end{pmatrix} + t\begin{pmatrix} 6 \\ 4 \\ 3 \end{pmatrix}$$

4 Show that each of the points $B(9, 11, -11)$ and $C(-5, -17, 24)$ lies on the line $L: \mathbf{r} = \begin{pmatrix} 3 \\ -1 \\ 4 \end{pmatrix} + t\begin{pmatrix} 2 \\ 4 \\ -5 \end{pmatrix}$. State the corresponding values of t. Given that A is $(3, -1, 4)$ state the ratio of AB to AC.

13.4 The angle between two lines

Whether two lines intersect or not, the angle between them is defined as the angle between their direction vectors, or its supplement if this angle is obtuse. We can therefore find the angle between two lines by using the scalar product of their direction vectors.

The point of intersection of two lines

In two dimensions, two lines are either parallel or they intersect.

In three dimensions, two lines may be parallel, they may intersect, or neither of these may happen. If they are not parallel and do not intersect, the lines are said to be 'skew'.

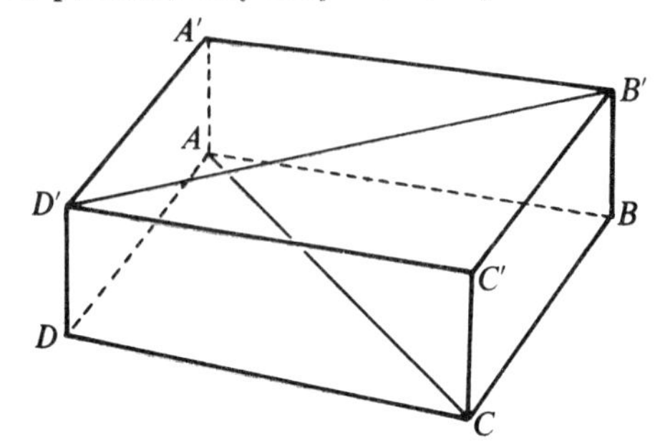

For example, in the diagram, the diagonals AC and $B'D'$ of the opposite faces of the rectangular box are skew. The diagonals of the floor and the ceiling in a room of this shape are either parallel to each other or they are skew.

Examples 13.4

1 Find the angle θ between the lines L_1 and L_2 given by the equations

$$L_1:\mathbf{r} = \begin{pmatrix}3\\1\\2\end{pmatrix} + s\begin{pmatrix}3\\5\\4\end{pmatrix} \quad \text{and} \quad L_2:\mathbf{r} = \begin{pmatrix}4\\5\\1\end{pmatrix} + t\begin{pmatrix}-6\\3\\2\end{pmatrix}.$$

The lines have direction vectors

$$\mathbf{d}_1 = \begin{pmatrix}3\\5\\4\end{pmatrix} \text{ and } \mathbf{d}_2 = \begin{pmatrix}-6\\3\\2\end{pmatrix} \text{ and } \mathbf{d}_1 . \mathbf{d}_2 = -18 + 15 + 8 = 5.$$

Also $|\mathbf{d}_1| = \sqrt{50} = 5\sqrt{2}$ and $|\mathbf{d}_2| = 7$, so $\cos\theta = \dfrac{5}{35\sqrt{2}} = \dfrac{1}{7\sqrt{2}}$.

$\therefore\ \theta = 84°$ to the nearest degree.

2 The lines L_1, L_2, L_3 have the vector equations

$$\mathbf{r} = \begin{pmatrix}1\\2\\3\end{pmatrix} + t\begin{pmatrix}3\\4\\5\end{pmatrix}, \quad \mathbf{r} = \begin{pmatrix}3\\2\\1\end{pmatrix} + s\begin{pmatrix}3\\6\\2\end{pmatrix}, \quad \mathbf{r} = \begin{pmatrix}3\\2\\1\end{pmatrix} + q\begin{pmatrix}3\\6\\9\end{pmatrix},$$

respectively. Find the common point (if any) of

a L_1 and L_2 **b** L_1 and L_3.

a By inspection, the lines are not parallel. For a common point, we need a value of t and a value of s so that the following three equations are all satisfied.

$1 + 3t = 3 + 3s$ (equating x-coordinates)
$2 + 4t = 2 + 6s$ (equating y-coordinates)
$3 + 5t = 1 + 2s$ (equating z-coordinates)

The first two equations give $t = 2$ and $s = \frac{4}{3}$, and these values do not satisfy the third equation. Hence the lines are skew.

b Again the lines are not parallel, and for a common point we require

$$1 + 3t = 3 + 3q$$
$$2 + 4t = 2 + 6q$$
$$3 + 5t = 1 + 9q.$$

All three equations are satisfied by $t = 2$, $q = \frac{4}{3}$, which give the common point as (7, 10, 13).

3 Find the length of the perpendicular from O to the line L given by

$$\mathbf{r} = \begin{pmatrix} 4 \\ 3 \\ 2 \end{pmatrix} + t\begin{pmatrix} 3 \\ -4 \\ 5 \end{pmatrix}.$$

Let the foot of the perpendicular from O to L be N, with position vector $\mathbf{n}$, given by the parameter s.

Let $\mathbf{m}$ be $\begin{pmatrix} 3 \\ -4 \\ 5 \end{pmatrix}$.

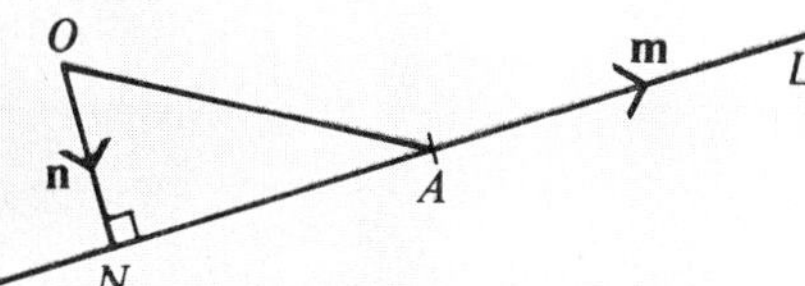

Method 1

$$\mathbf{n} = \begin{pmatrix} 4 + 3s \\ 3 - 4s \\ 2 + 5s \end{pmatrix} \text{ and } \mathbf{m}\,.\,\mathbf{n} = 0$$

$$\therefore\ 3(4 + 3s) - 4(3 - 4s) + 5(2 + 5s) = 0$$

$$\therefore\ s = -\frac{1}{5} \text{ and } \mathbf{n} = \frac{1}{5}\begin{pmatrix} 17 \\ 19 \\ 5 \end{pmatrix}$$

$$\therefore\ ON = \sqrt{27} = 3\sqrt{3}$$

Method 2

Let A be the point with position vector $\begin{pmatrix} 4 \\ 3 \\ 2 \end{pmatrix}$.

Then NA is the resolved part of $\overrightarrow{OA}$ in the direction of $\mathbf{m}$, so that

$$NA = \frac{\overrightarrow{OA}\,.\,\mathbf{m}}{m} = \frac{\begin{pmatrix} 4 \\ 3 \\ 2 \end{pmatrix}.\begin{pmatrix} 3 \\ -4 \\ 5 \end{pmatrix}}{\sqrt{50}} = \frac{10}{\sqrt{50}}.$$

From the triangle OAN, $ON^2 = OA^2 - NA^2 = 29 - \frac{100}{50}$

$$= 27$$

$$\therefore\ ON = 3\sqrt{3}.$$

Exercise 13.4A

1 Find to the nearest degree the angle between each of the following pairs of lines.

a $\mathbf{r} = \begin{pmatrix} 2 \\ 3 \\ -5 \end{pmatrix} + s\begin{pmatrix} 1 \\ 7 \\ 2 \end{pmatrix}$, and $\mathbf{r} = \begin{pmatrix} 4 \\ -2 \\ 3 \end{pmatrix} + t\begin{pmatrix} 2 \\ 3 \\ -1 \end{pmatrix}$

b $\mathbf{r} = \begin{pmatrix} 1 \\ 5 \\ -2 \end{pmatrix} + s\begin{pmatrix} 3 \\ -1 \\ 4 \end{pmatrix}$, and $\mathbf{r} = \begin{pmatrix} 4 \\ 6 \\ -1 \end{pmatrix} + t\begin{pmatrix} -2 \\ 3 \\ 1 \end{pmatrix}$

2 Determine whether the following pairs of lines intersect; if they do intersect, state the coordinates of their common point.

a $\mathbf{r} = \begin{pmatrix} -1 \\ 0 \\ 2 \end{pmatrix} + s\begin{pmatrix} 3 \\ 4 \\ -2 \end{pmatrix}$, and $\mathbf{r} = \begin{pmatrix} 1 \\ -2 \\ 4 \end{pmatrix} + t\begin{pmatrix} 4 \\ 3 \\ -1 \end{pmatrix}$

b $\mathbf{r} = \begin{pmatrix} 3 \\ -2 \\ 4 \end{pmatrix} + s\begin{pmatrix} 1 \\ 2 \\ 5 \end{pmatrix}$, and $\mathbf{r} = \begin{pmatrix} -5 \\ 2 \\ 2 \end{pmatrix} + t\begin{pmatrix} 2 \\ -1 \\ 3 \end{pmatrix}$

3 Find the length of the perpendicular from O to each of the following lines. State the coordinates of the foot of the perpendicular.

a $\mathbf{r} = \begin{pmatrix} 1 \\ 6 \\ -2 \end{pmatrix} + t\begin{pmatrix} 5 \\ -4 \\ 3 \end{pmatrix}$ **b** $\mathbf{r} = \begin{pmatrix} 3 \\ 4 \\ -2 \end{pmatrix} + t\begin{pmatrix} 1 \\ 2 \\ 1 \end{pmatrix}$

4 Verify that the point $A(1, 3, 4)$ is the foot of the perpendicular from O to the line

$$L: \mathbf{r} = \begin{pmatrix} 1 \\ 3 \\ 4 \end{pmatrix} + t\begin{pmatrix} 2 \\ 6 \\ -5 \end{pmatrix}.$$

Given that B is the reflection of O in L, write down the coordinates of B. Given that C and D are the points on L corresponding to $t = 1$ and $t = -1$ respectively, calculate the area of the rhombus $OCBD$, giving the answer in its simplest surd form.

5 The line L has the equation

$$\mathbf{r} = 3\mathbf{i} + 2\mathbf{j} - 5\mathbf{k} + t(4\mathbf{i} + \mathbf{j} + 2\mathbf{k}).$$

The point Q has coordinates $(8, 4, 5)$. Calculate the length of the perpendicular from Q to L, giving it in surd form.

6 Calculate the coordinates of the foot of the perpendicular from $Q(10, -2, -1)$ to the line

$$\mathbf{r} = \begin{pmatrix} 1 \\ -3 \\ 4 \end{pmatrix} + t\begin{pmatrix} 2 \\ 5 \\ -3 \end{pmatrix}.$$

Exercise 13.4B

1 Find to the nearest degree the angle between each of the following pairs of lines.

a $\mathbf{r} = \begin{pmatrix} 1 \\ 3 \\ 2 \end{pmatrix} + s\begin{pmatrix} 2 \\ 1 \\ 3 \end{pmatrix}$, and $\mathbf{r} = \begin{pmatrix} 5 \\ 12 \\ 13 \end{pmatrix} + t\begin{pmatrix} 1 \\ 4 \\ 4 \end{pmatrix}$

b $\mathbf{r} = \begin{pmatrix} 4 \\ 1 \\ 3 \end{pmatrix} + s\begin{pmatrix} 2 \\ 1 \\ -3 \end{pmatrix}$, and $\mathbf{r} = \begin{pmatrix} 2 \\ 0 \\ -4 \end{pmatrix} + t\begin{pmatrix} 4 \\ 2 \\ -1 \end{pmatrix}$

2 Determine whether the pairs of lines in question **1** intersect; if they do intersect, state the coordinates of their common point.

3 Find the length of the perpendicular from O to each of the following lines.

a $\mathbf{r} = \begin{pmatrix} 6 \\ 4 \\ 2 \end{pmatrix} + t\begin{pmatrix} 1 \\ 3 \\ 4 \end{pmatrix}$ **b** $\mathbf{r} = \begin{pmatrix} 1 \\ 4 \\ 10 \end{pmatrix} + t\begin{pmatrix} -2 \\ 1 \\ 4 \end{pmatrix}$

4 The line L has the equation

$$\mathbf{r} = \begin{pmatrix} 0 \\ 1 \\ -6 \end{pmatrix} + t\begin{pmatrix} 1 \\ -3 \\ 5 \end{pmatrix}.$$

The point Q has coordinates (1, 3, 2). Calculate the length of the perpendicular from Q to L, giving it in surd form.

5 Show that the lines

$$L\!:\mathbf{r} = \begin{pmatrix} 1 \\ 2 \\ 3 \end{pmatrix} + s\begin{pmatrix} 3 \\ 4 \\ 5 \end{pmatrix} \quad \text{and} \quad M\!:\mathbf{r} = \begin{pmatrix} 2 \\ -10 \\ 16 \end{pmatrix} + t\begin{pmatrix} -1 \\ 2 \\ 3 \end{pmatrix}$$

are skew. Verify that L and M are each perpendicular to $\mathbf{d}$, where $\mathbf{d} = \begin{pmatrix} 1 \\ -7 \\ 5 \end{pmatrix}$. Write down a vector equation in terms of a parameter u for the line N which passes through $A(1, 2, 3)$ and has direction vector $\mathbf{d}$. Show that N and M intersect and find their point of intersection B. Calculate AB, and interpret this length geometrically.

Miscellaneous Exercise 13

1 Calculate the resolved part of $4\mathbf{i} + 2\mathbf{j} + 6\mathbf{k}$ in the direction of $3\mathbf{i} - 4\mathbf{j} + \mathbf{k}$.

2 In the direction of the vector $4\mathbf{i} + 3\mathbf{k}$, the resolved part of the vector $x\mathbf{i} + 2\mathbf{j} - 5\mathbf{k}$ is 5. Find the value of x.

3 Verify that the point $A(9, -7, 8)$ lies on each of the lines

$$L\colon \mathbf{r} = \begin{pmatrix} 3 \\ 5 \\ -1 \end{pmatrix} + s\begin{pmatrix} 2 \\ -4 \\ 3 \end{pmatrix}, \qquad M\colon \mathbf{r} = \begin{pmatrix} -3 \\ -1 \\ 4 \end{pmatrix} + t\begin{pmatrix} 6 \\ -3 \\ 2 \end{pmatrix}.$$

4 Find the foot of the perpendicular from $P(6, 3, 5)$ to the line

$$\mathbf{r} = \begin{pmatrix} 2 \\ 3 \\ 1 \end{pmatrix} + t\begin{pmatrix} 1 \\ -1 \\ 2 \end{pmatrix}.$$

5 Determine whether the following lines intersect; if they do intersect state the coordinates of their common point. Calculate the angle between the lines, to the nearest degree.

$$L\colon \mathbf{r} = \begin{pmatrix} 2 \\ 9 \\ 13 \end{pmatrix} + s\begin{pmatrix} 1 \\ 2 \\ 3 \end{pmatrix}, \qquad M\colon \mathbf{r} = \begin{pmatrix} 3 \\ 7 \\ -2 \end{pmatrix} + t\begin{pmatrix} 1 \\ -2 \\ 3 \end{pmatrix}$$

6 The line L is given by the equation

$$\mathbf{r} = \begin{pmatrix} 2 \\ -3 \\ 4 \end{pmatrix} + t\begin{pmatrix} -3 \\ 4 \\ 6 \end{pmatrix}.$$

The line from $P(5, 1, 13)$ perpendicular to L meets L at Q. Find

a the coordinates of Q

b a vector equation for PQ

c the length of PQ

d the coordinates of the point S which is the reflection of P in L.

7 In the parallelogram $OABC$ the position vectors of A and B, with respect to O, are $2\mathbf{i} + \mathbf{j}$ and $\mathbf{i} + 2\mathbf{j} + 2\mathbf{k}$ respectively.

a Calculate the lengths of the diagonals OB and AC.

b Find the cosine of the acute angle between the diagonals.

c Find a vector equation of the line CB.

d P is the point with position vector $1.4\mathbf{i} + 2.2\mathbf{j} + 2\mathbf{k}$. Show that P lies on BC and that it is the foot of the perpendicular from A to BC.

(*AEB* 1984)

8 **a** Find a unit vector parallel to $\mathbf{i} - 2\mathbf{j} + \mathbf{k}$.

b Find a vector equation involving a parameter for the line L through the point A with position vector $\mathbf{i} + 2\mathbf{j} + \mathbf{k}$ and parallel to $\mathbf{i} - 2\mathbf{j} + \mathbf{k}$. Explain the geometric significance of the parameter.

c The point C has position vector $\mathbf{i} + \mathbf{j} + \mathbf{k}$. Calculate the length of AN, the projection of AC on L and hence the distance of C from L.

d Find the position vector of N and show that N lies on OC.

e Find a parametric vector equation for the line through N perpendicular to L and to OC.

(*S*)

Chapter 14

The binomial theorem and the binomial series

14.1 Pascal's triangle

The binomial theorem provides a method for expanding $(1 + x)^n$ in powers of x, where the index n is a positive integer. More generally, the theorem gives the expansion of $(a + b)^n$ in powers of a and b; the two numbers a and b give the theorem its name.

This theorem has many applications; students whose course includes probability will meet an important application there.

It can be verified by direct removal of brackets that the coefficients of successive powers of x in the expansions of $(1 + x)^n$ for $n = 1, 2, 3, 4$ are given by the following array.

$$\begin{array}{ccccccccc} & & & 1 & & 1 & & & \\ & & 1 & & 2 & & 1 & & \\ & 1 & & 3 & & 3 & & 1 & \\ 1 & & 4 & & 6 & & 4 & & 1 \end{array}$$

This array is known as Pascal's triangle, after the seventeenth-century French mathematician Pascal. The next row at any stage is formed by adding adjacent numbers in pairs on the last row, so that the next row above is

$$1 \qquad 1+4 \qquad 4+6 \qquad 6+4 \qquad 4+1 \qquad 1.$$

This row corresponds to the expansion

$$(1 + x)^5 = 1 + 5x + 10x^2 + 10x^3 + 5x^4 + x^5.$$

The *binomial theorem* states that for every positive integer n and for all x

$$(1 + x)^n = 1 + nx + \frac{n(n-1)}{1.2}x^2 + \frac{n(n-1)(n-2)}{1.2.3}x^3 + \ldots + x^n.$$

The pattern of the coefficients for successive powers of x should be carefully noted; the number of factors in the numerator and in the denominator in each term is equal to the power of x.

A proof of this theorem is given in **14.4**.

Examples 14.1

1 Verify that the expansion of $(1 + x)^5$ calculated from the binomial theorem is the same as that found above from Pascal's triangle.

By the theorem

$$(1 + x)^5 = 1 + 5x + \frac{5.4}{1.2}x^2 + \frac{5.4.3}{1.2.3}x^3 + \frac{5.4.3.2}{1.2.3.4}x^4 + \frac{5.4.3.2.1}{1.2.3.4.5}x^5$$

$$= 1 + 5x + 10x^2 + 10x^3 + 5x^4 + x^5,$$

as found above.

2 Use the theorem to expand $(1 + x)^{10}$.

$$(1 + x)^{10} = 1 + 10x + \frac{10.9}{1.2}x^2 + \frac{10.9.8}{1.2.3}x^3 + \frac{10.9.8.7}{1.2.3.4}x^4$$

$$+ \frac{10.9.8.7.6}{1.2.3.4.5}x^5 + \frac{10.9.8.7.6.5}{1.2.3.4.5.6}x^6$$

$$+ \frac{10.9.8.7.6.5.4}{1.2.3.4.5.6.7}x^7 + \frac{10.9.8.7.6.5.4.3}{1.2.3.4.5.6.7.8}x^8$$

$$+ \frac{10.9.8.7.6.5.4.3.2}{1.2.3.4.5.6.7.8.9}x^9 + x^{10}$$

$$= 1 + 10x + 45x^2 + 120x^3 + 210x^4 + 252x^5 + 210x^6$$

$$+ 120x^7 + 45x^8 + 10x^9 + x^{10}$$

Note that (i) each coefficient may be found from the previous one by multiplying by one factor and dividing by another, e.g. the coefficient of x^5 above is $210 \times \frac{6}{5} = 252$, and the coefficient of $x^6 = 252 \times \frac{5}{6} = 210$;

(ii) the coefficients show symmetry about the centre of the expansion, as is shown in Pascal's triangle. It was therefore unnecessary to write down the details in the above expansion after the term in x^5. For n even, as in this example, there is an odd number of terms in the expansion, and so there is one term in the 'centre'. For n odd, as in Example **1**, there is an even number of terms, and the coefficients in the two centre terms are equal.

3 Expand $(a + b)^5$ in powers of a and b.

$$a + b = a\left(1 + \frac{b}{a}\right), \text{ so } (a + b)^5 = a^5\left(1 + \frac{b}{a}\right)^5.$$

Using the expansion in Example **1** with $\frac{b}{a}$ in place of x gives

$$(a + b)^5 = a^5\left(1 + 5\frac{b}{a} + 10\frac{b^2}{a^2} + 10\frac{b^3}{a^3} + 5\frac{b^4}{a^4} + \frac{b^5}{a^5}\right)$$

$$= a^5 + 5a^4b + 10a^3b^2 + 10a^2b^3 + 5ab^4 + b^5.$$

Note the pattern of this result; in each term the sum of the indices of a and of b is 5.

4 Calculate the value of $(1.02)^6$ correct to four decimal places by using the binomial theorem.

$(1 + x)^6 = 1 + 6x + 15x^2 + 20x^3 + 15x^4 + 6x^5 + x^6$

Using $x = 0.02$ gives

$(1.02)^6 = 1 + 0.12 + 6(10)^{-3} + 1.6(10)^{-4} + 2.4(10)^{-6} + \dots.$

The last term here is too small to affect the fourth decimal place. Using the first five terms gives 1.12616, so to four decimal places $(1.02)^6 = 1.1262$.

This method is useful when a calculator is not available.

Exercise 14.1A

1 Expand $(1 + x)^7$

a by extending Pascal's triangle **b** by using the binomial theorem.

2 Expand $(1 + x)^9$ in ascending powers of x as far as the term in x^3. Hence write down the last four terms in the expansion.

3 Expand $(a + x)^6$ using Pascal's triangle.

4 Calculate the value of $(0.98)^7$ correct to four decimal places, using your answer to question **1**.

Exercise 14.1B

1 Expand $(1 + x)^8$

a by extending Pascal's triangle **b** by using the binomial theorem.

2 Expand $(1 + 2x)^{12}$ in ascending powers of x as far as the term in x^3. Hence write down the last four terms in the expansion, leaving powers of 2 in the answer.

3 Expand $(a + b)^{10}$ as far as the middle term.

4 Calculate the value of $(1.01)^8$ to four decimal places, using the answer to question **1**.

14.2 The expansion of $(a + b)^n$

Since $a + b = a\left(1 + \frac{b}{a}\right)$, it follows that

$$(a + b)^n = a^n\left(1 + \frac{b}{a}\right)^n$$

$$= a^n\left[1 + n\frac{b}{a} + \frac{n(n-1)}{1\,.\,2}\left(\frac{b}{a}\right)^2 + \ldots + \left(\frac{b}{a}\right)^n\right]$$

$$= a^n + na^{n-1}b + \frac{n(n-1)}{1\,.\,2}a^{n-2}b^2 + \ldots + b^n.$$

This identity is true for all a and b and all positive integers n.

Examples 14.2

1 Expand $(4 + x)^5$, leaving powers of 4 in the answer.

Using $a = 4$, $b = x$ and $n = 5$ in the above,

$$(4 + x)^5 = 4^5 + 5\,.\,4^4x + \frac{5\,.\,4}{1\,.\,2}\,.\,4^3x^2 + \frac{5\,.\,4\,.\,3}{1\,.\,2\,.\,3}\,.\,4^2x^3 + 5\,.\,4x^4 + x^5$$

$$= 4^5 + 5\,.\,4^4x + 10\,.\,4^3x^2 + 10\,.\,4^2x^3 + 20x^4 + x^5.$$

2 Write down in unsimplified form the term in x^4 in the expansion of $(3 + x)^9$.

The term in x^4 contains 3^5 and the coefficient is $\frac{9\,.\,8\,.\,7\,.\,6}{1\,.\,2\,.\,3\,.\,4}$.

So the term is $\frac{9\,.\,8\,.\,7\,.\,6}{1\,.\,2\,.\,3\,.\,4}3^5x^4$.

3 Write down the term in x^7 in the expansion of $(2 - 3x)^{10}$, leaving powers of 2 and 3 in the answer.

The term in x^7 contains $(-3)^7$, 2^3 and the coefficient

$\frac{10\,.\,9\,.\,8\,.\,7\,.\,6\,.\,5\,.\,4}{1\,.\,2\,.\,3\,.\,4\,.\,5\,.\,6\,.\,7}$, which is 120.

So the term is $-120\,.\,2^3\,.\,3^7x^7$.

4 Write down the fifth term in the expansion of $(2 + x)^9$ in ascending powers of x.

(Note that the value of the fifth term depends on whether the expansion is in ascending or descending powers of x; the term in a particular power of x does not.)

The expansion starts with the term 2^9x^0; the fifth term contains x^4. It also contains 2^5 and the coefficient $\frac{9.8.7.6}{1.2.3.4} = 126$; so the term is $126 . 2^5x^4 = 4032x^4$.

5 Expand $\left(x^2 + \frac{1}{2x}\right)^6$ in descending powers of x.

From Pascal's triangle or otherwise the coefficients for the index 6 are 1, 6, 15, 20, 15, 6, 1.
The expansion is

$$x^{12} + 6x^{10}\left(\frac{1}{2x}\right) + 15x^8\left(\frac{1}{2x}\right)^2 + 20x^6\left(\frac{1}{2x}\right)^3$$

$$+ 15x^4\left(\frac{1}{2x}\right)^4 + 6x^2\left(\frac{1}{2x}\right)^5 + \left(\frac{1}{2x}\right)^6$$

$$= x^{12} + 3x^9 + \frac{15}{4}x^6 + \frac{5}{2}x^3 + \frac{15}{16} + \frac{3}{16x^3} + \frac{1}{64x^6}.$$

Exercise 14.2A

1 Expand $(2 + x)^7$, leaving powers of 2 in the answer.

2 Write down in unsimplified form
a the term in x^6 in the expansion of $(5 + x)^{11}$
b the term in x^7 in the expansion of $(3 + 4x)^{12}$.

3 Find the seventh term in the expansion of $(2 - 3x)^{10}$ in ascending powers of x, leaving powers of 2 and 3 in the answer.

4 Expand $\left(x + \frac{3}{x}\right)^8$ in descending powers of x as far as the term in x^2.

Exercise 14.2B

1 Expand $(x - 3y)^6$ in descending powers of x as far as the term in x^3.

2 Write down in unsimplified form
a the term in x^5 in the expansion of $(3 - x)^8$
b the term in x^8 in the expansion of $(4 + 5x)^{13}$.

3 Find the ninth term in the expansion of $(a + x)^{11}$ in ascending powers of x.

4 Expand $\left(2x - \frac{1}{2x}\right)^9$ in descending powers of x as far as the term in x^{-3}.

14.3 The binomial coefficients

The binomial theorem states that for every positive integer n and every x

$$(1 + x)^n = 1 + nx + \frac{n(n-1)}{1.2}x^2 + \ldots + x^n.$$

For $r \geqslant 1$ the coefficient of x^r in this expansion is

$$\frac{n(n-1)(n-2)\ldots(n-r+1)}{1.2.3\ldots r}.$$

This is written in the shorter form $\binom{n}{r}$, the top number n being the first factor in the numerator and the bottom number r being the last factor in the denominator; r is also the number of factors in the numerator and in the denominator.

The number $\binom{n}{r}$ is the *general binomial coefficient*. The symbol $\binom{n}{0}$ is defined as unity, i.e. $\binom{n}{0} = 1$. Using this notation the binomial theorem may be written in the shorter form

$$(1 + x)^n = \sum_{r=0}^{n} \binom{n}{r} x^r.$$

The number $\binom{n}{r}$ may be written in a condensed form by using factorial notation.

Factorial n is written $n!$ and is defined by $n! = n(n-1)(n-2)(n-3)\ldots 3.2.1$; $0!$ is defined as 1.

Using this notation $\binom{n}{r} = \frac{n!}{r!(n-r)!}$, by multiplying numerator and denominator by $(n-r)!$

Examples 14.3

1 Simplify $\binom{9}{3}$ and $\binom{9}{6}$.

$$\binom{9}{3} = \frac{9.8.7}{1.2.3} = 84 \qquad \binom{9}{6} = \frac{9.8.7.6.5.4}{1.2.3.4.5.6} = \frac{9.8.7}{1.2.3} = 84$$

since the last three factors in the numerator and the denominator are the same.

Note that $\binom{9}{3}$ and $\binom{9}{6}$ are the coefficients of x^3 and x^6 respectively in the expansion of $(1 + x)^9$, and by symmetry are equal.

2 Calculate $\binom{8}{3}+\binom{8}{4}$ and $\binom{9}{4}$.

$$\binom{8}{3}+\binom{8}{4}=\frac{8.7.6}{1.2.3}+\frac{8.7.6.5}{1.2.3.4}=\frac{8.7.6}{1.2.3}\left(1+\frac{5}{4}\right)=56.\frac{9}{4}=126$$

$$\binom{9}{4}=\frac{9.8.7.6}{1.2.3.4}=126$$

3 Calculate $\binom{8}{6}\div\binom{8}{5}$.

$$\binom{8}{6}=\frac{8.7.6.5.4.3}{1.2.3.4.5.6}=\frac{8.7}{1.2}\qquad\binom{8}{5}=\frac{8.7.6.5.4}{1.2.3.4.5}=\frac{8.7.6}{1.2.3}$$

$$\therefore\binom{8}{6}\div\binom{8}{5}=\frac{1}{2}$$

4 Verify by using factorial notation that $\binom{n}{r}=\binom{n}{n-r}$.

$$\binom{n}{r}=\frac{n!}{r!(n-r)!}$$

$$\binom{n}{n-r}=\frac{n!}{(n-r)![n-(n-r)]!}=\frac{n!}{(n-r)!r!}=\binom{n}{r}$$

This result corresponds to the symmetry of Pascal's triangle about the centre line.

5 Verify by using factorial notation that $\binom{n}{r-1}+\binom{n}{r}=\binom{n+1}{r}$.

$$\binom{n}{r-1}+\binom{n}{r}=\frac{n!}{(r-1)!(n-r+1)!}+\frac{n!}{r!(n-r)!}$$

$$=\frac{n!}{(r-1)!}\left[\frac{1}{(n-r+1)(n-r)!}+\frac{1}{r(n-r)!}\right]$$

$$=\frac{n!}{(r-1)!(n-r)!}\left[\frac{1}{n-r+1}+\frac{1}{r}\right]$$

$$=\frac{n!}{(r-1)!(n-r)!}\left[\frac{r+n-r+1}{r(n-r+1)}\right]$$

$$=\frac{n!}{(r-1)!(n-r)!}\left[\frac{(n+1)}{r(n+1-r)}\right]$$

$$=\frac{(n+1)!}{r(r-1)!(n+1-r)(n-r)!}=\frac{(n+1)!}{r!(n+1-r)!}=\binom{n+1}{r}$$

This result corresponds to the property of Pascal's triangle which gives the rule for forming each row from the previous row.

6 Prove that, for every positive integer n, $\sum_{r=0}^{n}\binom{n}{r} = 2^n$.

$$\sum_{r=0}^{n}\binom{n}{r} = \binom{n}{0} + \binom{n}{1} + \binom{n}{2} + \ldots + \binom{n}{n}.$$

This is the result of replacing x by 1 in the expansion of $(1 + x)^n$, so its value is $(1 + 1)^n = 2^n$.

7 Find in its simplest form the ratio of the term in x^6 to the term in x^7 in the expansion of $(2 + 3x)^{10}$.

$$\frac{\text{the term in } x^6}{\text{the term in } x^7} = \frac{\binom{10}{6}2^4 3^6 x^6}{\binom{10}{7}2^3 3^7 x^7} = \frac{\binom{10}{6}2}{\binom{10}{7}3x} = \frac{10!}{6!4!} \cdot 2 \cdot \frac{7!3!}{10!3x} = \frac{7}{6x}$$

$\therefore$ the ratio is $7{:}6x$.

Exercise 14.3

1 Simplify **a** $\binom{12}{5}$ and $\binom{12}{7}$ **b** $\binom{15}{3}$ and $\binom{15}{12}$.

2 Calculate $\binom{9}{2} + \binom{9}{3}$ and $\binom{10}{3}$.

3 Calculate $\binom{11}{3} + \binom{11}{4}$ and $\binom{12}{4}$.

4 Calculate **a** $\binom{10}{5} \div \binom{10}{4}$ **b** $\binom{12}{7} \div \binom{12}{6}$.

5 Write $\frac{(2n)!}{(n!)^2}$ as a binomial coefficient in the notation $\binom{N}{R}$.

6 Prove that $\binom{n}{0} - \binom{n}{1} + \binom{n}{2} - \ldots + (-1)^n\binom{n}{n} = 0$.

7 Find in its simplest form the ratio of the term in x^5 to the term in x^6 in the expansion of $(3x + 4)^9$.

14.4 A proof of the binomial theorem

The theorem may be proved by several methods. The following proof uses calculus.

Since $(1 + x)^n$ for any positive integer n is a polynomial of degree n and has the value 1 at $x = 0$, we may write

$$(1 + x)^n = 1 + a_1x + a_2x^2 + a_3x^3 + \ldots + a_rx^r + \ldots + a_nx^n \quad (1)$$

where the coefficients $a_1, a_2, \ldots$ are independent of x.

To determine these coefficients, in succession, differentiate both sides of (1) with respect to x, giving

$$n(1 + x)^{n-1} = a_1 \,.\, 1 + 2a_2x + 3a_3x^2 + \ldots + ra_rx^{r-1} + \ldots + na_nx^{n-1}. \quad (2)$$

Putting $x = 0$ in both sides of (2) gives

$$n = a_1 \qquad \text{or} \qquad a_1 = n.$$

Differentiating both sides of (2) gives

$$n(n-1)(1 + x)^{n-2} = 2a_2 \,.\, 1 + 3 \,.\, 2a_3x + \ldots + r(r-1)a_rx^{r-2} + \ldots + n(n-1)a_nx^{n-2}. \quad (3)$$

Putting $x = 0$ in both sides of (3) gives

$$n(n-1) = 2a_2 \,.\, 1 \qquad \text{or} \qquad a_2 = \frac{n(n-1)}{1 \,.\, 2}.$$

Differentiating both sides of (3) gives

$$n(n-1)(n-2)(1 + x)^{n-3} = 3 \,.\, 2a_3 \,.\, 1 + \ldots + r(r-1)(r-2)a_rx^{r-3} + \ldots + n(n-1)(n-2)a_nx^{n-3}. \quad (4)$$

Putting $x = 0$ in both sides of (4) gives

$$n(n-1)(n-2) = 3 \,.\, 2 \,.\, 1a_3 \qquad \text{or} \qquad a_3 = \frac{n(n-1)(n-2)}{1 \,.\, 2 \,.\, 3}.$$

Continuing to differentiate and replace x by zero leads after r applications to the result

$$n(n-1)(n-2) \ldots [n-(r-1)](1 + x)^{n-r} = r(r-1)(r-2) \ldots 3 \,.\, 2 \,.\, 1a_r.$$

Putting $x = 0$ in both sides and rearranging gives

$$a_r = \frac{n(n-1)(n-2) \ldots (n-r+1)}{1 \,.\, 2 \,.\, 3 \ldots r} = \binom{n}{r}.$$

In particular, $a_n = \dfrac{n!}{n!} = 1.$

Replacing a_1, a_2, a_3, a_r and a_n in (1) by the values found gives

$$(1+x)^n = 1 + nx + \frac{n(n-1)}{1 \,.\, 2}x^2 + \frac{n(n-1)(n-2)}{1 \,.\, 2 \,.\, 3}x^3 + \ldots + \binom{n}{r}x^r + \ldots + x^n,$$

and the theorem is proved.

Note: In **12.4** the rule for differentiating x^n was proved without using the binomial theorem, and this rule may therefore be used here to prove the binomial theorem. It is possible to obtain the rule for differentiating x^n by using the binomial theorem, but in that case a different proof of the binomial theorem must be used.

Examples **14.4** provide more illustrations of the use of the theorem.

Examples 14.4

1 In the expansion of $\left(x^2+\frac{1}{2x}\right)^6$ find

a the term in x^3 **b** the term independent of x.

$$x^2+\frac{1}{2x}=x^2\left(1+\frac{1}{2x^3}\right) \qquad \therefore \left(x^2+\frac{1}{2x}\right)^6=x^{12}\left(1+\frac{1}{2x^3}\right)^6$$

a the term in x^3 is given by the term in $\frac{1}{x^9}$ in

$\left(1+\frac{1}{2x^3}\right)^6$, i.e. the term in $\left(\frac{1}{2x^3}\right)^3$.

$$\therefore \text{ the term is } x^{12}\binom{6}{3}\left(\frac{1}{2x^3}\right)^3=\frac{6.5.4\,x^3}{1.2.3\;8}=\frac{5}{2}x^3.$$

b the term independent of x is $x^{12}\binom{6}{4}\left(\frac{1}{2x^3}\right)^4=\frac{15}{16}$.

2 Expand $(1+x+x^2)^5$ in ascending powers of x as far as the term in x^2.

This 'trinomial' may be expanded by the binomial theorem by writing $x+x^2$ as y; to expand as far as the term in x^2, only terms up to y^2 are needed.

$$\begin{aligned}\text{Then } (1+x+x^2)^5 &= (1+y)^5\\ &= 1+5y+10y^2+\text{higher powers}\\ &= 1+5(x+x^2)+10(x+x^2)^2+\dots\\ &= 1+5x+5x^2+10x^2+\text{higher powers}\\ &= 1+5x+15x^2, \text{ as far as the term in } x^2.\end{aligned}$$

3 Find the term in x^4 in the expansion of $\left(x+\frac{1}{x}\right)^2(1+x)^4$.

$$\left(x+\frac{1}{x}\right)^2(1+x)^4=\left(x^2+2+\frac{1}{x^2}\right)(1+4x+6x^2+4x^3+x^4)$$

The term in x^4 is obtained from $x^2 \,.\, 6x^2$ and $2 \,.\, x^4$, so the term is $8x^4$.

4 Expand $(1-x)^3(1+2x)^4$ in ascending powers of x as far as the term in x^2.

$$\begin{aligned}(1-x)^3(1+2x)^4 &= (1-3x+3x^2\dots)(1+4\,.\,2x+6\,.\,4x^2\dots)\\ &= (1-3x+3x^2)(1+8x+24x^2)+\dots\\ &= 1+8x+24x^2-3x(1+8x)+3x^2+\dots\\ &= 1+5x+3x^2+\dots\end{aligned}$$

Exercise 14.4

1 Find the term in x^4 in the expansion of $\left(x + \frac{3}{x}\right)^8$.

2 Find the term independent of x in the expansion of

a $\left(x + \frac{1}{3x^2}\right)^9$ **b** $\left(4x^2 + \frac{1}{x}\right)^6$ **c** $\left(3x^2 + \frac{1}{3x^3}\right)^{10}$.

3 Find the coefficient of x^{-2} in the expansion of $\left(2x - \frac{1}{2x}\right)^8$.

4 Expand $(1 + 2x + 3x^2)^5$ in ascending powers of x as far as the term in x^2.

5 Expand $(1 - x + 2x^2)^6$ in ascending powers of x as far as the term in x^2.

6 Find the term in x^3 in the expansion of $\left(x - \frac{1}{x}\right)^2 (1 + x)^5$.

7 Find the first three terms in the expansion in ascending powers of x of $(1 + 2x)^2(1 - 3x)^3$.

8 Write down the expansion of $(1 + x)^5$. Hence express $(1 + \sqrt{3})^5$ in the form $p + q\sqrt{3}$ where p and q are integers. *State* a similar expression for $(1 - \sqrt{3})^5$.

9 In the expansion of $(1 + x)^{14}$ show that the coefficients of x^8, x^9 and x^{10} are in arithmetic progression.

10 In the expansion of $(1 + 2x)^n$ in powers of x the coefficient of x^8 is twice the coefficient of x^7. Find n.

14.5 The binomial series

This chapter so far has been concerned with the expansion of $(1 + x)^n$ where $n \in \mathbb{N}$. In this case $(1 + x)^n$ is a polynomial of degree n and the binomial theorem provides a way of writing it as a sum of $n + 1$ terms instead of as a product of n factors.

For all other values of n, $(1 + x)^n$ is not a polynomial.

If n is a negative integer then $(1 + x)^n$ is the reciprocal of a polynomial. Also $(1 + x)^{\frac{1}{2}}$ is a square root; for all n of the form $\frac{p}{q}$ where p and q are integers and $q \geqslant 2$, $(1 + x)^n$ is the qth root of $(1 + x)^p$.

If the binomial expansion is written with n replaced by k, we have

$$(1 + x)^k = 1 + kx + \frac{k(k-1)}{1.2}x^2 + \frac{k(k-1)(k-2)}{1.2.3}x^3 + \dots \qquad (1)$$

and, for any k which is not a positive integer, no coefficient on the right-hand side can be zero, so that the series is 'infinite'. It can be proved that, *provided* $|x| < 1$, this infinite series converges to the sum $(1 + x)^k$.

It is essential in the case of the infinite binomial series that the first number in the bracket is 1; any other number must be removed as a factor before the expansion is used. Removal of this factor must be done with care; many errors are made at this stage.

The binomial series provides a set of approximating polynomials for $(1 + x)^k$; if only the first two terms are used, it is a linear approximation; if the first three terms are used, it is a quadratic approximation, and so on.

Examples 14.5

1 Given that $|x| < 1$, expand $(1 + x)^{-1}$ as far as the term in x^3. State the coefficient of x^r. Write down the first four terms in the expansion of $(1 - x)^{-1}$, and the term in x^r.

Using (1) above, with $k = -1$,

$$(1 + x)^{-1} = 1 + (-1)x + \frac{(-1)(-2)}{1\,.\,2}x^2 + \frac{(-1)(-2)(-3)}{1\,.\,2\,.\,3}x^3 + \ldots$$

$$= 1 - x + x^2 - x^3 + \ldots \text{ for } |x| < 1.$$

A study of the working above shows that the terms will continue in this pattern with alternating signs. The term in x^r is $(-1)^r x^r$.

To obtain the expansion of $(1 - x)^{-1}$, change the sign of x in the above expansion, giving

$$(1 - x)^{-1} = 1 + x + x^2 + x^3 + \ldots + x^r + \ldots \text{ for } |x| < 1. \qquad (2)$$

Note: an alternative way to establish (2) is to start with the right side, which is an infinite geometric series with first term 1 and common ratio x. The sum of this series is given by the formula $\dfrac{a}{1 - r}$ for $|r| < 1$, and this gives the sum as $\dfrac{1}{1 - x}$ or $(1 - x)^{-1}$, for $|x| < 1$. Similarly the expansion of $(1 + x)^{-1}$ is an infinite geometric series with common ratio $-x$. Thus these particular cases of the binomial series are series which have already been met in Chapter 3.

2 Given that $|x| < 1$, expand $(1 + x)^{-2}$ as far as the term in x^3, and state the coefficient of x^r.

$$(1 + x)^{-2} = 1 + (-2)x + \frac{(-2)(-3)}{1\,.\,2}x^2 + \frac{(-2)(-3)(-4)}{1\,.\,2\,.\,3}x^3 + \ldots$$

$$= 1 - 2x + 3x^2 - 4x^3 + \ldots$$

A study of the above working shows that this pattern will continue, with alternating signs and the numerical coefficient of each power of x being one greater than the power of x. The coefficient of x^r is $(-1)^r(r + 1)$.

3 Given that $|x| < \frac{1}{2}$, expand $(1 + 2x)^{\frac{1}{2}}$ as far as the term in x^4. Hence calculate $\sqrt{1.02}$ correct to seven decimal places.

$$(1 + 2x)^{\frac{1}{2}} = 1 + \frac{1}{2} \, . \, 2x + \frac{\frac{1}{2}\left(-\frac{1}{2}\right)(2x)^2}{1\,.\,2} + \frac{\frac{1}{2}\left(-\frac{1}{2}\right)\left(-\frac{3}{2}\right)(2x)^3}{1\,.\,2\,.\,3}$$

$$+ \frac{\frac{1}{2}\left(-\frac{1}{2}\right)\left(-\frac{3}{2}\right)\left(-\frac{5}{2}\right)(2x)^4}{1\,.\,2\,.\,3\,.\,4} + \ldots$$

$$= 1 + x - \frac{x^2}{2} + \frac{x^3}{2} - \frac{5}{8}x^4 + \ldots$$

Put $x = 0.01$, giving

$$(1.02)^{\frac{1}{2}} = 1 + 0.01 - \frac{0.0001}{2} + \frac{0.000001}{2} - \frac{5}{8}(10)^{-8} + \ldots$$

The next term will not affect the seventh decimal place, and $\sqrt{1.02} = 1.0099505$ to seven decimal places.

4 Expand each of the following as far as the term in x^2. State the values of x for which each series is convergent.

a $(4 + x)^{-\frac{1}{2}}$ **b** $(2 + x)^{-3}$ **c** $\left(\frac{1}{8} + x\right)^{\frac{1}{3}}$

a $(4 + x)^{-\frac{1}{2}}$

$$= 4^{-\frac{1}{2}}\left(1 + \frac{x}{4}\right)^{-\frac{1}{2}}$$

$$= \frac{1}{2}\left[1 - \frac{1}{2} \, . \, \frac{x}{4} + \frac{\left(-\frac{1}{2}\right)\left(-\frac{3}{2}\right)}{1\,.\,2}\left(\frac{x}{4}\right)^2 + \ldots\right] \text{ for } \left|\frac{x}{4}\right| < 1$$

$$= \frac{1}{2}\left(1 - \frac{1}{8}x + \frac{3}{128}x^2 + \ldots\right) \text{ for } |x| < 4$$

The series is convergent for $|x| < 4$.

b $(2 + x)^{-3}$

$$= 2^{-3}\left(1 + \frac{x}{2}\right)^{-3}$$

$$= \frac{1}{8}\left(1 - 3\frac{x}{2} + \frac{(-3)(-4)}{1\,.\,2}\left(\frac{x}{2}\right)^2 + \ldots\right) \text{ for } \left|\frac{x}{2}\right| < 1$$

$$= \frac{1}{8}\left(1 - \frac{3}{2}x + \frac{3}{2}x^2 + \ldots\right) \text{ for } |x| < 2$$

The series is convergent for $|x| < 2$.

c $\left(\frac{1}{8}+x\right)^{\frac{1}{3}}$

$= \left(\frac{1}{8}\right)^{\frac{1}{3}} \left[(1+8x)^{\frac{1}{3}}\right]$

$= \frac{1}{2}\left[1+\frac{1}{3}.8x+\frac{\left(\frac{1}{3}\right)\left(-\frac{2}{3}\right)}{1.2}(8x)^2+\ldots\right]$ for $|8x|<1$

$= \frac{1}{2}\left(1+\frac{8}{3}x-\frac{64}{9}x^2+\ldots\right)$ for $|x|<\frac{1}{8}$

The series is convergent for $|x|<\frac{1}{8}$.

Exercise 14.5A

In each question, the expansion is to be in ascending powers of x.

1 Given that $|x|<1$, expand each of the following as far as the term in x^3.
a $(1+x)^{-3}$ **b** $(1+x)^{-\frac{1}{2}}$ **c** $(1-x)^{\frac{1}{4}}$

2 Given that $|x|<\frac{1}{3}$, expand $(1+3x)^{\frac{1}{3}}$ as far as the term in x^3. Hence calculate $\sqrt[3]{1.03}$ correct to five decimal places.

3 Expand $(1+x)(1+x^2)^{\frac{1}{2}}$ as far as the term in x^3.

4 Expand each of the following as far as the term in x^3. State the values of x for which each series is convergent.
a $(1-2x)^{-1}$ **b** $(1-4x)^{\frac{1}{2}}$ **c** $\frac{1+x}{1+2x}$ **d** $\frac{1+x}{2+x}$

5 Expand $\sqrt{\left(\frac{1+x}{4+x}\right)}$ as far as the term in x^2. State the values of x for which the series is convergent.

6 Expand $(1+x+x^2)^{\frac{1}{2}}$ as far as the term in x^3.

Exercise 14.5B

In each question the expansion is to be in ascending powers of x.

1 Given that $|x|<1$, expand each of the following as far as the term in x^3.
a $(1-x)^{\frac{1}{3}}$ **b** $(1+x)^{-4}$ **c** $(1-x)^{-\frac{3}{2}}$

2 Given that $|x|<\frac{1}{2}$, expand $(1-2x)^{\frac{1}{2}}$ as far as the term in x^3. Hence calculate $\sqrt{0.98}$ correct to five decimal places.

3 Expand $(1+2x-x^2)(1-x^2)^{-2}$ as far as the term in x^3.

4 Expand each of the following as far as the term in x^3. State the values of x for which each series is convergent.
a $(3+x)^{-2}$ **b** $(4+x)^{-\frac{1}{2}}$ **c** $\frac{2+3x}{2-3x}$

5 Expand $(1-2x+3x^2)^{-2}$ as far as the term in x^2.

Exercise 14.5C

1 By writing $\dfrac{x+2}{x-2}$ in the form $\dfrac{1+\dfrac{2}{x}}{1-\dfrac{2}{x}}$, expand $\dfrac{x+2}{x-2}$ in ascending powers of $\dfrac{1}{x}$ as far as the term in $\dfrac{1}{x^2}$. State the values of x for which the series is convergent.

2 Expand $\sqrt{\left(\dfrac{x+4}{x-4}\right)}$ in ascending powers of $\dfrac{1}{x}$ as far as the term in $\dfrac{1}{x^2}$. State the values of x for which the series is convergent.

3 By writing $2-x$ in the form $1+(1-x)$, expand $(2-x)^{-1}$ in ascending powers of $1-x$ as far as the term in $(1-x)^3$. Find the values of x for which the series is convergent.

4 Expand $\left(1+\dfrac{x-1}{x}\right)^{-2}$ in ascending powers of $\dfrac{x-1}{x}$ as far as the term in $\left(\dfrac{x-1}{x}\right)^3$. Find the values of x for which the series is convergent.

Miscellaneous Exercise 14

1 In the expansion of $\left(x+\dfrac{1}{x^2}\right)^{10}$, find and simplify the term in

a x **b** $\dfrac{1}{x^5}$.

2 In the expansion of $\left(x^2+\dfrac{1}{2x}\right)^9$, find and simplify the constant term.

3 Expand $(1+2x+3x^2)^5$ in ascending powers of x as far as the term in x^3.

4 Write down the first four terms in the expansion in ascending powers of x of

a $(1+x)^6$ **b** $(1-x)^6$.

Hence, without using tables or calculator, calculate $(1.01)^6-(0.99)^6$ correct to five significant figures.

5 Write down the third and fourth terms in the expansion in ascending powers of x of $(a+bx)^n$.

Given that these terms are equal, find a simple relation between a, b, x and n.

Given that $a=1$, $b=0.1$, $x=0.5$ and n is an integer greater than unity, find n.

Calculate the term in x^3 in the expansion of $(3-x)^2(1+2x)^5$.

7 Write down the first three terms in the expansion of $(1 + kx)^8$ in ascending powers of x.

Given that, when $x = 2$, the sum of these terms is 4, and that, when $x = -2$, the sum of these terms is 12, find the value of the constant k.

8 Expand $\left(x + \frac{1}{x}\right)^3$ in descending powers of x.

Given that $x + \frac{1}{x} = -1$, prove that $x^3 + \frac{1}{x^3} = 2$, and find the value of $x^5 + \frac{1}{x^5}$.

9 Given that $(1 + ax)^n = 1 - 12x + 63x^2 + \ldots$, find a and n.

10 Find a quadratic approximation for each of the following.

a $(1 + 2x)^{\frac{1}{2}}(1 + 3x)^{-\frac{1}{3}}$ **b** $(1 + 2x - 4x^2)^{\frac{1}{2}}$ **c** $\frac{1 + 2x}{\sqrt{(4 + x)}}$

11 Determine the value of the constant k given that in the expansion of $\frac{1 - kx^2}{(1 - x^2)^{\frac{1}{2}}}$ in ascending powers of x for $|x| < 1$, the coefficient of x^2 is zero. Using this value of k, find the first three non-zero terms of the expansion. *(L)*

12 Expand $(1 - \lambda x)^{-\frac{1}{2}}$ and $(1 + \mu x)^{\frac{1}{2}}$ in ascending powers of x up to and including the terms in x^3 and state the set of values of x for which *both* expansions are valid if $\lambda > \mu > 0$.

Neglecting x^3 and higher powers, find positive values of λ and μ for which

$$2x(1 + 7x) = (1 - \lambda x)^{-\frac{1}{2}} - (1 + \mu x)^{\frac{1}{2}}$$ *(L)*

13 Use the binomial theorem to expand $(x + y)^4$. Hence, by expanding the left-hand side, show that

$$(x + y)^4 - 4xy(x + y)^2 + 2x^2y^2 = x^4 + y^4.$$

A positive number x and a negative number y exist such that $x + y = 2$ and $x^4 + y^4 = 706$. Use the above identity to form a quadratic equation in (xy) and find the value of (xy). Hence find x and y. *(OLE)*

Chapter 15

Linear relations

15.1 Introduction

This short chapter describes an isolated and straightforward topic of particular relevance to students studying science.

In much scientific work, observations of two related variables are made, and an algebraic relation between the two variables is required. Usually the form of the relation is known or suspected, and the values of some constants have to be determined. The following examples show some of the techniques that can be used.

In each example a straight line through a set of points is obtained by drawing the line which appears to fit the points as well as possible. There are mathematical techniques for obtaining a 'best fit' for a given set of points, but they are outside the scope of this text.

In the first example the relation to be found is linear. In the other examples the first stage in the solution is to transform the relation to a linear form.

Examples 15.1

1 Two variables x and y are known to satisfy a linear relation.

Approximate measurements of corresponding values for the two variables give the following results.

x	2.1	3.2	4.8	8.7
y	2.4	3.2	3.9	5.6

Find y in terms of x, giving the coefficients to two significant figures.

Since x and y are known to satisfy a linear relation, this relation can be written in the form $y = a + bx$. The graph of y against x will be a straight line; a will be the intercept on the y-axis and b will be the gradient. Since the observed values are approximate measurements, the 'best' line through the points is drawn and approximate values for a and b are taken from this.

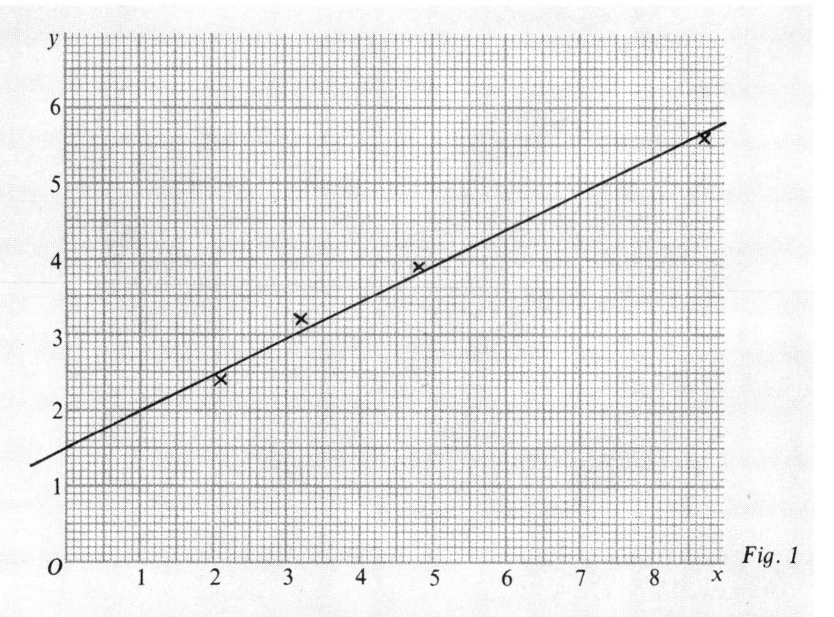

Fig. 1

The intercept on the y-axis is 1.5, so $a = 1.5$.

The gradient of the line is calculated by taking two suitable and widely spaced points, e.g. (0, 1.5) and (5, 3.9), giving the gradient as $\dfrac{3.9 - 1.5}{5} = 0.48$, so $b = 0.48$. The required relation is therefore

$$y = 1.5 + 0.48x.$$

2 A ball is released from rest at time $t = 0$, at a point on an inclined plane. At t seconds from the time of release the ball is x metres from the top of the slope. Measurements of x are made at one-second intervals, with the following results.

t	1	2	3	4	5
x	2.8	4.4	7.8	11.8	17.2

Show that these values approximately satisfy a relation of the form $x = a + bt^2$, and estimate the values of a and b to two decimal places.

Let $T = t^2$. Then we have to show that $x = a + bT$. We therefore draw the graph of x against T. It is helpful to tabulate values of T and x first.

T	1	4	9	16	25
x	2.8	4.4	7.8	11.8	17.2

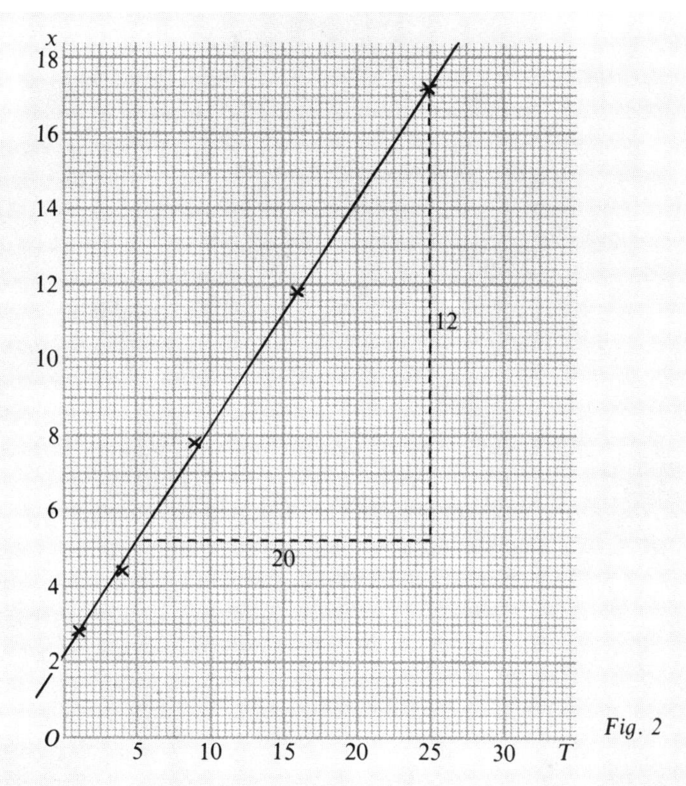

Fig. 2

The points lie close to a line, showing that the values do approximately satisfy a relation of the given form. The x-intercept is 2.2 and the gradient is 0.6, therefore $a = 2.2$ and $b = 0.6$, to one decimal place.

3 Approximate measurements of corresponding values of variables x and y give the following results.

x	5.8	6.4	7.2	8.1
y	46.6	54.6	65.6	79.6

Confirm that these values satisfy a relation of the form $y = kx^n$, and find values of k and n, giving your answers to two significant figures.

In this case, to transform the relation to a linear form, logarithms are used. Taking the natural logarithm of each side of the given equation gives

$$\begin{aligned} \ln y &= \ln (kx^n) \\ &= \ln k + \ln (x^n) \\ &= \ln k + n \ln x. \end{aligned}$$

Let $Y = \ln y$, $X = \ln x$, then

$$Y = \ln k + nX. \qquad (1)$$

This is a linear relation in Y and X, so we now plot Y against X.

$X = \ln x$	1.76	1.86	1.97	2.09
$Y = \ln y$	3.84	4.00	4.18	4.38

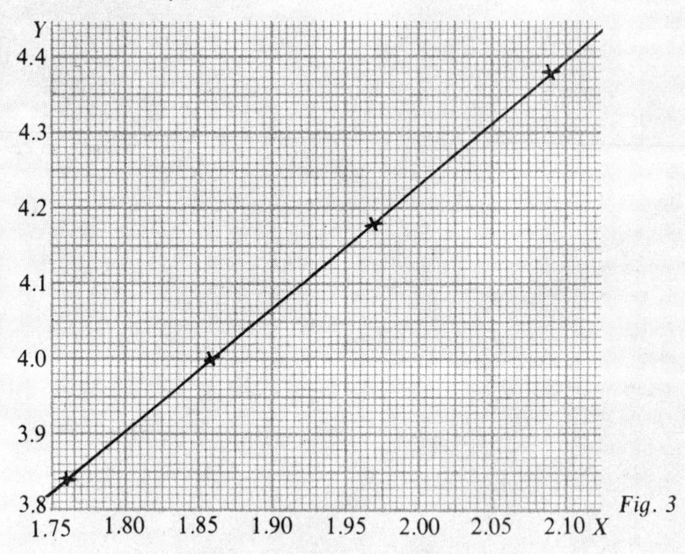

Fig. 3

Note that for the values in the table it is not convenient to start either axis at zero. For this reason the intercept cannot be used to find $\ln k$; a different method is used here.

The points plotted are a good fit to the line drawn, so y and x do approximately satisfy a relation of the given form. The gradient of the line is 1.64. The point (2.00, 4.23) lies on the line, so its equation is

$$Y - 4.23 = 1.64(X - 2.00) \qquad \text{or} \qquad Y = 0.95 + 1.64X.$$

From equation (1), $n = 1.6$ to two significant figures, and $\ln k = 0.95$, giving $k = e^{0.95} = 2.6$ to two significant figures.

4 In a biology experiment, measurements of the number of micro-organisms in 1 cc of nutrient medium are made at one-hourly intervals. The following results are obtained.

Time T (hours)	0	1	2	3	4	5
Number N	183	224	255	305	396	452

Assuming that the variables satisfy a relation of the form $N = ab^T$, estimate the values of a and b to two significant figures.

If $\quad N = ab^T$,

then $\ln N = \ln a + \ln (b^T)$

$\ln N = \ln a + T \ln b$.

Let $\quad Y = \ln N,$
then $\quad Y = \ln a + T \ln b. \qquad (2)$

So we plot Y against T.

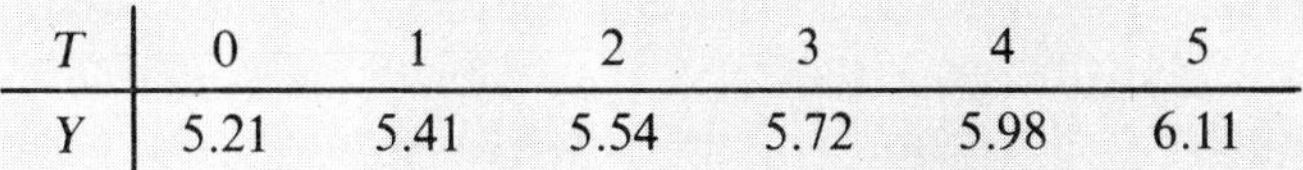

T	0	1	2	3	4	5
Y	5.21	5.41	5.54	5.72	5.98	6.11

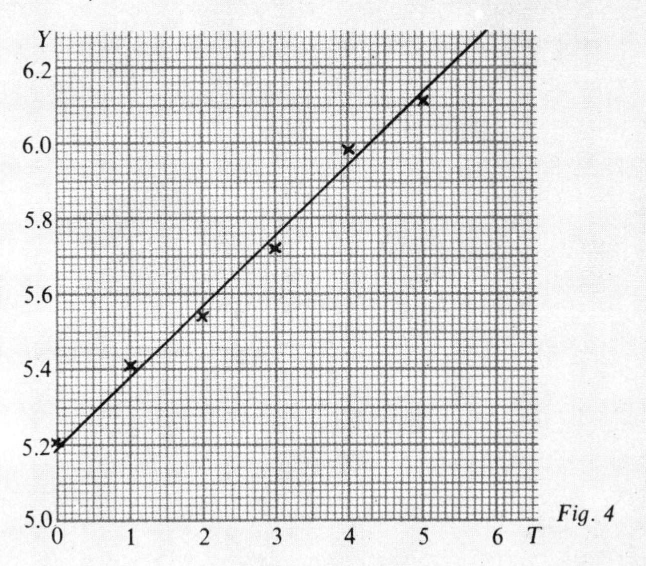

Fig. 4

The Y-intercept is 5.19 and the gradient of the line is 0.186.
Comparing with equation (2) gives

$\ln a = 5.19, \qquad \ln b = 0.186$

$\therefore \quad a = 180, \qquad b = 1.2 \quad$ to two significant figures.

Miscellaneous Exercise 15

1 Rewrite the following equations in suitable form to display a linear relationship in each case between two of the variables, x, $\ln x$, y, and $\ln y$.

a $\dfrac{2}{x} + \dfrac{3}{y} = \dfrac{4}{xy}$ $\qquad$ **b** $5x = 6^y$ $\qquad$ (L)

2 Two variables x and y are known to be related by an equation either of the form $y = ab^x$, where a and b are constants, or $y = cx^n$, where c and n are constants.

Explain how to decide which of these relations is correct by attempting to draw appropriate straight line graphs.

Explain how the appropriate pair of constants a and b, or c and n could be obtained from the straight line graph. (L)

3

v	5	10	15	20	25
R	149	175	219	280	359

The table shows corresponding values of variables R and v obtained in an experiment. By drawing a suitable linear graph, show that these pairs of values may be regarded as approximations to values satisfying a relation of the form $R = a + bv^2$, where a and b are constants.

Use your graph to estimate the values of a and b, giving your answers to 2 significant figures. *(L)*

4 A physics experiment yields the following readings connecting time T and pressure P in appropriate units.

T	0.12	0.17	0.23	0.41	0.75	1.60
P	0.07	1.29	1.71	2.50	2.95	3.24

It is hoped that these results obey a formula of the type $P = A \times \frac{1}{T} + B$, where A and B are constants to be found. Explain what quantities should be plotted on a graph so that, if the results do obey such a formula, the graph will prove to be a straight line and A and B can be deduced from it.

Carry out this process, show that five of the readings are a close fit to such a formula and find A and B. Assuming that T is correct, state which value of P appears to be wrong and estimate what it should be to fit the formula.

Explain also, in plain language, what the formula predicts will happen to the pressure as time increases further. *(MEI)*

5 Measured values of x and y are given in the following table.

x	2	3	4	5	6
y	40	23	18	15	13

It is known that x and y are related by the equation $x^2y = a + bx^2$.

Explain how a straight line graph may be drawn to represent the given equation and draw it for the given data.

Use the graph to estimate the values of a and b. *(C)*

6 The variables x and y are known to satisfy an equation of the form

$$y = a + b\sqrt{x},$$

where a and b are constants. Corresponding approximate values of x and y (each rounded to one decimal place) were obtained experimentally and are given in the following table.

x	3.2	6.8	16.0	25.2	33.6	40.4
y	4.0	5.0	6.6	8.2	9.0	9.8

By drawing a suitable linear graph, estimate the values of a and b, giving both answers to one decimal place. *(JMB)*

7 The variables x and y satisfy a law of the form $x^n y = k$, where n and k are constants. Measured values of x and y are given in the table below.

x	1.2	1.6	2.0	2.6	3.5	4.5
y	11.0	6.31	3.98	2.36	1.32	0.79

By plotting a suitable straight line graph, estimate the values of n and k. Use your graph to estimate the value of y when $x = 3$. (*AEB* 1983)

8 Pairs of numerical values (x, y) are collected from an experiment and it is possible that either of the two following equations may be applicable to these data.

(i) $ax^2 + by^3 = 1$, where a and b are constants

(ii) $y = cx^d$, where c and d are constants

In each case explain carefully how you would use a graph to examine the validity of the equation. Explain how you would estimate the values of the constants if you found the equation to be approximately valid from your graph. (*AEB* 1981)

9 Corresponding values of s and t are as shown.

s	1.5	3	5	8	10
t	275	800	2000	3550	5000

By drawing a suitable graph either on log-log paper or on ordinary graph paper, show that all but one of the pairs are related approximately by the equation $t = As^p$ where A and p are constants.
Find suitable values for A and p. (*AEB* 1980)

10 It is assumed that variables x and y satisfy a relationship of the form $y = a(1 + x)^n$, where a and n are constants. Show graphically, using log-log paper or otherwise, that the values of x and y given in the following table approximately support this assumption. Use your graph to find approximate values for a and n.

x	1	2	3	4	5
y	3.16	3.62	3.99	4.30	4.56

(*AEB* 1981)

11 The air resistance, R newtons, to a vehicle is expected to follow a law of the type

$$R = av^b$$

where v m/s is the speed and a and b are constants. Experimental observations give the following results.

v	10	20	30	40
R	73	260	545	920

By drawing a graph on log-log or other graph paper, show that these values support the expectation.

Use your graph to find

(i) the values of a and b (ii) the value of R at 35 m/s

(iii) the speed at which the resistance is 400 N. (*AEB* 1983)

12 A student performs an experiment and records the following data for two variables y and x.

x	0.5	2	4	7	8
y	1.4	2.8	4.0	5.3	5.7

He believes that there is a relationship between y and x of the form

$$y = ax^b.$$

By plotting $\lg y$ against $\lg x$ show that this relationship holds and find a and b to 2 significant figures.

After completing the experiment, the student realised that he should have measured y when $x = 6$. Obtain, from your graph, an estimate to 2 significant figures, of the value of y when $x = 6$. *(L)*

13

x	0.5	1.5	3.0	4.5	5.5	6.0	7.5
$\ln y$	0.6	1.6	3.6	5.4	6.8	7.2	9.0

The table gives a set of corresponding values for x and $\ln y$, where the variables x and y are known to satisfy a relation of the form $y = ab^x$, where a, b are constants.

Show, by plotting $\ln y$ against x, or otherwise, that the values are not consistent with this relation, but that they are consistent if two of the $\ln y$ entries are assumed to be incorrect.

Estimate the corrected values of $\ln y$ and calculate the values of a and b, correct to one decimal place. *(L)*

14 Measurements are made of two related quantities x and y, and corresponding values are observed. It is known that the relation between x and y is of the form

$$\frac{1}{x} + \frac{1}{y} = \frac{1}{a}.$$

Explain how the value of a may be found by plotting $\frac{1}{y}$ against $\frac{1}{x}$.

In an experiment to determine the focal length of a convex lens, the distance u of the object and the distance v of its image were measured in centimetres from the centre of the lens. The readings obtained are given by the following table.

u (cm)	20	25	30	35	40	45	50
v (cm)	50	33	32	24	22	21	20

Given that $\frac{1}{u} + \frac{1}{v} = \frac{1}{f}$, plot a suitable graph to determine the constant f.

Eliminate any pairs of readings which you consider suspect, and use the remainder to estimate f to the nearest millimetre. *(L)*

Answers

The Examining Boards listed in the Acknowledgements on page ii bear no responsibility whatever for the answers to examination questions given here, which are the sole responsibility of the author.

Chapter 1

Functions

Exercise 1.1A

1 a $\left\{\frac{1}{2}, \frac{1}{5}, \frac{1}{10}, \frac{1}{17}\right\}$ **b** $\{1, 2\}$ **c** $\{1, 2, 4, 8\}$

2 $\{y : y \geqslant 4\}$ **3** $\{y : y \leqslant 1\}$ **4** $\{y : y \geqslant 3\}$

xercise 1.1B

1 a $\{4, 5, 8\}$ **b** $\{0, 1\}$ **c** $\{0, 1, 2, 3\}$

2 $\{y : y \geqslant 5\}$ **3** $\{y : y \geqslant 0\}$ **4** $\{y : y \leqslant 4\}$

5 $\left\{y : 0 < y \leqslant \frac{1}{3}\right\}$ **6** $\{y : y < 1\}$

xercise 1.2A

1 a $3(x-1), 3x-1, 9x, x-2$

b $(x+5)^2, x^2+5, x^4, x+10$

c $2^{x+3}, 2^x+3, 2^{(2^x)}, x+6$

2 $(2x)^3, (2x)^3-3, 2(x-3), [2(x-3)]^3$

3 $20x+5, 20x-13$

4 a $\{y : y \geqslant 0\}, \mathbb{R}$

b $\sqrt{(x-2)}, \{x : x \geqslant 2\}, \{y : y \geqslant 0\}$

c $\sqrt{x}-2, \{x : x \geqslant 0\}, \{y : y \geqslant -2\}$

ercise 1.2B

$\frac{1}{x-4}, x \neq 4; \frac{1}{x}-4, x \neq 0; x, x \neq 0$

$\{y : y > 0\}$ **3** $ad+b = bc+d$

a $\frac{x-1}{2x+3}, x \neq 1$ or $-\frac{3}{2}$

b $\frac{2+3x}{1-x}, x \neq 0$ or 1

a $\{y : y < 3\}, \{y : 0 < y < 1\}$

b $3 - \frac{1}{x+1}, \{x : x > 0\}$

c $\frac{1}{4-x}, \{x : 0 < x < 3\}$

a $\{y : y > 0\}, \{y : y \geqslant 3\}$

b $\frac{1}{x+2}, \{x : x \geqslant 0\}, \left\{y : 0 < y \leqslant \frac{1}{2}\right\}$

c $\frac{1}{x-1}+3, \{x : x > 1\}, \{y : y > 3\}$

rcise 1.3A

a $\frac{x+2}{5}$ **b** $\frac{5x-4}{3}$

$\sqrt{(2x+3)}-4$ **3** $\frac{3x+1}{x-2}$ **4** $\frac{x+3}{1-2x}$

Exercise 1.3B

1 a $2x-3$ **b** $\frac{3x+5}{2}$

2 a $\frac{\sqrt[5]{(4x-3)}+1}{2}$ **b** $\frac{4x+2}{3-x}$ **c** $\frac{2x+4}{3x-1}$

Exercise 1.4A

1 a $|x| = 4; x = \pm 4$ **b** $x = \pm 2; x^2 = 4$

c $-5 < x < 5; x^2 < 25$

d $x < -6, x > 6; x^2 > 36$

Chapter 2

Polynomials, algebraic fractions, the remainder theorem and the factor theorem

Exercise 2.1A

1 a $2x^2+x-3, -4x^2+10x+15, 8x^3-6x^2-33x-18$

b $5x^2+3x-3, -x^2-12x+3, 6x^4+11x^3-18x^2-x+2$

c $2x^4+4x^3-2x+4, 2x^4-8x^3+4x+1, 8x^7-4x^5+2x^4+12x^3-6x+3$

2 $-10, 0$ **3 a** -1 **b** 6

4 $9x^4-30x^3+13x^2+20x+4$

Exercise 2.1B

1 a $12x^2-x-11, -16x^2+18x+8, 20x^3-18x^2-11x+6$

b $9x^2+8x-1, -2x^2-24x+8, 6x^4+4x^3-15x^2+12x-2$

c $6x^3+5x^2+15x-15, -8x^3+10x^2-20x+10, 10x^5+19x^3-20x^2-15x+12$

2 a 8 **b** 1 **3 a** -20 **b** 24

4 -20

Exercise 2.2A

1 a $\frac{7x-7}{(x-3)(x+4)}$ **b** $\frac{x-14}{(x-2)(x-5)}$

c $\frac{5x^2+x-6}{(x+2)(x+3)(x-2)}$ **d** $\frac{2x^2+21x+3}{(x-3)(x+3)(x+4)}$

e $\frac{4}{x-3}$ **f** $\frac{x+3}{x-5}$

g $\frac{5x+1}{(x+1)^2}$ **h** $\frac{3x^2+9x-46}{(x-4)(x-6)(x-2)}$

i $\frac{3(x+5)}{x(x-1)}$ **j** $\frac{x(x+7)}{(x+1)(x+5)}$

Exercise 2.2B

1 a $\frac{5x^2+2x+8}{(x+4)(x-6)}$ **b** $\frac{-x^2+29x}{(x-2)(x+4)}$

c $\frac{-x^2+29x-11}{(2x-1)(x+4)(x+6)}$ **d** $\frac{(x+4)(4x-3)}{x(3x-2)}$

e $\frac{(x+3)(x-1)}{(4x-1)(x+2)}$ **f** $\frac{2x^2+5xy-y^2}{(x-y)^2(x+y)}$

g $\frac{a+2b}{3a-b}$ **h** $\frac{x-y}{(x+2y)^2}$

Exercise 2.3A

1 a $x^2+2x-1, -4$ b $x^2+x+6, 10$

2 a $x^2+5x+15, 40$ b $3x^2+\frac{3}{2}x+\frac{11}{4}, -\frac{1}{4}$

3 $1+\frac{2}{x+2}$

4 a $x^2+3x-1, -7x+3$ b $x+2, 0$ c $x-3, 0$

Exercise 2.3B

1 a $x^2-6x+23, -73$
b $x^2+x-\frac{1}{3}, -\frac{8}{3}$
c $x^2-x+1, 0$
d $4x^2+2x+1, 0$
e $2x^2+\frac{3}{2}x-\frac{3}{4}, -\frac{25}{4}$
f $x^4+2x^3+4x^2+8x+16, 0$

2 a $x^2+5, 0$ b $x^2+4, 0$

3 a $1+\frac{3}{x-1}$ b $1+\frac{3}{x+2}$
c $2+\frac{7}{x-2}$ d $\frac{3}{2}-\frac{11}{2(2x+1)}$

Exercise 2.4A

1 a 2 b 0 c 1 d -40 e $-1\frac{1}{4}$ f $\frac{13}{9}$

Exercise 2.4B

1 a 0 b -1 c $\frac{34}{9}$ d 0 e 0 f $2a^6$

2 $12x-26$

Exercise 2.5A

1 a $(x-1)(x-2)(x+5)$ b $(x-2)(x+1)(x+3)$
c $(x-1)^2(x-2)$ d $(x-3)(x-4)(x+2)$

2 $(2x-1), (x-4)$ 3 $(2x-1)(x^2+2x+3)$

4 $(3x-1)(x^2+x+1)$

Exercise 2.5B

1 a $(x-1)(x-3)(x+4)$ b $(x+1)(x^2-6x+10)$
c $(x-3)(x^2+4x+5)$ d $(x+2)(x^2+x+3)$

2 $(3x-2), (x+3)$

3 $(2x+1)(x^2-2x+3)$

4 $(x-2)(x+2)(x^2+4)$

5 $(x-2)((x^4+2x^3+4x^2+8x+16)$

Exercise 2.6

1 a $(x-2)(x^2+2x+4)$
b $(x+3)(x^2-3x+9)$
c $(x+1)(x^4-x^3+x^2-x+1)$
d $(x-2)(x+2)(x^2+2x+4)(x^2-2x+4)$
e $(x+5)(x^2-5x+25)$
f $(x-5)(x+5)(x^2+25)$
g $(2x-1)(4x^2+2x+1)$
h $(3-x)(9+3x+x^2)$

Miscellaneous Exercise 2

1 $\frac{(x^2+2x+4)(x+2)}{(x^2-3x+9)(x-1)}$

2 $\frac{-3x^2+8x-1}{(x+1)^2(x^2-x+1)}$

3 $\frac{x^2-x+1}{x+2}$

4 $\frac{4-2x}{x+1}; x \neq \pm 1$

5 $\frac{(ap+br)x+aq+bs}{(cp+dr)x+cq+ds}$; $cp+dr=0$; $x \neq -\frac{s}{r}$

Chapter 3

Arithmetic and geometric series

Exercise 3.1A

1 a $30, 4n-2$ b $-8, 8-2n$
c $6\frac{1}{2}, \frac{5+n}{2}$ d $9.3, 10.1-0.1n$

2 a 17 b 177 c 51 d 31

3 102 4 4.1

Exercise 3.1B

1 a $3+2n$ b $3.8+0.2n$
c $25-5n$ d $\frac{2+4n}{3}$

2 a 64 b 41 c 102 d 98

3 22

Exercise 3.2A

1 a $\sum_{r=1}^{n} r^2$ b $\sum_{r=1}^{10} \frac{1}{r}$
c $\sum_{r=0}^{n-1} 2r$ d $\sum_{r=1}^{n} r(r+1)$

2 a $1^3+2^3+3^3+\ldots+n^3$
b $3+3^2+3^3+\ldots+3^{2n}$
c $4+7+10+13+16+19$
d $1-4+4^2-4^3+4^4-4^5$

3 a 101, 2600 b $-45, -1025$
c 5.9, 172.5 d 9, 275

4 $55, \frac{5}{2}$ 5 $188\frac{1}{2}$ 6 3, 7, 11

Exercise 3.2B

1 a $\sum_{r=2}^{n} 2r$ b $\sum_{r=3}^{n} \frac{1}{r^2}$
c $\sum_{r=1}^{4} 3(2^{n-1})$ d $\sum_{r=1}^{n} \frac{1}{(2r-1)(2r+1)}$

2 a $1+\frac{1}{2}+\ldots+\frac{1}{2^{n-1}}$
b $1-x+x^2-\ldots+x^{2n}$
c $1.2.3+2.3.4+\ldots+7.8.9$
d $2+2+\ldots+2$ (n terms)

3 a 182, 560 b $-108, -2940$ c 72.8,

4 2 6 31 7 $8, 11, 3n+5$

Exercise 3.3A

1 a $4\times3^5, 4\times3^{n-1}$ **b** $2\times10^5, 2\times10^{n-1}$

c $\frac{1}{2}(-4)^5, \frac{1}{2}(-4)^{n-1}$ **d** $6\left(\frac{1}{3}\right)^5, 6\left(\frac{1}{3}\right)^{n-1}$

2 ±3 **3** 4.4

4 a 7.16×10^8 **b** 8.00 **c** 8.33

5 $\frac{1-x^n}{1-x}$; $(1-x)(1+x+x^2+\ldots+x^{n-1})$

xercise 3.3B

1 a $2.4^5, 2.4^{n-1}$ **b** $12\left(-\frac{1}{4}\right)^4, 12\left(-\frac{1}{4}\right)^{n-1}$

c $0.2(0.1)^6, 0.2(0.1)^{n-1}$

2 ±3

3 a $18(1-3^{-20})$ **b** $1-2^{20}$ **c** $\frac{81}{4}(1-3^{-20})$

4 $\frac{x^n-a^n}{x-a}$; $(x-a)(x^{n-1}+ax^{n-2}+\ldots+a^{n-1})$

5 £633·59

ercise 3.4A

a $\frac{2}{3}, 6$ **b** $-\frac{1}{2}, \frac{2}{9}$

c 0.9, 10 **d** 1.1, divergent

a $|x|<\frac{1}{3}, \frac{1}{1-3x}$ **b** $|x|>2, \frac{x}{x-2}$

c $1<x<3, \frac{1}{x-1}$

a $\frac{2}{9}$ **b** $\frac{6}{11}$ **c** $\frac{41}{333}$ **d** $\frac{7}{330}$

ercise 3.4B

a $\frac{1}{9}, \frac{27}{8}$ **b** $-\frac{3}{4}, \frac{16}{7}$

c $\frac{12}{11}$, divergent **d** $\frac{2}{3}$, 192

a $|x|<\frac{1}{5}, \frac{1}{1-5x}$ **b** $|x|<4, \frac{4}{4+x}$

c $|x|<1, \frac{1}{1-x^2}$ **d** $|x|<\frac{1}{2}, \frac{1}{1-8x^3}$

a $\frac{5}{9}$ **b** $\frac{3}{11}$ **c** $\frac{176}{333}$ **d** $\frac{1}{660}$

cellaneous Exercise 3

14 950 **2** 29

i) 43, 62 (ii) 36, 54

26, 3 **5** $6, \frac{729}{16}$

i) 4.75 cm, 6.5 cm (ii) 4.5 cm, 6.75 cm

i) $4\frac{3}{4}$ cm (ii) 33 cm

$-\frac{1}{2}, \frac{2}{3}a$

3000 **b** $\frac{3}{2}, 5$

Chapter 4

Trigonometry 1

Exercise 4.1A

1 a $-40°, \pm140°$ **b** $-110°, \pm70°$
c $-170°, \pm10°$ **d** $20°, \pm160°$
e $100°, \pm80°$

2 a $-35°$ **b** $-128°$ **c** $25°$ **d** $160°$

3 a $35°, 145°$ **b** $-18°, -162°$ **c** $\pm85°$

4 a $15°, -165°$ **b** $65°, -115°$ **c** $-80°, 100°$

5 $P(2, 3.5), Q(-4.6, 3.9), R(8.7, -5)$
$QR=16, RP=11, PQ=7$

6 a 2 or $\frac{1}{4}$ **b** $-166°, -117°, 14°, 63°$

8 a $2\cos\theta+3$; domain = set of all angles;
range $=\{y: 1\leqslant y\leqslant 5\}$
b $\cos^2\theta+3$; domain as **a**;
range $=\{y: 3\leqslant y\leqslant 4\}$
c $\frac{1}{\cos\theta}$; domain = set of all angles except odd multiples of 90°;
range $=\{y: |y|\geqslant 1\}$

Exercise 4.1B

1 a $-90°$ **b** $-105°$ **c** $-79°$ **d** $-130°$

2 a $10°$ **b** $130°$ **c** $-95°$ **d** $-72°$

3 a $-140°$ **b** $-5°$ **c** $91°$ **d** $70°$

4 a $\pm58°$ **b** $-27°, -153°$ **c** $-52°, 128°$

5 a $-127°$ **b** $113°$

6 a $\frac{1}{3}$ or $-\frac{1}{2}$ **b** $\pm120°, \pm71°$

7 a $(13, 67°)$ **b** $(13, -113°)$
c $(\sqrt{8}, -45°)$ **d** $(\sqrt{8}, 135°)$

9 a $3\sin\theta+1$; domain = set of all angles;
range $=\{y: -2\leqslant y\leqslant 4\}$
b $\sin^3\theta+2$; domain as **a**;
range $=\{y: 1\leqslant y\leqslant 3\}$
c $\frac{1}{\sin^2\theta}$; domain = set of all angles except multiples of 180°;
range $=\{y: y\geqslant 1\}$

Exercise 4.2

1 a $\pm69°$ **b** $-34°, -146°$ **c** $-38°, 142°$

2 a $136°, 224°$ **b** $193°, 347°$ **c** $68°, 248°$

3 a $\pm24°, \pm156°$
b $17°, -163°, 73°, -107°$
c $-35°, 145°, 55°, -125°$

4 Graph has half-turn symmetry about O.

5 Each point for which $\theta\leqslant360°$ on the graph is mapped to another point on the graph by a translation 180° parallel to the θ-axis.

Exercise 4.3A

1 120° 2 −135° 3 a $\pm\frac{12}{13}$ b $\pm\frac{5}{12}$

4 $P(1, \sqrt{3}), Q(-2, 2\sqrt{3}); \sqrt{12}$

5 63.4°, −116.6°
6 ±45°, ±135°
7 ±60°, ±120°
8 30°, 150°, −90°
9 ±120°
10 ±60°, ±120°
11 ±90°, ±41.4°
12 48.6°, 131.4°
13 ±120°, ±48.2°
14 180°, ±66.4°
15 ±48.2°, ±60°
16 21.8°, −158.2°, −26.6°, 153.4°
17 $\frac{x^2}{a^2}+\frac{y^2}{b^2}=1$
18 $\frac{x^2}{9}-\frac{y^2}{4}=1$
19 $\frac{x^2}{16}-\frac{y^2}{9}=1$
20 −150°, −60°, 30°, 120°
21 ±15°, ±165°

Exercise 4.3B

1 −60° 2 −124.1° 3 $\pm\frac{5}{4}$

4 ±30°, ±150°
5 ±45°, ±135°
6 56.3°, −123.7°, 63.4°, −116.6°
7 ±41.4°
8 0°, 180°
9 ±78.5°
10 −30°, −150°
11 26.6°, −153.4°, −71.6°, 108.4°
12 $\frac{16}{x^2}+\frac{9}{y^2}=1$
13 $(x-1)^2+(y-2)^2=1$
14 $(x-2)^2-(y-3)^2=25$
15 $x^2+y^2=2$
16 $-112\frac{1}{2}°, -22\frac{1}{2}°, 67\frac{1}{2}°, 157\frac{1}{2}°$
17 $\pm 22\frac{1}{2}°, 157\frac{1}{2}°$

Exercise 4.4

1 $A=80°, b=7.5, c=4.9$
2 $A=82.2°, B=53.6°, C=44.2°$
3 $a=7.9, B=78.0°, C=48.0°$
4 $B=45°, a=4.7, c=2.1$
5 $c=4.9, A=28.2°, B=46.8°$
6 $C=99°, a=6.0, b=3.5$
7 $C=78.5°, A=62.6°, B=38.9°$
8 $b=8.0, A=72.2°, C=51.8°$
10 13.0 cm, 3.0 cm; 29.8 cm², 6.8 cm²
11 31.2° or 148.8°; 6.3 cm or 20.2 cm
12 300 m, 270 m
13 2.5 cm, 1.4 cm
14 7.3 cm, 9.8 cm, 31.9 cm²

Miscellaneous Exercise 4

1 ±48.2°, ±60°
2 63.4°, −116.6°, 59.0°, −121.0°
3 ±27.7°, ±152.3°
4 −122.9°, −32.9°, 57.1°, 147.1°
5 a $\tan^2\theta+1; \{\theta: -90°<\theta<90°\}; \{y: y\geqslant 1\}$
b $\frac{1}{\tan\theta-1}; \{\theta: -90°<\theta<90°, \theta\neq 45°\}; \{y: y\neq 0\}$
6 $(s-1)(2s+1)(s+2)$; −150°, −30°, 90°
8 4.3 km, 257°
9 a 22° b 2.5 km c 098°
d (i) 4.4 km (ii) 11.1 km
10 a 140 m b 200 m c 42°
11 a 5 km b 330° c 7.05 km

Chapter 5

Rational and irrational numbers, surds, quadratic equations

Exercise 5.1A

1 a 125 b 21 c 10 d $\frac{2}{5}$

2 a $5\sqrt{2}$ b $4\sqrt{5}$ c $7\sqrt{2}$ d $6\sqrt{3}$ e 9

3 a $\frac{2\sqrt{7}}{21}$ b $\frac{3}{13}(4+\sqrt{3})$ c $\frac{3\sqrt{2}-2}{7}$
d $\frac{4}{17}(5-2\sqrt{2})$

Exercise 5.1B

1 a 56 b 13 c $\frac{7}{8}$

2 a $5\sqrt{3}$ b $6\sqrt{5}$ c $11\sqrt{2}$ d $8\sqrt{}$

3 a $\frac{4\sqrt{5}}{15}$ b $2\frac{(6+\sqrt{7})}{29}$ c $\frac{3}{2}(2+\sqrt{3})$
d $\frac{15-2\sqrt{5}}{41}$

4 For example, $\sqrt{2}$ and $\sqrt{8}$

5 a $\frac{7}{3}\sqrt{6}$ b $\frac{25}{7}\sqrt{7}$

Exercise 5.2A

1 1.24, −3.24
2 −0.59, −3.41
3 5.45, 0.55
4 4.56, 0.44
5 1.87, 0.1
6 2.12, −

Exercise 5.2B

1 3.45, −1.45
2 5.16, −1.16
3 7.32, 0.68
4 No solutions
5 −0.42, −
6 1.40, −0.

Exercise 5.3

1 5.16, −1.16
2 −0.22, −2.28
3 1.55, −0.80
4 No solutions
5 0.79, −2.12
6 No solutions
7 0.39, −3.89
8 No solutions
9 0.74, −1.34
10 0.84, −0.59

Exercise 5.4A

1 a 40; real, not rational b −23; not real
c −16; not real d 136; real, not rat
e −23; not real f 25; real, rational
g 0; real, rational

2 $k \leqslant 9$

3 $p = 2\sqrt{3}$, root $-\sqrt{3}$; $p = -2\sqrt{3}$, root $\sqrt{3}$

4 $|p| \geqslant 2\sqrt{7}$

xercise 5.4B

1 $k \geqslant -16$

2 $s = -2\sqrt{5}$, root $-\sqrt{5}$; $s = 2\sqrt{5}$, root $\sqrt{5}$

3 $s < -\sqrt{40}$, $s > \sqrt{40}$

4 $k \leqslant -2$, $k \geqslant 2$; $k = \pm 2$

xercise 5.5

1 **a** $\frac{5}{3}, \frac{4}{3}$ **b** $-3, -\frac{3}{2}$ **c** $\frac{3}{4}, \frac{5}{4}$

d $\frac{2}{7}, \frac{3}{7}$ **e** $-\frac{3}{8}, -\frac{1}{2}$ **f** $\frac{4}{5}, -\frac{2}{5}$

2 **a** $x^2 - 7x + 3 = 0$ **b** $2x^2 + 5x + 8 = 0$
c $3x^2 + 4x + 2 = 0$ **d** $7x^2 - 6x - 2 = 0$

xercise 5.6A

1 **a** $3x^2 - 18x + 4 = 0$ **b** $3x^2 + 3x - 5 = 0$
c $x^2 - 27x + 27 = 0$ **d** $3x^2 - 63x + 49 = 0$
e $9x^2 - 75x + 1 = 0$ **f** $9x^2 - 21x - 5 = 0$

2 $8x^2 - 136x - 27 = 0$

ercise 5.6B

a $x^2 + 14x + 32 = 0$ **b** $x^2 - 13x + 38 = 0$
c $x^2 = 0$ **d** $16x^2 - 33x + 4 = 0$

$x^2 - (p^4 - 4p^2q + 2q^2)x + q^4 = 0$

ercise 5.7

$27x^2 - 108x + 8 = 0$

$x^2 - 3x - 10 = 0$

a $4x^2 + 19x + 19 = 0$ **b** $2x^2 + 15x - 36 = 0$

$S_3 = p^3 - 3pq$

ercise 5.8

$2p^2 = 9q$ **2** $p^2 - 9 = 4q$

a $0 < k \leqslant 9$ **b** $k < 0$

$q = 16 - s^2$, $-4 < s < 4$

rcise 5.9

a 0.2, 2.3 **b** 3.7, −1.2 **c** 0.2, 3.4

a 2.4, −0.4 **b** 1.3, −2.3 **c** 2.4, −0.9
d 0.2, −1.9

rcise 5.10A

$(-8, -\frac{1}{2})$, $(1, 4)$ **2** $(1, 2)$, $(3, -4)$

$\frac{1}{7}, \frac{5}{7})$, $(1, -1)$ **4** $(6, 15)$

rcise 5.10B

$0, -5)$, $(3, 4)$ **2** $(2, \frac{1}{2})$, $(1, 1)$

$1, 2)$, $(2, 1)$ **4** $(\frac{3}{2}, 1)$

$-1 \leqslant m \leqslant 1$; $y = x + 1$, $y = -(x + 1)$

cellaneous Exercise 5

$= s$, $h = 0$ **2** $a = b$ **3** 2, for example

$\frac{3 \pm \sqrt{3}}{2}$ **b** $\frac{3 \pm \sqrt{3}}{3}$

$^2 - q(p^2 - 2q)x + q^4 = 0$

6 $9q - 2p^2$ **7** 1, −3

10 (i) $p^3 - 3pq$ (ii) $q + q^2 + 3pq - p^3$

11 $x = 1, y = 1$; $x = 2, y = -1$

12 $(3, 1)$, $(-\frac{17}{7}, -\frac{12}{7})$

13 $(2, 4)$, $(3, 2)$

14 (i) $b^2 = 4ac$ (ii) $-\frac{b}{a}$

a $\pm\frac{3}{2}$ **b** (i) $x^2 - 6x - 10 = 0$ (ii) 3

Chapter 6

Coordinate geometry 1: lines and circles

Exercise 6.1A

1 (i) **a** $(\frac{7}{2}, \frac{21}{2})$ **b** $\sqrt{34}$ **c** $\frac{3}{5}$ **d** 31°

(ii) **a** $(-\frac{1}{2}, -6)$ **b** $\sqrt{29}$ **c** $\frac{2}{5}$ **d** 22°

(iii) **a** $(-1, 5)$ **b** $6\sqrt{5}$ **c** $\frac{1}{2}$ **d** 27°

2 $2\sqrt{5}$, $2\sqrt{17}$ **3** $(12, 1)$ **4** $(-3, 5)$, -1

Exercise 6.1B

1 **a** $(4, \frac{11}{2})$ **b** $\sqrt{13}$ **c** $-\frac{3}{2}$ **d** −56°

2 **a** $(2, -\frac{7}{2})$ **b** $\sqrt{73}$ **c** $\frac{3}{8}$ **d** 21°

4 $(7, -1)$

Exercise 6.2A

1 **a** yes **b** no **c** yes

2 **a** $y = 2x - 7$ **b** $3x + y = 11$
c $4x - 3y + 23 = 0$ **d** $4x - 5y + 12 = 0$
e $5x + 2y = 22$

3 $\frac{x}{7} + \frac{y}{3} = 1$ **4** $3x + 2y = 10$

Exercise 6.2B

1 **a** $4x - 5y = 23$
b $2x + 3y = 13$
c $2x - 5y + 34 = 0$
d $2x + 3y = 5$
e $x - y\sqrt{3} + 2\sqrt{3} - 4 = 0$
f $x + y\sqrt{3} + 2\sqrt{3} - 4 = 0$

2 $2x - 5y = 1$

3 **a** 37° **b** −50°

4 **a** $5x + 2y = 10$ **b** $5x + 2y + 10 = 0$
c $5y - 2x = 10$

Exercise 6.3A

1 $2x - 3y = 5$; $\frac{2}{3}$

3 $(8, \frac{5}{2})$ **4** 18°, $(1, -1)$

5 **a** $5x - 2y + 1 = 0$ **b** $4x + 3y = 7$
c $x - 6y + 17 = 0$

6 $y = 2x - 7$ **7** $\frac{14}{5}$; no, opposite side

Exercise 6.3B

2 $x = 4t$, $y = 3 + 3t$ (or others)
3 a $63°$ b $65°$
4 $(-2, 9)$
5 a $3x - 4y = 18$ b $2x + 5y + 33 = 0$
6 $2y = x + 7$; 4, (5, 6)
7 $5x - y + 30 = 0$, $5x + 25y - 48 = 0$

Exercise 6.4A

1 $3x + 2y = 13$
2 $xx_1 + yy_1 = a^2$
3 a $x^2 + y^2 - 6x - 2y + 6 = 0$
b $x^2 + y^2 + 4x - 10y + 26 = 0$
4 a circle; $(3, -2)$, $\sqrt{11}$ b circle; $(-4, 1)$, 1
c not a circle d circle; $(-2, \frac{4}{3})$, $\frac{2}{3}\sqrt{13}$
5 (5, 2); (5, 5), (5, −1)
6 a $3x + 4y = 45$
7 $2\sqrt{3}$

Exercise 6.4B

1 $x + y\sqrt{3} = 8$
2 $x \cos \phi + y \sin \phi = a$
3 $(\frac{11}{2}, 4)$
4 $x = 4$, $x + y = 13$; (4, 9), $\sqrt{20}$; $x^2 + y^2 - 8x - 18y + 77 = 0$
5 (6, 5)
6 (1, 6), (5, 4)

Miscellaneous Exercise 6

1 a $(\frac{11}{2}, \frac{7}{2})$, $3y = x + 5$ b $(\frac{5}{2}, \frac{5}{2})$
2 $(\frac{5}{2}, -1)$, $(\frac{11}{2}, 5)$
3 (i) $5x + y = 4$, $x - 5y = 6$
(iii) 52 units^2 (iv) (0, 30)
4 $(-7, 1)$; 30 units^2; $\frac{6}{13}\sqrt{65}$
5 (i) $A(2, 0)$, $B(0, 6)$, $C(9, 3)$
(iii) 27 units^2 (iv) (7, 9)
6 a $(x - 1)^2 + (y - 2)^2 = 5$
7 $(x - 9)^2 + (y + 1)^2 = 117$; $2x - 3y + 18 = 0$
8 a (1, 5) b $x + y = 8$ c (3, 7)
9 a $x + 3y = 18$
b (i) $(\frac{9}{2}, \frac{9}{2})$
(ii) $x^2 + y^2 - 9x - 9y + 28 = 0$
c (1, 5)
10 (1, 2), $2\sqrt{2}$
(i) $x + y = 7$ (iii) $(x - 4)^2 + (y - 1)^2 = 10$
11 (i) $(\frac{3}{2}, 0)$ (ii) $\frac{5}{2}$
(iii) $(-1, 0)$, (4, 0), $(0, -2)$, (0, 2)
(3, 2); $(\frac{17}{3}, 0)$
12 (i) $x^2 + y^2 + x - 4y - 3 = 0$
(ii) $(-\frac{1}{2}, 2)$ (iii) $\frac{\sqrt{29}}{2}$
(iv) (2, 1) (v) $5x - 2y - 8 = 0$
(vi) $44°$
13 10, (8, 9); $x^2 + y^2 - 22x - y + 40 = 0$; $6x - 17y + 105 = 0$
14 $\frac{|a + 4|}{5}$; 1; $3x + 4y = 7$

Chapter 7

Indices; exponential and logarithmic functions

Exercise 7.1

1 $\frac{1}{5}$
2 8
3 125
4 4
5 9
6 $\frac{1}{7}$
7 27
8 4
9 $\frac{2}{3}$
10 13
11 32
12 $\frac{1}{100}$
13 $\frac{1}{6}$
14 0.4
15 $\frac{1}{1000}$
16 32
17 $\frac{7}{12}$
18 $\frac{8}{27}$
19 $\frac{4}{9}$
20 100
21 32

Exercise 7.2A

3 $2^{x+1} + 2$, $\mathbb{R}$, $\{y : y > 2\}$
4 ± 1

Exercise 7.2B

3 a 2^x, $\mathbb{R}$, $\{y : y > 0\}$
b 2^{2x-1}, $\mathbb{R}$, $\{y : y > 0\}$
4 3^{4x}, 3^{8x}, 3^{64x}

Exercise 7.3A

1 a $\log_5 125 = 3$ b $\log_2\left(\frac{1}{8}\right) = -3$
c $\log_4 32 = \frac{5}{2}$ d $\log_3\left(\frac{1}{27}\right) = -3$
2 a $5^{-2} = \frac{1}{25}$ b $8^{\frac{1}{3}} = 2$
c $100^{\frac{1}{2}} = 10$ d $c^a = d$
3 a 3 b −8 c 4.5
d 2.5 e $\frac{2}{3}$ f 0
g $\frac{2}{3}$ h −1 i c

Exercise 7.3B

1 a $\log_7 343 = 3$ b $\log_6\left(\frac{1}{36}\right) = -2$
c $\log_9 27 = \frac{3}{2}$ d $\log_p r = q$
e $\log_r t = -s$
2 a $27^{\frac{2}{3}} = 9$ b $5^4 = 625$
c $9^{3.5} = 2187$ d $b^c = \frac{1}{\sqrt{a}}$
3 a −3 b 2.5 c 3.5 d 8 e

Exercise 7.4A

1 a $\log r + \log s$ b $\log s - \log t$
c $2 \log r$ d $\frac{1}{2}(\log s + \log t)$
e $-3 \log t$ f $2 + 3 \log_{10} r$
g $\frac{1}{2} \log r + \frac{1}{3} \log s$ h $\frac{3}{2} \log r + \frac{5}{2} \log s$

2 **a** $\log 63$ **b** $\log 2000$
c $\log 15$ **d** $\log_{10} 450$
e $\log_2 8pq^2$ **f** $\log \dfrac{r^2s^3}{9t^4}$
g $\log p^{\frac{1}{2}}q^{\frac{2}{3}}$

3 **a** 2.807 **b** 1.431 **c** 0.8390 **d** -1.369

4 18; 2.58×10^8 **5** 2080; 3 h 32 min p.m.

6 **a** $3 \log_{10} x$ **b** $10^{\frac{x}{3}}$ **c** $(\log_{10} x)^3$ **d** $10^{x^{\frac{1}{3}}}$

xercise 7.4B

1 **a** $\log a + \log b + \log c$
b $\log b + \log c - \log a$
c $2 \log a + 3 \log b + 4 \log c$
d $\dfrac{3}{2} \log a$
e $-3 \log b - 2 \log c$
f $b \log a + a \log b + ab \log c$

a $\log 24$ **b** $\log 9$ **c** $\log 9$ **d** $\log 20$

a 1.61 **b** 2.03 **c** 1.67 **d** 0.126

5, 22 **5** 1989

a $-\log_{10} x$, $\{x : x > 0\}$, $\mathbb{R}$
b 10^{-x}
c $\dfrac{1}{\log_{10} x}$
d $10^{\frac{1}{x}}$, $\{x : x > 0\}$, $\{y : y > 1\}$

scellaneous Exercise 7

a 343 **b** $\dfrac{1}{8}$ **c** $\dfrac{4}{9}$ **d** $\dfrac{4}{11}$

9.548 **4** 0.6309, 1.262 **5** 0, 1.58 **6** 1217

a $\log (x-2)^2$ **b** $\log \dfrac{x-4}{x-2}$
c $\log \dfrac{x^2+2x+4}{(x-2)^2}$ **d** $\log (x+3)^2$
e $\log \dfrac{(x-1)^4}{x+1}$ **f** $\log \dfrac{(x+1)^2(x-1)^3}{x^4}$

a (i) $b = a^c$ (ii) $a = b^{\frac{1}{c}}$ (iii) 6 (iv) 9 (v) 6
b 0 **c** 2.28

37°C; 15 min **10** **a** 1.3 **b** $2\frac{1}{2}$ h

a $\log \sqrt{x}$ **b** 10^{2x} **c** $\sqrt{(\log_{10} x)}$ **d** 10^{x^2}

$2 + \log_2 x$, $\{x : x > 1\}$, $\{y : y > 2\}$
2^{x-2}, $\{x : x > 2\}$, $\{y : y > 1\}$

hapter 8

ctors 1

cise 8.1A

$\begin{pmatrix} 4 \\ 3 \end{pmatrix}, \begin{pmatrix} 7 \\ 8 \end{pmatrix}, \begin{pmatrix} 3 \\ 5 \end{pmatrix}, \begin{pmatrix} -3 \\ -5 \end{pmatrix}$

$\begin{pmatrix} -2 \\ 1 \end{pmatrix}, \begin{pmatrix} 3 \\ 4 \end{pmatrix}, \begin{pmatrix} 5 \\ 3 \end{pmatrix}, \begin{pmatrix} -5 \\ -3 \end{pmatrix}$

$\begin{pmatrix} 1 \\ -3 \end{pmatrix}, \begin{pmatrix} -4 \\ 5 \end{pmatrix}, \begin{pmatrix} -5 \\ 8 \end{pmatrix}, \begin{pmatrix} 5 \\ -8 \end{pmatrix}$

$\begin{pmatrix} 1 \\ 2 \end{pmatrix}, \begin{pmatrix} -2 \\ -4 \end{pmatrix}, \begin{pmatrix} -3 \\ -6 \end{pmatrix}, \begin{pmatrix} 3 \\ 6 \end{pmatrix}$

2 $\begin{pmatrix} 2 \\ 6 \end{pmatrix}, \begin{pmatrix} 3 \\ 9 \end{pmatrix}$; 2 : 3

3 (1, 7); $\begin{pmatrix} 4 \\ 6 \end{pmatrix}$, (5, 13); $\begin{pmatrix} -6 \\ -9 \end{pmatrix}$, (−1, 4)

4 (2, 8), (10, 2)

5 $\begin{pmatrix} 4 \\ 2 \end{pmatrix}$, (9, 11); each $\begin{pmatrix} 2 \\ 5 \end{pmatrix}$

Exercise 8.1B

1 **a** $\begin{pmatrix} 5 \\ 2 \end{pmatrix}, \begin{pmatrix} 3 \\ 6 \end{pmatrix}, \begin{pmatrix} -2 \\ 4 \end{pmatrix}, \begin{pmatrix} 2 \\ -4 \end{pmatrix}$

b $\begin{pmatrix} 4 \\ -3 \end{pmatrix}, \begin{pmatrix} 6 \\ 1 \end{pmatrix}, \begin{pmatrix} 2 \\ 4 \end{pmatrix}, \begin{pmatrix} -2 \\ -4 \end{pmatrix}$

c $\begin{pmatrix} -2 \\ -1 \end{pmatrix}, \begin{pmatrix} -3 \\ 4 \end{pmatrix}, \begin{pmatrix} -1 \\ 5 \end{pmatrix}, \begin{pmatrix} 1 \\ -5 \end{pmatrix}$

d $\begin{pmatrix} -4 \\ 2 \end{pmatrix}, \begin{pmatrix} 1 \\ -1 \end{pmatrix}, \begin{pmatrix} 5 \\ -3 \end{pmatrix}, \begin{pmatrix} -5 \\ 3 \end{pmatrix}$

2 $\begin{pmatrix} 2 \\ -3 \end{pmatrix}, \begin{pmatrix} 6 \\ -9 \end{pmatrix}$; 1 : 3

3 (3, 2); $\begin{pmatrix} -12 \\ 9 \end{pmatrix}$, (−9, 11)

4 (1, −2), (−3, 8)

5 (7, 4), (11, 7), (1, 12)

Exercise 8.2A

1 **a** $\begin{pmatrix} -1 \\ 3 \end{pmatrix}$ **b** $\begin{pmatrix} -10 \\ 2 \end{pmatrix}$ **c** $\begin{pmatrix} -3 \\ -5 \end{pmatrix}$
d $\begin{pmatrix} -7 \\ 0 \end{pmatrix}$ **e** $\begin{pmatrix} -7 \\ 0 \end{pmatrix}$ **f** $\begin{pmatrix} 7 \\ -7 \end{pmatrix}$
g $\begin{pmatrix} 2 \\ 8 \end{pmatrix}$ **h** $\begin{pmatrix} 13 \\ -4 \end{pmatrix}$ **i** $\begin{pmatrix} 1 \\ -10 \end{pmatrix}$

2 **a** $\mathbf{f} = \mathbf{a} + \mathbf{b}$ **b** $\mathbf{g} = \mathbf{f} + \mathbf{c}$ **c** $\mathbf{g} = \mathbf{e} - \mathbf{d}$
d $\mathbf{g} = \mathbf{a} + \mathbf{b} + \mathbf{c}$ **e** $\mathbf{e} = \mathbf{f} + \mathbf{c} + \mathbf{d}$

3 rhombus **a** $\mathbf{g} = \mathbf{b}$ **b** $\mathbf{c} = \mathbf{a} - \mathbf{d}$ **c** $\mathbf{c} = \mathbf{e}$

4 $\overrightarrow{CD} = -\mathbf{a}$, $\overrightarrow{AB} = \mathbf{b} - \mathbf{a}$, $\overrightarrow{MC} = \mathbf{b} - \mathbf{a}$

Exercise 8.2B

1 **a** $\begin{pmatrix} -2 \\ 2 \end{pmatrix}$ **b** $\begin{pmatrix} 2 \\ -3 \end{pmatrix}$ **c** $\begin{pmatrix} -2 \\ 4 \end{pmatrix}$
d $\begin{pmatrix} -2 \\ -1 \end{pmatrix}$ **e** $\begin{pmatrix} -10 \\ 9 \end{pmatrix}$

2 **a** $\mathbf{t} = \mathbf{p} + \mathbf{q}$ **b** $\mathbf{u} = \mathbf{q} + \mathbf{r}$
c $\mathbf{s} = -\mathbf{p} - \mathbf{q} - \mathbf{r}$ **d** $\mathbf{r} = -\mathbf{t} - \mathbf{s}$

Exercise 8.3A

1 **a** $4\mathbf{i} - 2\mathbf{j}$ **b** $-5\mathbf{i} + 3\mathbf{j}$ **c** $-7\mathbf{i} + 5\mathbf{j}$
d $17\mathbf{i} - 10\mathbf{j}$

2 **a** $-5\mathbf{i} - \mathbf{j}$ **b** $5\mathbf{i} - 5\mathbf{j}$ **c** $-6\mathbf{j}$

3 $-2\mathbf{i} + 3\mathbf{j}$, $-4\mathbf{i} + 6\mathbf{j}$; collinear, 1 : 2

4 **a** $2\mathbf{i} - 4\mathbf{j}$ **b** $3\mathbf{i} + 2\mathbf{j}$
$\mathbf{i} + 6\mathbf{j}$, $2\mathbf{i} + 12\mathbf{j}$

Exercise 8.3B

1 a $-3\mathbf{i}+4\mathbf{j}$ **b** $7\mathbf{i}-6\mathbf{j}$ **c** $-2\mathbf{i}+6\mathbf{j}$ **d** $2\mathbf{i}-\mathbf{j}$
2 a $4\mathbf{i}+2\mathbf{j}$ **b** $-6\mathbf{i}+2\mathbf{j}$ **c** $2\mathbf{i}-4\mathbf{j}$
3 $6\mathbf{i}-2\mathbf{j}$, $12\mathbf{i}-4\mathbf{j}$; collinear, 1 : 2
4 $4\mathbf{i}+5\mathbf{j}$; $7\mathbf{i}+8\mathbf{j}$

Exercise 8.4A

1 a 5, 53.1° **b** 5, 126.9° **c** $\sqrt{74}$, −125.5° **d** $\sqrt{13}$, −56.3°
2 a $\begin{pmatrix}2\\3\end{pmatrix}$, $\sqrt{13}$, 56.3° **b** $\begin{pmatrix}-3\\5\end{pmatrix}$, $\sqrt{34}$, 121.0° **c** $\begin{pmatrix}5\\10\end{pmatrix}$, $5\sqrt{5}$, 63.4°
3 $(3\sqrt{3}+3, 8)$ **4** $(4-4\sqrt{2}, -2+4\sqrt{2})$
5 $(-2, 6-5\sqrt{3})$ **6** $\begin{pmatrix}5+4\sqrt{2}\\4\sqrt{2}\end{pmatrix}$
7 1.7, 151.4° **8** $\begin{pmatrix}2.5\\-0.95\end{pmatrix}$, $\begin{pmatrix}6.5\\2.9\end{pmatrix}$

Exercise 8.4B

1 a $\sqrt{2}$, 45° **b** $\sqrt{5}$, −26.6° **c** 13, 112.6° **d** $\sqrt{13}$, −146.3°
2 a $\begin{pmatrix}5\\4\end{pmatrix}$, $\sqrt{41}$, 38.7° **b** $\begin{pmatrix}5\\-12\end{pmatrix}$, 13, −67.4° **c** $\begin{pmatrix}-1\\1\end{pmatrix}$, $\sqrt{2}$, 135°
3 $(-7, 4+5\sqrt{3})$ **4** $(5-2\sqrt{2}, -3-2\sqrt{2})$
5 $\begin{pmatrix}3-2\sqrt{3}\\2\end{pmatrix}$ **6** $\begin{pmatrix}-1.4\\5.5\end{pmatrix}$, $\begin{pmatrix}5.0\\2.1\end{pmatrix}$
7 $\begin{pmatrix}4.8\\-1.1\end{pmatrix}$; 5.0; −12.3° to x-axis

Exercise 8.5A

1 a $\begin{pmatrix}4\\-5\\6\end{pmatrix}$ **b** $\begin{pmatrix}0\\3\\8\end{pmatrix}$ **c** $\begin{pmatrix}7\\0\\-2\end{pmatrix}$
2 a $2\mathbf{i}-4\mathbf{j}+3\mathbf{k}$; 5.4 **b** $5\mathbf{i}+\mathbf{j}-2\mathbf{k}$; 5.5 **c** $-3\mathbf{i}+5\mathbf{j}+7\mathbf{k}$; 9.1 **d** $4.2\mathbf{i}-3.4\mathbf{j}-2.6\mathbf{k}$; 6.0
3 a $2\mathbf{i}-4\mathbf{j}+3\mathbf{k}$ **b** $5\mathbf{i}-10\mathbf{j}-4\mathbf{k}$
4 a $\frac{1}{\sqrt{61}}(-6\mathbf{i}+3\mathbf{j}-4\mathbf{k})$ **b** $\frac{2}{\sqrt{61}}(6\mathbf{i}-3\mathbf{j}+4\mathbf{k})$
5 $4\mathbf{i}+2\mathbf{j}+2\mathbf{k}$, $2\mathbf{i}+\mathbf{j}+\mathbf{k}$; 2 : 1
6 11, $\frac{1}{11}\begin{pmatrix}6\\7\\6\end{pmatrix}$; $\frac{6}{11}, \frac{7}{11}, \frac{6}{11}$
7 54°, 126° **8** 57°, 123°

Exercise 8.5B

1 a $\begin{pmatrix}3\\5\\-2\end{pmatrix}$, 6.2 **b** $\begin{pmatrix}4\\-2\\-1\end{pmatrix}$, 4.6 **c** $\begin{pmatrix}0\\-2\\3\end{pmatrix}$, 3.6
2 a $5\mathbf{i}-2\mathbf{j}+4\mathbf{k}$ **b** $-3\mathbf{i}+7\mathbf{k}$ **c** $-2\mathbf{j}+5\mathbf{k}$
3 a $\mathbf{i}-\mathbf{j}-\mathbf{k}$ **b** $2\mathbf{i}-2\mathbf{j}-2\mathbf{k}$
4 a $\frac{1}{3}(2\mathbf{i}+\mathbf{j}-2\mathbf{k})$; $\mathbf{b}=-4\hat{\mathbf{a}}$
b $\frac{1}{5\sqrt{2}}(3\mathbf{i}-5\mathbf{j}+4\mathbf{k})$; $\mathbf{b}=-4\hat{\mathbf{a}}$
c $\frac{1}{\sqrt{3}}(\mathbf{i}+\mathbf{j}-\mathbf{k})$; $\mathbf{b}=-4\hat{\mathbf{a}}$
5 $5\mathbf{i}-2\mathbf{j}+\mathbf{k}$, $15\mathbf{i}-6\mathbf{j}+3\mathbf{k}$; 1 : 3
6 77°, 103° **7** $12\mathbf{i}-12\mathbf{j}+6\mathbf{k}$

Exercise 8.6

1 1, 1, 1; 0, 0, 0
2 (i) $\frac{6}{\sqrt{2}}$ (ii) 0 (iii) −4 (iv) 15 (v) $15\sqrt{}$
3 (i) 9.7 (ii) −9.3
4 (i) angle is between 0° and 90°
(ii) angle is between 90° and 180°

Exercise 8.7A

1 1, acute angle **3** $\frac{4}{5}$
4 (i) 8, 36.9° (ii) 3, 79.1° (iii) 18, 25.8°
5 $\frac{\sqrt{5}}{2}$ **6** 106.9°
7 a $A=10.4°$, $B=19.4°$, $C=150.2°$
b $A=86.4°$, $B=32.8°$, $C=60.8°$
8 5.9, 3.7; 50.8°, 129.2°

Exercise 8.7B

1 $-\frac{5}{2}$
2 (i) 0, 90° (ii) 31, 20.0° (iii) 11, 56.9°
3 $6\sqrt{2}$
4 a $A=82.7°$, $B=18.1°$, $C=79.2°$
b $A=71.2°$, $B=55.8°$, $C=53.0°$
5 120°; $\frac{9\sqrt{3}}{2}$
6 a 3.3 **b** 63.0°, 117.0° **c** $4\sqrt{6}$
7 $\begin{pmatrix}7\\4\\1\end{pmatrix}$

Exercise 8.8A

1 4, −20; −16, 24 **2** 8.83, 12.8, 46.7, 6.83
4 $\sqrt{\frac{11}{3}}, \frac{2}{\sqrt{3}}$

Exercise 8.8B

1 $6s-15t$; 5 : 2 **2** 120°
3 $\sqrt{88}$, $\sqrt{18}$, 3; 86°

Miscellaneous Exercise 8

1 $\mathbf{b} - \frac{7}{4}\mathbf{a}$

a $\frac{4}{7}$ **b** $\frac{4}{7}\mathbf{b}$

4 : 3

2 $\mathbf{d} = \frac{\mathbf{b}+\mathbf{c}}{2}$, $\mathbf{e} = \frac{\mathbf{c}+\mathbf{a}}{2}$, $\mathbf{f} = \frac{\mathbf{a}+\mathbf{b}}{2}$

$\overrightarrow{FH} = \frac{1}{6}(2\mathbf{c} - \mathbf{a} - \mathbf{b})$, $\overrightarrow{HC} = \frac{1}{3}(2\mathbf{c} - \mathbf{a} - \mathbf{b})$

H lies on CF and divides CF in ratio 2 : 1;
H is point of intersection of AD, BE, CF.

3 (i) $\frac{\mathbf{a}+\mathbf{b}}{2}$ (ii) $\frac{\mathbf{a}+\mathbf{d}}{2}$ (iii) $\frac{\mathbf{d}-\mathbf{b}}{2}$

(iv) $\frac{\mathbf{d}-\mathbf{b}}{2}$ (v) $\frac{\mathbf{b}+\mathbf{d}}{2}$ (vi) $\frac{\mathbf{a}+\mathbf{b}+\mathbf{c}+\mathbf{d}}{4}$

4 $\begin{pmatrix}-2\\5\\-3\end{pmatrix}, \begin{pmatrix}2\\9\\1\end{pmatrix}$; $AB = \sqrt{38}$, $AC = \sqrt{86}$;

$\cos A = \sqrt{\frac{19}{43}}$; $B = 90°$; 0

5 **a** $2\mathbf{a} + \mathbf{b}, \mathbf{a} + 2\mathbf{b}$ **c** 143.1°

6 $k\mathbf{p} + 2\mathbf{q}, \mathbf{p} - 2\mathbf{q}$; 10 cm

7 **a** $-\frac{\mathbf{b}+\mathbf{c}}{2}$, $\mathbf{a} - \frac{\mathbf{b}+\mathbf{c}}{2}$ **b** $\frac{1}{2}$

8 (i) 10, 9 (ii) $-\frac{2}{3}, 15\sqrt{5}$
(iii) $y = 6, z = -5$ (v) $5\sqrt{5}$

Chapter 9

ansformations of graphs: the adratic and bilinear functions

ercise 9.1

(−1, 10) **4** (4, −6)
(2, −4) **5** $(1, -\frac{9}{4})$
$(-2, -\frac{4}{3})$

ercise 9.2

$(x+2)^2 + 1$ **5** $2\left[(x+3)^2 - \frac{15}{2}\right]$

$(x-3)^2 + 5$ **6** $3\left[(x-1)^2 + \frac{1}{3}\right]$

$(x-2)^2 - 2$ **7** $-3\left[(x-1)^2 + \frac{1}{3}\right]$

$(x-3)^2 - 5$ **8** $4\left[\left(x - \frac{5}{8}\right)^2 + \frac{7}{64}\right]$

rcise 9.3

41 **2** −23 **3** −23 **4** 0

Exercise 9.4A

1 $(x-5)(x-3)$; $(4, -1)$, min.
2 $(x-6)(x+2)$; $(2, -16)$, min.
3 $(x+1)(x+3)$; $(-2, -1)$, min.
4 $(3-x)(x+1)$; $(1, 4)$, max.
5 $x(x+2)$; $(-1, -1)$, min.
6 $x(3-x)$; $(\frac{3}{2}, \frac{9}{4})$, max.
7 $(3-x)(3+x)$; $(0, 9)$, max.
8 $(\sqrt{3}-x)(\sqrt{3}+x)$; $(0, 3)$, max.

Exercise 9.4B

1 $(x-4)(x-1)$; $\{y : y \geqslant -2\frac{1}{4}\}$
2 $(x+5)(x-2)$; $\{y : y \geqslant -12\frac{1}{4}\}$
3 $x(x-2)$; $\{y : y \geqslant -1\}$
4 $(x+3)(x+4)$; $\{y : y \geqslant -\frac{1}{4}\}$
5 $(2x-1)(x-4)$; $\{y : y \geqslant -6\frac{1}{8}\}$
6 $(3x-2)(x+1)$; $\{y : y \geqslant -2\frac{1}{12}\}$
7 $(4x+1)(x+2)$; $\{y : y \geqslant -3\frac{1}{16}\}$
8 $(x-\sqrt{2})(x+\sqrt{2})$; $\{y : y \geqslant -2\}$

Exercise 9.5

1 $\{y : 0 \leqslant y \leqslant 8\}$ **4** $\{y : -4 \leqslant y \leqslant 2\frac{1}{4}\}$
2 $\{y : -6 \leqslant y \leqslant 6\}$ **5** $\{y : 2 \leqslant y \leqslant 10\}$
3 $\{y : -4 \leqslant y \leqslant 5\}$

Exercise 9.6

In these answers a single figure indicates the scale factor of a stretch parallel to the y-axis; two possible answers are given in each case.

1 $\begin{pmatrix}-3\\0\end{pmatrix}, -4, \begin{pmatrix}0\\1\end{pmatrix}$ or $-4, \begin{pmatrix}-3\\1\end{pmatrix}$

2 $\begin{pmatrix}2\\0\end{pmatrix}, 8, \begin{pmatrix}0\\3\end{pmatrix}$ or $8, \begin{pmatrix}2\\3\end{pmatrix}$

3 $\begin{pmatrix}1\\0\end{pmatrix}, 3, \begin{pmatrix}0\\-1\end{pmatrix}$ or $3, \begin{pmatrix}1\\-1\end{pmatrix}$

4 $\begin{pmatrix}3\\0\end{pmatrix}, 5, \begin{pmatrix}0\\2\end{pmatrix}$ or $5, \begin{pmatrix}3\\2\end{pmatrix}$

Exercise 9.7

1 $(3, 0), (0, 3)$; $x = 1, y = 1$
2 $(-2, 0), (0, -2)$; $x = 4, y = 1$
3 $(\frac{1}{2}, 0), (0, -1)$; $x = -1, y = 2$
4 $(1, 0), (0, -\frac{1}{6})$; $x = -2, y = \frac{1}{3}$
5 $(\frac{2}{3}, 0), (0, -\frac{2}{3})$; $x = -3, y = 3$
6 $(2, 0), (0, -2)$; $x = 1, y = -1$

Miscellaneous Exercise 9

1 **a** $(3x-2)(x+5)$ **b** $x(5-2x)$
c $(3-2x)(3+2x)$ **d** $(x-1)(x+1)(x-2)$
e $(x+1)(x+3)(3-x)$ **f** $(x+1)(x-3)(2x-1)$

2 $\frac{3x+2}{x-1}$ **5** $\frac{3x-5}{4}, x \neq 3$

10 $\dfrac{(ap+bs)x+aq+bs}{(cp+ds)x+aq+ds}, \begin{pmatrix} ap+bs & aq+bs \\ cp+ds & aq+ds \end{pmatrix};$

$\dfrac{(pa+qc)x+pb+qd}{(ra+sc)x+rb+sd}, \begin{pmatrix} pa+qc & pb+qd \\ ra+sc & rb+sd \end{pmatrix}.$

The pattern of the numbers in f(x), g(x) and fg(x) corresponds to the pattern of the numbers in **M**, **N** and **MN**.

11 $\dfrac{dx-b}{-cx+a}, \begin{pmatrix} d & -b \\ -c & a \end{pmatrix}, \dfrac{1}{ad-bc}\begin{pmatrix} d & -b \\ -c & a \end{pmatrix}$

If $ad-bc=1$, then $f^{-1}(x)$ may be written down by forming $\mathbf{M}^{-1}$ and using the pattern of the numbers. If $ad-bc \neq 0$, then $f^{-1}(x)$ may be found as above, followed by multiplication by $ad-bc$.

Chapter 10

Trigonometry 2

Exercise 10.1A

1 cos 20° **5** tan 70°
2 sin 50° **6** $\tan(30°+\theta)$
3 cos 100° **7** $\cos(\theta-45°)$ or $\sin(\theta+45°)$
4 tan 55°

8 a $\dfrac{1+\sqrt{3}}{2\sqrt{2}}$ **b** $\dfrac{\sqrt{3}+1}{\sqrt{3}-1}$ **c** $\dfrac{\sqrt{3}-1}{2\sqrt{2}}$ **d** $\dfrac{1-\sqrt{3}}{2\sqrt{2}}$

9 $-\dfrac{19}{8}$

10 30°, −150° **12** 18.4°, −161.6°, 26.6°, −153.4°

11 −45°, 135° **13** $\dfrac{63}{65}$

Exercise 10.1B

1 a $\dfrac{1+\sqrt{3}}{2\sqrt{2}}$ **b** $\dfrac{\sqrt{3}-1}{\sqrt{3}+1}$ **c** $-\left(\dfrac{1+\sqrt{3}}{2\sqrt{2}}\right)$

2 $\dfrac{16}{13}, -\dfrac{8}{19}$

3 49.1°, −130.9° **5** 67.2°, −112.8°
4 72.1°, −107.9°

6 $\pm\dfrac{2}{\sqrt{5}}, \pm\dfrac{4}{3\sqrt{5}}+\dfrac{1}{3}$

Exercise 10.2A

1 a $\dfrac{1}{2}$ **b** $\dfrac{1}{\sqrt{3}}$ **c** $\dfrac{1}{\sqrt{2}}$ **d** $\dfrac{1}{2\sqrt{2}}(\sqrt{2}-1)$ **e** $\dfrac{1}{4}$

f $-\dfrac{\sqrt{3}}{2}$

2 $\pm\dfrac{4}{5}, \pm\dfrac{4}{3}, \pm\dfrac{24}{7}$ **3** $\dfrac{12}{13}$

4 ±90°, 60°, 120° **6** 0°, 180°, ±63.4°, ±116.6°
5 −41.8°, −138.2° **7** ±60°

8 a $y=1-2x^2$ **b** $y=\dfrac{2x}{1-x^2}$ **c** $y=\dfrac{1-x^2}{1+x^2}$

9 a $\dfrac{2}{1+t^2}$ **b** $\dfrac{1+2t+t^2}{1+t^2}$ **c** $\dfrac{1-2t+t^2}{1+t^2}$

Exercise 10.2B

1 $-\dfrac{12}{13}, -\dfrac{120}{169}, \dfrac{119}{169}$

2 $\dfrac{5}{4}, -\dfrac{3}{5}, -\dfrac{24}{25}$

3 0°, 180°, ±82.8° **6** ±24.1°, ±155.9°, 0°, 180°

4 ±90°, 180° **7** −45°, 135°, −18.4°, 161.6°
5 −30°, −150°

8 a $2y=x^2-2$ **b** $y=\dfrac{2x}{x^2-1}$ **c** $y=\dfrac{2x}{1+x^2}$

Exercise 10.3

1 2.6 cm
2 1.6 radians = 91.7°
3 0.62, 5.6 cm
4 1.70, 84.8 cm²
5 a 3.7 cm **b** 1.0 cm²
6 1

Exercise 10.4A

1 a ±1.819 **b** 0.355, 2.786 **c** −1.305, 1.83

2 a $(2n+1)\dfrac{\pi}{3}$ **b** $\dfrac{\pi}{8}+n\pi, \dfrac{3\pi}{8}+n\pi$

c $\dfrac{2\pi}{3}+2n\pi$

3 a ±0.723 **b** 0.245, −2.897, 1.107, −2.034

c $\pm\dfrac{\pi}{2}$, 0.100, 3.041

4 a max. 14, $t=\dfrac{\pi}{4}, \dfrac{5\pi}{4}$; min. 6, $t=\dfrac{3\pi}{4}, \dfrac{7\pi}{4}$

b $0, \dfrac{\pi}{2}, \pi, \dfrac{3\pi}{2}, 2\pi$

c $\dfrac{7\pi}{12}, \dfrac{11\pi}{12}, \dfrac{19\pi}{12}, \dfrac{23\pi}{12}$

d 0.424, 1.147, 3.566, 4.288

5 a 0.540 **b** 0.158 **c** 0.858 **d** 0.654

6 a $\sin 2x, -1 \leqslant y \leqslant 1$
b $2\sin x+2\pi, 2\pi-2 \leqslant y \leqslant 2\pi+2$

Exercise 10.4B

1 a $\pm\dfrac{\pi}{6}+n\pi$ **b** $(4n-1)\pi$ **c** $\dfrac{n\pi}{3}-\dfrac{\pi}{18}$

2 a $\dfrac{\pi}{2}$, 0.848, 2.294 **b** $\pm\dfrac{\pi}{3}$, ±2.301

c 0, π, ±0.714, ±2.428

3 a −1 cm, 4.427 cm, 9 cm

b $\dfrac{\pi}{3}$ seconds **c** $\dfrac{2\pi}{3}$ seconds

4 a $\sin\sqrt{x}, \{x: 0 \leqslant x \leqslant \pi^2\}, \{y: 0 \leqslant y \leqslant 1\}$
b $\sqrt{(\sin x)}, \{x: 0 \leqslant x \leqslant \pi\}, \{y: 0 \leqslant y \leqslant 1\}$

Exercise 10.5

1 translation $\begin{pmatrix} \frac{\pi}{4} \\ 0 \end{pmatrix}$; stretch, scale factor 3 parallel to y-axis; either order.

2 stretch, scale factor $\frac{1}{3}$ parallel to x-axis; stretch, scale factor 2 parallel to y-axis; either order.

3 translation $\begin{pmatrix} -\frac{\pi}{6} \\ 0 \end{pmatrix}$; stretch, scale factor 2 parallel to y-axis; either order.

4 stretch, scale factor 2 parallel to x-axis; stretch, scale factor 4 parallel to y-axis; either order.

5 translation $\begin{pmatrix} \frac{\pi}{3} \\ 1 \end{pmatrix}$, followed by stretch, scale factor 3 parallel to y-axis; *or* stretch, scale factor 3 parallel to y-axis, followed by translation $\begin{pmatrix} \frac{\pi}{3} \\ 3 \end{pmatrix}$

iscellaneous Exercise 10

$0, \frac{1}{2}, 75°, 15°$ **3** (i) $\pm\frac{\sqrt{5}}{3}$ (ii) $\frac{1}{9}$ (iii) $\pm\frac{7\sqrt{5}}{27}$

$-\cos 2\alpha$ **5** $\frac{t-1}{t+1}$

$\pm 35.3°, \pm 144.7°$ **7** $\sqrt{2}-1, 112\frac{1}{2}°$

$0°, 180°$ **9** **a** (i) $\frac{1}{8}$ (ii) $-\frac{31}{32}$

$\frac{77}{85}$, 15.4 cm **11** (iii) $\frac{\sqrt{7}}{2\sqrt{2}}$

$0°, 180°, -90°, 48.6°, 131.4°$

(i) 1.85, 4.99 (ii) 13.0

(i) $r^2\theta$ (ii) $r^2\left(\theta - \frac{1}{2}\sin 2\theta\right)$

(iii) $\frac{r^2}{2}(\pi \sin^2\theta - 2\theta + \sin 2\theta)$

160 cm² (i) 30 (ii) 60 cm

1.2 **18** $\frac{12}{\sqrt{5}}$, 2.30

1 h 46 min, 4 h 14 min, 7 h 46 min, 10 h 14 min

a $p = 5, q = 2$ **c** 2 hours

hapter 11

equalities

rcise 11.1A

$x \leqslant 7$ **4** $x < 1$

$x \geqslant \frac{3}{2}$ **5** $\{x : x \geqslant 1\}$

$x > 2$

Exercise 11.1B

1 $x \leqslant -\frac{5}{3}$

2 $x \geqslant 1$

3 $x \geqslant 1$

4 $-\frac{3}{2} \leqslant x \leqslant 2$

5 $\{x : -5 \leqslant x \leqslant 5\}$

Exercise 11.2A

1 $x \leqslant -1, x \geqslant 5$

2 $\frac{1}{2} < x < 4$

3 all x

4 $-4 \leqslant x \leqslant 2$

5 $\{x : 1 - \sqrt{5} \leqslant x \leqslant 1 + \sqrt{5}\}$

Exercise 11.2B

1 $x \leqslant -4, x \geqslant \frac{2}{3}$

2 $-1 < x < 9$

3 no solution

4 $x \leqslant -1, x \geqslant 9$

5 $\{x : x \leqslant 3 - \sqrt{6}\} \cup \{x : x \geqslant 3 + \sqrt{6}\}$

Exercise 11.3A

1 $-1 \leqslant x \leqslant \frac{3}{2}, x \geqslant 4$

2 $x \leqslant -2, -\frac{3}{2} < x < 1$

3 $x \geqslant 0, x = -4$

4 $x < -1, x > -\frac{1}{2}$

5 $\{x : -1 < x < 0\} \cup \{x : x > 7\}$

6 $\{x : -1 < x < 6\} \cup \{x : x > 7\}$

Exercise 11.3B

1 $x < -3, -2 < x < \frac{5}{3}$

2 $-\frac{1}{2} < x < 3, x > 4$

3 $x \leqslant 2, x = 3$

4 $1 < x < \frac{5}{3}$

5 $x < -1, x > 1$

6 $x < -2, x > -1$

7 $\{x : 2 < x < 3\}$

8 $\left\{x : x < \frac{2}{5}\right\} \cup \{x : 2 < x < 3\}$

Exercise 11.4A

1 $x < 1$

2 $x \geqslant \frac{7}{4}$

3 $x < -4, x > \frac{1}{2}$

4 $-6 \leqslant x \leqslant 6$

5 $x < 1, x > \frac{11}{3}$

6 $x > \frac{1}{2}$

7 $x < \frac{1}{2}$

Exercise 11.4B

1 $x < 1$

2 $x < \frac{7}{4}$

3 $x < 0, x > 4$

4 $x \leqslant -4, -2 \leqslant x \leqslant 2, x \geqslant 4$

5 $x \leqslant -3, -2 \leqslant x \leqslant 1, 1 \leqslant x \leqslant 2, x \geqslant 3$

6 $x < 1$

7 $\frac{5}{8} \leqslant x \leqslant \frac{3}{4}$

Miscellaneous Exercise 11

1 $\{x : x < -1\} \cup \{x : x > 3\}$

2 $x < -1, 0 < x < 2$

3 **a** $x < -1, x > 4$ **b** $x < -3, \ -2 < x < 1$

4 **a** $x < 1, x > 6$ **b** $-\frac{1}{3} < x < \frac{1}{6}, x > \frac{1}{2}$

5 $x < 1, x > \frac{5}{2}$ **6** $\left\{x : x < -\frac{4}{3}\right\} \cup \{x : x > -1\}$

7 $x = 1, y = 0; x = -3, y = 1$
$\{x : -3 < x < -1\} \cup \{x : 1 < x < 3\}$

8 $\{x : x < -2\} \cup \{x : x > 2\}$ **9** $\{x : x < -3\frac{1}{2}\}$

10 $\{x : -4 < x < 0\}$

11 **a** $\{x : -1 < x < 0\} \cup \{x : x > 1\}$
b $\{x : x < -\sqrt{2}\} \cup \{x : 1 < x < \sqrt{2}\} \cup \{x : x > 2\}$
c $\left\{x : x < \frac{1}{2}\right\} \cup \{x : x > 2\}$

12 $(x + 1)(2x - 1)(x - 4)$
a $-1 < x < \frac{1}{2}, x > 4$
b $x < -4, \ -\frac{1}{2} < x < \frac{1}{2}, x > 4$

13 $\left\{x : -1 \leqslant x \leqslant \frac{1}{2}\right\}$;
$\left\{\theta : -\pi \leqslant \theta \leqslant \frac{\pi}{6}\right\} \cup \left\{\theta : \frac{5\pi}{6} \leqslant \theta \leqslant \pi\right\}$

14 $\{x : x > -1\}$ **15** $\{k : k \leqslant 2\} \cup \{k : k \geqslant 9\}$

16 $\{m : m < 8 - 4\sqrt{5}\} \cup \{m : m > 8 + 4\sqrt{5}\}$; $8 \pm 4\sqrt{5}$

Chapter 12

Calculus 1

Exercise 12.1

1 77, 253 **a** 77 per hour **b** 253 per hour
120 per hour

Exercise 12.2

1 **a** 2 **b** 1 **c** $-\frac{4}{3}$ **d** -2 **e** $\frac{4}{3}$ **f** 0 **g** $\frac{1}{2}$

2 **a** A, B or B, C or A, C or E, F
b C, D or D, E or C, E
c A, D or B, D or A, E or B, E
d D, F or C, F

Exercise 12.3

3

g(AB)	8	8	2	2	6	6	7	6.5	6.3	6.1	6.001

b $g(AB) = a + b$

Exercise 12.4A

1 $10x + 7$ **4** $6x - \frac{8}{x^3}$ **7** $4x^3 + 6 - \frac{18}{x^3}$

2 $3x^2 + 12x - 9$ **5** $\frac{1}{\sqrt{x}} - \frac{3}{x\sqrt{x}}$ **8** $\frac{1}{2\sqrt{x}} + 3\sqrt{x}$

3 $12x^2 - \frac{5}{x^2}$ **6** $18x + 12$ **9** $\frac{3\sqrt{x}}{2} + \frac{2}{\sqrt{x}}$

Exercise 12.4B

1 $8x - 3$ **4** $16x + 2$ **7** $1 - \frac{4}{x^3}$

2 $3x^2 + 14x - 6$ **5** $2x - \frac{1}{2x^3}$ **8** $3\sqrt{x} + 3$

3 $12x + \frac{2}{x^2}$ **6** $2x^{-\frac{1}{2}} - x^{-\frac{3}{2}}$ **9** $\frac{7}{x^2} + \frac{10}{x^3}$

Exercise 12.5A

1 **a** $y = 6x + 4, 6y + x = 61$
b $4y = 3x + 4, 8x + 6y = 31$

2 $y = 3x - 3$

3 $y = 6x - 3, y = 6x - 35$

4 $3y = 2x + 5, (-\frac{9}{2}, -\frac{4}{3})$

Exercise 12.5B

1 **a** $3x + y = 11, 3y = x + 3$
b $6x + y + 7 = 0, 6y = x - 5$

2 $y = 8x - 7$

3 $y = 6x + 11, y = 6x - 21$

4 $y + 2x = 7, (\frac{1}{3}, \frac{19}{3})$

5 $y = 2(a - 2)x + 9 - a^2$
$y = 2x, y = -10x$

Exercise 12.6A

1 (0, 2), (2, −2) **2** (2, 14), (4, 10) **3** (1, 1)

4 (1, 3)

Exercise 12.6B

1 (2, −10), (−2, 22) **2** $(0, 1), (\frac{1}{3}, \frac{28}{27})$ **3** (−2,

Exercise 12.7A

1 **a** $x^2 + 5x + C$ **b** $\frac{3x^2}{2} - 4x + C$
c $x^3 - 2x^2 + 5x + C$ **d** $\frac{x^3}{3} - 3x^2 - 7x + C$
e $x^2 + \frac{2}{3}x^{\frac{3}{2}} + C$ **f** $\frac{x^4}{4} - \frac{1}{x} + C$
g $\frac{x^5}{5} - \frac{1}{3x^3} + C$ **h** $x^3 + 2\sqrt{x} + C$

2 $y = 2x^2 + 5x - 50$

3 $y = x^3 - 3x^2 + 2x + 4$

4 $y = 2x^2 - \frac{1}{x} + 4$

Exercise 12.7B

1 **a** $2x^2 - 5x + C$ **b** $2x^3 + \frac{3x^2}{2} - 2x$ -
c $\frac{x^3}{3} - 5x^2 + 3x + C$ **d** $-\frac{1}{x} - \frac{1}{x^2} - \frac{1}{3x^3}$
e $\frac{x^7}{7} + 2x - \frac{1}{5x^5} + C$

2 $y = x^2 + x - 17$ **3** $y = 2x^3 + 2x^2 - 5x$ -

4 $y = \frac{1}{3}\left(x^3 + \frac{1}{x^3} + 8\right)$; $y = 2$

Exercise 12.8

1 $3x^2+12x-3,\ 6x+12$
2 $3t^2-8t,\ 6t-8$
3 $18t,\ 18$
4 $12t^2+16t,\ 24t+16$
5 10 cm
6 20 cm 20 cm 10 cm

Exercise 12.9A

1 $5\ \mathrm{ms}^{-1}$, $-4\ \mathrm{ms}^{-1}$, $20\ \mathrm{ms}^{-1}$; $-7\ \mathrm{ms}^{-1}$
2 -29
3 $25\ \mathrm{ms}^{-1}$, 28 m
4 19, 83; $32\ \mathrm{ms}^{-1}$; $16\ \mathrm{ms}^{-1}$, $52\ \mathrm{ms}^{-1}$, $34\ \mathrm{ms}^{-1}$
5 $\frac{9}{4}$ m, -18 m; $0\ \mathrm{ms}^{-1}$, $-9\ \mathrm{ms}^{-1}$; $20\frac{1}{2}$ m
6 $x=2t^2-9t+10$; 2s, $2\frac{1}{2}$ s; $-1\ \mathrm{ms}^{-1}$, $1\ \mathrm{ms}^{-1}$

Exercise 12.9B

1 $-9\ \mathrm{ms}^{-1}$, $16\ \mathrm{ms}^{-1}$; $4\ \mathrm{ms}^{-2}$; $2\ \mathrm{ms}^{-2}$, $6\ \mathrm{ms}^{-2}$
2 $x=2t^3-2t^2+3t+4$
3 $v=3t^2-4t+6,\ x=t^3-2t^2+6t+4$
4 1 s, 3 s; 1 s, 4 m; 54 m; 62 m

Exercise 12.10A

1 $6(3x+1)$
2 $-20(1-4x)^4$
3 $\dfrac{-2}{(2x-3)^2}$
4 $6x(x^2+4)^2$
5 $\dfrac{1}{\sqrt{(2x+1)}}$
6 $\dfrac{-4x}{(x^2+3)^3}$
7 $3\left(x^2-\dfrac{1}{x}\right)^2\left(2x+\dfrac{1}{x^2}\right)$
8 $\dfrac{-4x}{(4x^2-1)^{\frac{3}{2}}}$
9 $\dfrac{-3(6x+5)}{(3x^2+5x+2)^4}$

Exercise 12.10B

$12(4x-5)^2$
$-12(2-3x)^3$
$\dfrac{-5}{(5x-2)^2}$
$4(x+1)(x^2+2x+3)$
$\dfrac{-3}{2\sqrt{(4-3x)}}$
$\dfrac{-4x}{(2x^2-5)^2}$
7 $\dfrac{6x^3}{\sqrt{(3x^4-2)}}$
8 $5(x^3+4x)^4(3x^2+4)$
9 $\dfrac{2}{\sqrt{x}}\left(\sqrt{x}+\dfrac{1}{\sqrt{x}}\right)^3\left(1-\dfrac{1}{x}\right)$

Exercise 12.11A

$(2x+1)^2(8x+1)$
$(4x+1)(36x-13)$
$2(x+2)(2x^2+8x+7)$
$5(5x+2)(7x^5+2x^4+6)$
$6(x-3)(x+3)^3(x-1)$
$\dfrac{2x^2+4}{\sqrt{(x^2+4)}}$
7 $\dfrac{x(3x+8)}{(3x+4)^2}$
8 $\dfrac{2x-x^4}{(x^3+1)^2}$
9 $\dfrac{5}{(3x+1)^2}$
10 $(2,0),\ (4,-4)$

Exercise 12.11B

1 $3x^2(3x-2)(5x-2)$
2 $(5x+3)^2(80x+27)$
3 $(2x-1)(8x^2-2x-20)$
4 $6-16x^3-15x^4$
5 $(x+1)^2(x-2)(5x-4)$
6 $\dfrac{6x^4+8}{(x^4+4)^{\frac{1}{2}}}$
7 $\dfrac{17}{(4x+3)^2}$
8 $\dfrac{6x}{(x^2+2)^2}$
9 $\dfrac{2}{(x^2+2)^{\frac{3}{2}}}$
10 $(-2,0),\ (1,-27)$

Miscellaneous Exercise 12

1 $X(8,0),\ Y(0,2),\ L(5,5),\ M(3,-3)$
2 **a** $-\frac{1}{4}, 2$ **b** $(2,0)$, min.; $(\frac{1}{2}, 6\frac{3}{4})$, max.
 d $13,\ -27$
3 **a** $(0,0)$, inflexion; $(-\frac{3}{4}, -\frac{27}{128})$, min.
 b $(0,0),\ (-1,0)$
4 g, where $g(x)=3-3x^2$
 $(1,0),\ (-1,-4);\ (0,-2)$
5 $(-1,5)$, max., $(3,-27)$, min.; $0<k<5$
6 4; $-5\ \mathrm{ms}^{-2}$; $\frac{14}{3}\ \mathrm{ms}^{-1}$
7 **a** 2, 4; $-1\ \mathrm{ms}^{-1}$ **b** $6\frac{2}{3}$ m, $5\frac{1}{3}$ m; 8 m
8 **c** 54π **d** -32
9 (i) $h=\dfrac{1000}{\pi r^2}$ (ii) $\dfrac{2000}{r}+8r^2\ \mathrm{cm}^2$
 5 cm, $\dfrac{40}{\pi}$ cm, 6p
10 **a** $2(2a+h)+3;\ 4a+3$ **b** $h=\dfrac{2R}{\sqrt{3}}$
11 **a** $60x^2(4x^3+1)^4$ **b** $\dfrac{x}{\sqrt{(x^2+9)}}$
 c $\dfrac{-24x}{(3x^2+2)^5}$ **d** $2x(x^5+2)^3(11x^5+2)$
 e $\dfrac{x^2-10x-3}{(x-5)^2}$ **f** $\dfrac{x^2(x+12)}{(x+4)^3}$
12 $\dfrac{6x}{(2x^2+1)^2}$; $\{x : x>0\}$; 0, -1
13 **a** $\dfrac{x(x+8)}{(x+4)^2}$ **b** $(0,0)$, min.; $(-8,-16)$, max.
 c $(-2,2),\ (-6,-18);\ -4,\ -36$
14 $-2, 1, 4$; $-2<x<1,\ x>4$;
 $(-2,-34)$ min.; $(1,47)$ max.; $(4,-34)$ min.
15 **a** turning points $(3,16),\ (-3,4)$

Chapter 13

Vectors 2

Exercise 13.1A

1 (i) $3\sqrt{2}$ (ii) 0 (iii) $-\dfrac{5}{2}$
2 (i) $\dfrac{11}{3\sqrt{5}}$ (ii) $-\dfrac{4}{\sqrt{14}}$
3 $4\sqrt{2}$N

Exercise 13.1B

1 (i) 2.6 (ii) -1.7 (iii) 0.97
2 (i) $-\dfrac{7}{\sqrt{26}}$ (ii) 0 (iii) $-\dfrac{3}{\sqrt{5}}$
3 $-\dfrac{7}{\sqrt{42}}$N

Exercise 13.2A

1 a $x = 3 + 4t,\ y = 5 + t;\ x - 4y + 17 = 0$
b $x = -2 + 3t,\ y = 7;\ y = 7$

2 $\mathbf{r} = \begin{pmatrix} 2 \\ 5 \end{pmatrix} + t\begin{pmatrix} 2 \\ 3 \end{pmatrix};\ 3x - 2y + 4 = 0$

3 $\frac{1}{5}\begin{pmatrix} 3 \\ 4 \end{pmatrix};\ (11, 7), (-7, -17)$

4 $102°$

Exercise 13.2B

1 a $x = 5 - 6t,\ y = -4 + t;\ x + 6y + 19 = 0$
b $x = -3,\ y = -5 + 2t;\ x = -3$

2 $\mathbf{r} = \begin{pmatrix} \frac{1}{2} \\ \frac{3}{4} \end{pmatrix} + t\begin{pmatrix} 1 \\ -4 \end{pmatrix}$

4 $61°$

5 $\frac{1}{\sqrt{5}}\begin{pmatrix} 1 \\ -2 \end{pmatrix};\ (-4 + 2\sqrt{5}, 1 - 4\sqrt{5}),$
$(-4 - 2\sqrt{5}, 1 + 4\sqrt{5})$

Exercise 13.3A

1 a $x = 3 + t,\ y = 2 - 4t,\ z = 5 + 7t$
$x - 3 = \frac{y - 2}{-4} = \frac{z - 5}{7}$
b $x = 2 + 4t,\ y = -5 + 3t,\ z = 6 - t$
$\frac{x - 2}{4} = \frac{y + 5}{3} = \frac{z - 6}{-1}$

2 $\mathbf{r} = \begin{pmatrix} 3 \\ -1 \\ 4 \end{pmatrix} + t\begin{pmatrix} 4 \\ 5 \\ -2 \end{pmatrix}$

3 a $\mathbf{r} = \begin{pmatrix} 2 \\ -4 \\ 1 \end{pmatrix} + t\begin{pmatrix} 1 \\ 1 \\ -6 \end{pmatrix}$ **b** $\mathbf{r} = \begin{pmatrix} -3 \\ 2 \\ 4 \end{pmatrix} + t\begin{pmatrix} 9 \\ 0 \\ 1 \end{pmatrix}$

4 no **5** yes **6** $(0, 1, -9)$

Exercise 13.3B

1 $\mathbf{r} = \begin{pmatrix} 4 \\ 5 \\ -2 \end{pmatrix} + t\begin{pmatrix} 3 \\ -1 \\ 4 \end{pmatrix}$

2 a $\mathbf{r} = \begin{pmatrix} 1 \\ -3 \\ 2 \end{pmatrix} + t\begin{pmatrix} 4 \\ 1 \\ 2 \end{pmatrix}$ **b** $\mathbf{r} = \begin{pmatrix} -7 \\ 3 \\ -1 \end{pmatrix} + t\begin{pmatrix} 3 \\ -2 \\ 2 \end{pmatrix}$

3 no **4** $t = 3, -4;\ AB : AC = 3 : 4$

Exercise 13.4A

1 a $40°$ **b** $75°$

2 a $(-7, -8, 6)$ **b** lines are skew

3 a $\frac{\sqrt{114}}{2}, (3\frac{1}{2}, 4, -\frac{1}{2})$ **b** $\frac{\sqrt{62}}{2}, (1\frac{1}{2}, 1, -3\frac{1}{2})$

4 $(2, 6, 8);\ 26\sqrt{10}$ **5** $3\sqrt{5}$ **6** $(3, 2, 1)$

Exercise 13.4B

1 a $33°$ **b** $41°$

2 a $(3, 4, 5)$ **b** $(10, 4, -6)$

3 a $\sqrt{30}$ **b** $\sqrt{33}$

4 $\sqrt{34}$

5 $\mathbf{r} = \begin{pmatrix} 1 \\ 2 \\ 3 \end{pmatrix} + u\begin{pmatrix} 1 \\ -7 \\ 5 \end{pmatrix};\ (3, -12, 13);\ 10\sqrt{3},$
AB is the shortest distance between L, M.

Miscellaneous Exercise 13

1 $\frac{10}{\sqrt{26}}$

2 10

4 $(4, 1, 5)$ **5** No intersection; $37°$

6 a $(-1, 1, 10)$ **b** $\mathbf{r} = \begin{pmatrix} 5 \\ 1 \\ 13 \end{pmatrix} + t\begin{pmatrix} 6 \\ 0 \\ 3 \end{pmatrix}$
c $3\sqrt{5}$ **d** $(-7, 1, 7)$

7 a $3, \sqrt{13}$ **b** $\frac{1}{3\sqrt{13}}$
c $\mathbf{r} = \mathbf{i} + 2\mathbf{j} + 2\mathbf{k} + t(2\mathbf{i} + \mathbf{j})$

8 a $\frac{1}{\sqrt{6}}(\mathbf{i} - 2\mathbf{j} + \mathbf{k})$
b $\mathbf{r} = \mathbf{i} + 2\mathbf{j} + \mathbf{k} + t(\mathbf{i} - 2\mathbf{j} + \mathbf{k})$
c $\frac{2}{\sqrt{6}}, \frac{1}{\sqrt{3}}$
d $\frac{4}{3}(\mathbf{i} + \mathbf{j} + \mathbf{k})$
e $\mathbf{r} = \frac{4}{3}(\mathbf{i} + \mathbf{j} + \mathbf{k}) + s(\mathbf{i} - \mathbf{k})$

Chapter 14

The binomial theorem and the binomial series

Exercise 14.1A

1 $1 + 7x + 21x^2 + 35x^3 + 35x^4 + 21x^5 + 7x^6 +$

2 $1 + 9x + 36x^2 + 84x^3, 84x^6 + 36x^7 + 9x^8 + x^9$

3 $a^6 + 6a^5x + 15a^4x^2 + 20a^3x^3 + 15a^2x^4 +$
$6ax^5$

4 0.8681

Exercise 14.1B

1 $1 + 8x + 28x^2 + 56x^3 + 70x^4 + 56x^5 + 28x^6 +$
$8x^7$

2 $1 + 24x + 264x^2 + 1760x^3,$
$220.2^9x^9 + 66.2^{10}x^{10} + 12.2^{11}x^{11} + 2^1$

3 $a^{10} + 10a^9b + 45a^8b^2 + 120a^7b^3 + 210a^6b^4 +$
252

4 1.0829

Exercise 14.2A

1 $2^7 + 7.2^6x + 21.2^5x^2 + 35.2^4x^3 + 35.2^3x^4 +$
$21.2^2x^5 + 7.2x^6$

2 a $\frac{11 . 10 . 9 . 8 . 7 . 6}{1 . 2 . 3 . 4 . 5 . 6}5^5x^6$
b $\frac{12 . 11 . 10 . 9 . 8 . 7 . 6}{1 . 2 . 3 . 4 . 5 . 6 . 7}3^5 4^7 x^7$

3 $210.2^4 3^6 x^6$

4 $x^8 + 24x^6 + 252x^4 + 1512x^2$

Exercise 14.2B

1 $x^6 - 18x^5y + 135x^4y^2 - 540x^3y^3$

2 a $-\dfrac{8.7.6.5.4}{1.2.3.4.5}3^3x^5$

b $\dfrac{13.12.11.10.9.8.7.6}{1.2.3.4.5.6.7.8}4^5 5^8 x^8$

3 $165a^3x^8$

4 $512x^9 - 1152x^7 + 1152x^5 - 672x^3 + 252x - 63x^{-1} + \dfrac{21}{2}x^{-3}$

Exercise 14.3

1 a both $= 792$ **b** both $= 455$

2 both $= 120$ **3** both $= 495$

4 a $\dfrac{6}{5}$ **b** $\dfrac{6}{7}$ **5** $\dbinom{2n}{r}$ **7** $2 : x$

Exercise 14.4

1 $252x^4$

2 a $\dfrac{28}{9}$ **b** 240 **c** 1890

3 -14

4 $1 + 10x + 55x^2$ **5** $1 - 6x + 27x^2$

6 $-14x^3$ **7** $1 - 5x - 5x^2$

8 $1 + 5x + 10x^2 + 10x^3 + 5x^4 + x^5$; $76 + 44\sqrt{3}, 76 - 44\sqrt{3}$

0 15

Exercise 14.5A

1 a $1 - 3x + 6x^2 - 10x^3$ **b** $1 - \dfrac{x}{2} + \dfrac{3x^2}{8} - \dfrac{5x^3}{16}$

c $1 - \dfrac{x}{4} - \dfrac{3x^2}{32} - \dfrac{7x^3}{128}$

$1 + x - x^2 + \dfrac{5x^3}{3}$; 1.00990 **3** $1 + x - \dfrac{x^2}{2} + \dfrac{x^3}{2}$

a $1 + 2x + 4x^2 + 8x^3$; $|x| < \dfrac{1}{2}$

b $1 - 2x - 2x^2 - 4x^3$; $|x| < \dfrac{1}{4}$

c $1 - x + 2x^2 - 4x^3$; $|x| < \dfrac{1}{2}$

d $\dfrac{1}{2}\left(1 + \dfrac{x}{2} - \dfrac{x^2}{4} + \dfrac{x^3}{8}\right)$; $|x| < 2$

$\dfrac{1}{2}\left(1 + \dfrac{3x}{8} - \dfrac{21x^2}{128}\right)$; $|x| < 4$ **6** $1 + \dfrac{x}{2} + \dfrac{3x^2}{8} - \dfrac{3x^3}{16}$

Exercise 14.5B

a $1 - \dfrac{x}{3} - \dfrac{x^2}{9} - \dfrac{5x^3}{81}$

b $1 - 4x + 10x^2 - 20x^3$

c $1 + \dfrac{3x}{2} + \dfrac{15x^2}{8} + \dfrac{35x^3}{16}$

$1 - x - \dfrac{x^2}{2} - \dfrac{x^3}{2}$; 0.98995

$1 + 2x + x^2 + 4x^3$

4 a $\dfrac{1}{9}\left(1 - \dfrac{2x}{3} + \dfrac{x^2}{3} - \dfrac{4x^3}{27}\right)$; $|x| < 3$

b $\dfrac{1}{2}\left(1 - \dfrac{x}{8} + \dfrac{3x^2}{128} - \dfrac{5x^3}{1024}\right)$; $|x| < 4$

c $1 + 3x + \dfrac{9x^2}{2} + \dfrac{27x^3}{4}$; $|x| < \dfrac{2}{3}$

5 $1 + 4x + 6x^2$

Exercise 14.5C

1 $1 + \dfrac{4}{x} + \dfrac{8}{x^2}$; $|x| > 2$ **2** $1 + \dfrac{4}{x} + \dfrac{8}{x^2}$; $|x| > 4$

3 $1 - (1 - x) + (1 - x)^2 - (1 - x)^3$; $0 < x < 2$

4 $1 - 2\left(\dfrac{x-1}{x}\right) + 3\left(\dfrac{x-1}{x}\right)^2 - 4\left(\dfrac{x-1}{x}\right)^3$; $x > \dfrac{1}{2}$

Miscellaneous Exercise 14

1 a $120x$ **b** $\dfrac{252}{x^5}$ **2** $\dfrac{21}{16}$

3 $1 + 10x + 55x^2 + 200x^3$

4 a $1 + 6x + 15x^2 + 20x^3$

b $1 - 6x + 15x^2 - 20x^3$; 0.12004

5 $\dfrac{n(n-1)}{1.2}a^{n-2}b^2x^2, \dfrac{n(n-1)(n-2)}{1.2.3}a^{n-3}b^3x^3$;
$3a = (n-2)bx$; $n = 62$

6 $490x^3$ **7** $1 + 8kx + 28k^2x^2$; $k = -\dfrac{1}{4}$

8 $x^3 + 3x + \dfrac{3}{x} + \dfrac{1}{x^3}$; -1 **9** $a = -\dfrac{3}{2}, h = 8$

10 a $1 + \dfrac{x^2}{2}$ **b** $1 + x - \dfrac{5x^2}{2}$ **c** $\dfrac{1}{2} + \dfrac{15x}{16} - \dfrac{29x^2}{256}$

11 $\dfrac{1}{2}$; $1 + \dfrac{x^4}{8} + \dfrac{x^6}{8}$ **12** $1 + \dfrac{\lambda}{2}x + \dfrac{3\lambda^2}{8}x^2 + \dfrac{5\lambda^3}{16}x^3$
$1 + \dfrac{\mu}{2}x - \dfrac{\mu^2}{8}x^2 + \dfrac{\mu^3}{16}x^3$; $|x| < \dfrac{1}{\lambda}$;
$\lambda = 6, \mu = 2$

13 $(xy)^2 - 8xy - 345 = 0$;
$xy = -15, x = 5, y = -3$

Chapter 15

Linear relations

Miscellaneous Exercise 15

1 a $3x + 2y = 4$ **b** $\ln x + \ln 5 = y \ln 6$

3 $a = 140, b = 0.35$

4 $A = -0.4, B = 3.5$; 1.29 wrong, 1.15

5 $a = 115, b = 10.5$

6 $a = 1.7, b = 1.3$

7 $n = 2, k = 16$; $y = 1.8$

9 $A = 140, p = 1.6$

10 $a = 2.51, n = 0.33$

11 (i) $a = 1.2, b = 1.8$ (ii) 720 (iii) 25 m/s

12 $a = 2.0, b = 0.50$; $y = 4.9$

13 1.8, 6.6; $a = 1.0, b = 3.3$

14 143 mm

Index